Preface

There are many texts available in the area of building technology, each with their own merits. Each new book in the field attempts to provide something extra, something different to set it apart from the rest. The result is an ever-expanding quantum of information for the student to cope with. Whilst such texts are invaluable as reference sources, they are often difficult to use as learning vehicles. This text seeks to provide a truly different approach to the subject of construction technology associated with houses. Rather than being a reference source (although it may be used as such), the book provides a learning vehicle for students of construction and property related subjects.

A genuine learning text

The text is structured so that it provides a logical progression and development of knowledge from first principles to more advanced concepts relating to the technology of house construction. The content is aimed at students wishing to gain an understanding of the subject matter without the need to consult several different and costly volumes. Unlike reference texts that are used for selectively accessing specific items of information, this book is intended to be read as a continuous learning support vehicle. Whilst the student can access specific areas for reference the major benefit can be gained by reading the book from the start, progressing through the various chapters to gain a holistic appreciation of the various aspects of house construction.

Key learning features

- The learning process is supported by several key features that make this text different from its competitors. These are embedded at strategic positions to enhance the learning process.

- Case studies include photographs and commentary on specific aspects of the technology of house construction. Thus students can visualise details and components in a real situation.

- Reflective summaries are included at the end of each section to encourage the reader to reflect on the subject matter and to assist in reinforcing the knowledge gained.

- Review tasks aid in allowing the reader to consider different aspects of the subject at key points in the text.

- Comparative studies allow the reader to quickly compare and contrast the features of different details or design solutions and are set out in a simple to understand tabular format.

- The hot links incorporated into each section identify key texts or sources of information to support the reader's potential needs for extra information on particular topics.

- In addition, the pop-up boxes are used to expand on certain details discussed in the main text without causing readers to divert their attention from the core subject matter.

Website

A website supporting this book and designed to enhance the learning process can be found at http://www.palgrave.com/science/engineering/howard. This is separated into a lecturer's zone and a student zone.

- The lecturer's zone has series of 'Studios' that the lecturer can use with students to support the learning process. The studios are designed to build upon the information contained within the book to provide a challenging and interesting series of case based learning situations. The studios are set around case study material and they encourage the students to access and interpret information from a variety of defined sources such as British Standards, BRE digests and other published material. Each of the studios is structured to create a scenario within which students are required to consider a range of options for the solution of design and construction problems based on the knowledge developed by using the book, but also requiring wider, directed research.
  The studios may be used as learning vehicles, tutorial tasks and assessed submissions if delivered appropriately.

  In addition to the studio tasks the lecturer's zone incorporates detailed descriptions relating to the case study materials together with addition photographs and visual materials suitable for use in formal lectures and tutorials to follow the structure and format of the book.

- The student zone contains outline answers to the review tasks, plus further photographs from the Case Studies in the book, with accompanying commentary.

The overall aim of the text and website is to inspire students of construction and property related disciplines to develop an understanding of the principles of construction associated with low-rise housing. The format is intended to be easily accessible and the support features will allow the reader to progress through the text in a progressive manner without undue complexity. The text is written in a clear and concise fashion and should provide all that students require to support the development of their learning in the area of house construction.

This book is intended to be an accessible tool to support the learning process it is not an expansive reference book. With the aid of the book it is envisaged that students will be able to navigate their way through the typical syllabus of a construction technology programme dealing with the construction of houses. The need to buy several expensive texts should be a thing of the past....

Acknowledgements

The authors would like to express their thanks to the following people for their support and contribution to the book:

Paul Hodgkinson:	for his time and effort in creating the illustrations contained within the book.
Robin Hughes:	for his advice and commentary on the preliminary drafts
Redrow Homes:	for their kind permission to use examples of their buildings for illustrating the case studies and for granting unlimited access to their construction sites
Julie and Mal:	for their support and understanding during the writing of this text

part one

Introduction to house construction

chapter one

Functions of buildings

Aims

After studying this chapter you should be able to:

- Appreciate the main physical functions of buildings
- Describe the factors that must be considered in creating an acceptable living environment
- Discuss links between these factors and the design of modern dwellings
- Recognise the sources and nature of loads applied to building elements and the ways in which they affect those elements
- Appreciate the influence of the choice of materials and the selection of design features on building performance

This chapter contains the following sections:

1.1   Physical and environmental functions of buildings

1.2   Forces exerted on and by buildings

1.3   Structural behaviour of elements

( ) Hot links

- Building Regulations Approved Document A, Structure
- BS 648: Schedule of weights of building materials
- BS 5250: Code of practice for control of condensation in buildings
- BS ISO 6243: Climatic data for building design. Proposed system of symbols (refers to structural design of buildings)
- BS 6399 Part 1: Loadings for buildings. Code of practice for dead and imposed loads
- BS EN ISO 7730: Moderate thermal environments. Determination of the PMV and PPD indices and specification of the conditions for thermal comfort

1.1 Physical and environmental functions of buildings

Introduction

After studying this unit you should be aware of the nature of buildings as environmental enclosures. You should appreciate the nature of the building user's need to moderate the environment and you should understand how built form has evolved to allow this to be achieved. You should also have an awareness of the link between environmental needs and the form of the building fabric and should be able to recognise the key features of building form that affect the internal environment. In addition, you should understand the nature of physical forces exerted on and by buildings and you should be familiar with the terminology associated with this aspect of building performance. You should have comprehension of the implications of the need to satisfy these requirements upon building design. Given a variety of scenarios you should be able to recognise the key features of the building structure and fabric and should be able to relate these to its physical and environmental performance.

Included within this unit are the following areas:

● The building as an environmental envelope

● Performance requirements of building fabric

The building as an environmental envelope

Overview

The ways in which the internal environments of buildings are controlled have become very sophisticated as the needs of occupiers have evolved. The degree to which we are able to moderate the internal environmental conditions using the building enclosure and building services is great. However, it is easy to take for granted some of the features of buildings that affect the internal environment and to overlook the basis of the evolution of these features. Dwellings are generally designed to be aesthetically pleasing. Many of the details that we associate with building style and aesthetics have their origins in the need to satisfy functional needs. As buildings have developed, the role of building services to control heat, light and ventilation has become more significant. It is easy to forget that these services rely on the existence of an appropriate building envelope in order to achieve the required level of performance. The dwelling as we now know it has its origins in the simplest form of building enclosure, created by people to protect them from the extremes of the environment. The factors that led people to develop such enclosures in historic times are still evident today, and the function of dwellings, although now much more sophisticated, is still essentially the same as it was then. One of the primary functions of the building fabric is to create an environmental envelope.

Buildings and the control of the internal environment

Historically people have sought to modify and control the environment in which they live. In prehistoric times caves and other naturally occurring forms of shelter were used as primitive dwellings, providing protection from the external environment. As civilisation has developed, so the nature of people's shelter has become more refined and complex, developing from caves and natural forms of shelter to simple artificial enclosures, such as those used throughout history by nomadic peoples worldwide. The ways in which the structures created by humans have developed have depended upon the nature of the climate in specific locations and the form of building materials available locally. This resulted in the development of vernacular forms of building, based on the use of readily available local materials. As a consequence, identifiable styles of buildings developed in different areas, each adapting the form of the building to satisfy functional requirements with available materials and technologies. The ability to transport building materials over relatively large distances is a recent development. In Britain, for example, this was limited prior to the industrial revolution by the lack of effective transport networks. The advent of canals and rail links allowed materials to be transported over relatively large distances. Hence the extent of vernacular architecture has reduced, with materials from a wide variety of locations being incorporated into more modern buildings to satisfy functional requirements in the most efficient and cost-effective way possible.

Examples of vernacular architecture are found in the UK and throughout the world. In areas such as the Middle Eastern desert regions, where diurnal temperatures vary considerably, being very hot during the day and cool at night, buildings of massive construction are common. Such buildings are referred to as 'thermally heavy' structures. The intense heat of the day is partly reflected by the use of white surface finishes, and that which is not reflected is absorbed by the building fabric rather than being transmitted into the occupied space. As a result of the slow thermal reaction of the building, this stored heat is released at the times of day when the external temperatures may be very low, acting as a form of storage heater. The effects of direct solar gain are reduced by the use of a limited number of small window openings.

In areas where the climate is consistently warm and humid, such as the Far East, a very different approach to building design is required. In such situations, rare breezes may be the only cooling medium that can remove the oppressive heat and humidity of the internal environment. Since this cooling and dehumidifying effect takes place in a short period, the building must be able to react

During the course of a typical day the air temperature will vary as a result of climatic conditions. The variation during a single day is referred to as the diurnal range.

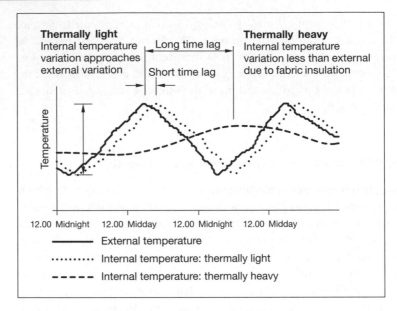

Figure 1.1 ● Thermal response of building fabric.

quickly to maximise any potential benefit. Hence, a 'thermally light' structure is essential to transmit external changes to the interior with minimal delay. The nature of buildings in such areas reflects these requirements, with lightweight building fabric and many large openings to allow cooling breezes to pass through the building (Figure 1.1).

There is a great difference in the properties of thermally light buildings and thermally heavy buildings. The fabric of the thermally light building is generally light in weight, with little capacity to absorb and store heat. Thus these buildings display fast response to external temperature changes. Thermally heavy buildings, in contrast, tend to be massive in their construction form, with dense walls that absorb heat readily. This form insulates the interior from external changes as a result of slow reaction times. The selected construction form must be matched to climate, user needs and the building services that are present to actively modify the internal environment.

The use of protective structures or enclosures is not the only method utilised in the moderation of people's environments. Since fire was first discovered and used by primitive people to provide light and heat, the use of energy to aid in environmental moderation has been fundamental. Although the use of built enclosures can moderate the internal environment and reduce the effects of extremes in the external climate, the active control and modification of the internal environment requires the input of energy. The use of buildings to house people, equipment and processes of differing types, exerting differing demands in terms of internal environment, has resulted in the development of buildings and associated services capable of controlling the internal conditions within desired parameters with great accuracy.

The nature of people's perceptions of comfort within buildings has also developed. The simple exclusion of rain and protection from extreme cold or heat are no longer sufficient to meet human needs. The provision of an acceptable internal condition relies on a number of factors, which include:

- *Thermal insulation and temperature control*
  The fabric of a modern dwelling must ensure that the levels of heat transfer between the interior and the external environment are within acceptable limits. In some cases this is aimed at minimising heat loss during cold periods; in others the aim is to minimise heat gain. In both of these situations the fabric must possess good levels of insulation in order to fulfil its functional requirement.

- *Acoustic insulation*
  In most situations it is desirable to shield the internal environment within a dwelling from the noise of the external surroundings. In addition, the need to maintain levels of privacy demands that the external envelope of the building be capable of insulating against the passage of noise to a reasonable level.

- *Provision of light*
  The interior of a dwelling must be provided with sufficient levels of natural or artificial light to allow the users to undertake their daily activities without hindrance. In addition, the levels of lighting maintained affect the perceptions of the comfort of the internal environment. Areas that are not provided with natural lighting would not be considered as being fit for human habitation.

- *Control of humidity and ventilation*
  In any building environment there is an acceptable range of relative humidity within which most people will feel comfortable. If the environment is subject to humidity levels above or below this range the occupants will feel discomfort; hence the humidity levels must be controlled. This is normally achieved in dwellings by the provision of appropriate levels of ventilation. The daily activities undertaken within a dwelling produce significant amounts of water vapour from cooking, washing and so on. Ventilating the interior to allow this vapour to migrate to the exterior is an effective method of humidity control. The provision of opening window areas facilitates ventilation and air movement within the dwelling, providing a constantly changing air supply to the interior.

- *Exclusion of contaminants*
  One of the functions fulfilled by the provision of appropriate levels of ventilation is the effective removal or exclusion of contaminants. Smoke, odours and other contaminants that are present in the air will be removed as a result of providing appropriate levels of air movement and, more importantly, air change through ventilation.

In the Northern hemisphere the Sun shines from the south. Hence most solar gain is on south-facing elevations, while most heat is lost on north-facing elevations. This affects the design of buildings such that larger windows tend to be placed to maximise heat gain, with smaller windows on north-facing walls to reduce heat loss.

The extent to which each of these plays a part in the creation of an acceptable environment varies from situation to situation. As the construction industry seeks to develop a more sustainable approach to its activities there is a move towards more natural mechanisms for environmental control. Many new buildings are designed to maximise natural light and ventilation, with the aim of reducing energy costs. Similarly, the benefits of solar gain may be maximised in the design of dwellings with differing sizes of window on different elevations depending on orientation. Large windows on southerly elevations maximise solar gain, while small openings on northerly elevations minimise heat loss. Factors such as this will play an increasing part in the design of buildings as we move towards a more sustainable approach to the built environment.

Figure 1.2 illustrates these requirements and the ways in which they are met in modern construction forms.

The construction of buildings using materials that were readily available locally was common in Britain prior to the Industrial Revolution. After this the ability to transport materials via the canal and railway systems resulted in more widespread use of some materials. The adoption of slate for roof coverings is a good example of this. In the UK the local availability of slate is limited to quite restricted areas, such as North Wales and the Lake District. However, the use of slate as a roofing material was widespread. In some countries the use of local materials and techniques is still commonplace and the wide variety of vernacular building styles reflects this. As previously noted, the form of these buildings is also affected by the nature of the local climate and the need to moderate the internal environment. Figure 1.3 shows an example of a regional vernacular style.

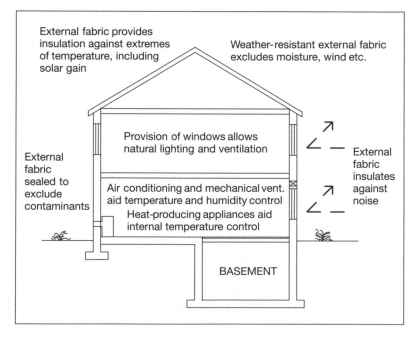

Figure 1.2 ● The building as an environmental modifier.

These dwellings are located in Thailand. The lightweight construction form is created by the use of locally available materials. The large openings allow air to pass through the building to cool the interior quickly.

Figure 1.3 ● Vernacular forms of architecture.

Review task

What performance differences do we expect from *thermally light* buildings compared with *thermally heavy buildings*?

Reflective summary

With reference to the building as an environmental shelter, remember:

— We need to preserve heat and keep out rain and noise, while allowing light in.

— Thermally heavy structures tend to be physically heavy and intercept heat by absorption.

— Some functions are not so easily measured, e.g. aesthetics (how the building looks).

Performance requirements of building fabric

Overview

The requirement to provide an acceptable internal environment is merely one of the performance requirements of modern buildings. The level of performance of buildings depends upon several factors and the emphasis placed upon individual performance requirements varies from situation to situation. Statutes and guidelines, such as the Building Regulations, set out minimum standards. These standards must always be satisfied irrespective of perceptions of the performance of the building fabric. The increasing role of the building as an asset has also affected the ways in which buildings have been designed to maximise the long-term value and minimise the maintenance costs of the structure and fabric.

The performance requirements of buildings include:

- Structural stability

- Durability

- Thermal insulation

- Exclusion of moisture and protection from weather

- Acoustic insulation

- Flexibility

- Aesthetics

Each of these performance requirements is important, although in certain instances some aspects of performance may take on more significance than others. A good example of this is the issue of durability. The level of durability required is linked to the required lifespan of the building. In some cases the intended functional life of the building may be short. In these situations the level of durability required clearly takes on less importance than in a situation where the lifespan is intended to be longer. Notwithstanding this, the relative importance of the various requirements is generally considered to be equal, and each of the requirements must be addressed to some extent. It is therefore worthwhile considering each in turn.

Structural stability

In order to satisfactorily fulfil the functions required of it, a building must be able to withstand the loads imposed upon it without suffering deformation or collapse. This necessitates the effective resistance of loads or their transfer through the structure to the ground. In dwellings of traditional structure the mechanisms for dealing with these loads are rather different from those of a timber frame building. The principles of each are dealt with later within this book and will not be explored in detail here. However, it is important to note that whatever the form of the building structure, the loads must be dealt with effectively. Generally this is achieved either by transferring them to some intermediate supporting element or to the supporting strata. Individual elements or components of the structure must also possess sufficient strength to cope with the forces that are established within them as a result of the various forms of load that exist within buildings.

Durability

The long-term performance of the structure and fabric demands that the component parts of the building are able to withstand the vagaries and hostilities of the environment in which they are placed without deterioration. The ability of the parts of the building to maintain their integrity and functional ability for the required period of time is fundamental to the ability of the building to perform in the long term. This factor is particularly affected by the occurrence of fires in buildings. The issue of durability affects the design of the building fabric and the selection of building materials and components. Great care must be taken in the specification of materials and components, as well as in the detailed design of the building, if premature failure is to be avoided. Durability is generally considered to be a variable benchmark of building performance, in that it is linked to the intended design life of the building rather than being an absolute measure of performance.

The selection of building materials and design details affects the durability of the completed building. In the process of selection, designers are mindful of the intended 'design life' of the building. Some buildings are intended to have quite short design lives, as they are temporary in nature. Dwellings will normally be expected to be more durable and are typically designed for a lifespan in excess of 60 years. In practice, most achieve lifespans well above this.

Thermal insulation

The needs to maintain internal conditions within fixed parameters and to conserve energy dictate that the external fabric of a given building provides an acceptable standard of resistance to the passage of heat. The level of thermal insulation that is desirable in an individual instance is, of course, dependant upon the use of the building, its location and so on. As the costs of energy increase and the awareness of environmental issues becomes more widespread, so the issue of energy consumption increases in importance. The Building Regulations set down minimum requirements for thermal performance of building enclosures. These requirements will undoubtedly increase in the future, and the design of the building fabric will evolve accordingly.

Exclusion of moisture and protection from weather

The passage of moisture from the exterior, whether in the form of ground water rising through capillary action, precipitation or other possible sources should be resisted by the building envelope. The ingress of moisture to the building interior can have several undesirable effects, such as the decay of timber elements, deterioration of surface finishes and decorations and risks to the health of the occupants, in addition to effects upon certain processes carried out in the building. Hence, details must be incorporated into the design of the building structure and fabric to resist the passage of moisture to the interior of the building from all undesirable sources. The exclusion of wind and water is essential to the satisfactory performance of any building fabric. In addition, the associated issue of exclusion of contaminants is increasingly recognised. One example of this is the potentially deleterious effect of radioactive radon gas upon the occupants of buildings. In areas where this is likely, specific design details must be introduced to minimise the potential risk associated with ingress of the gas.

Acoustic insulation

The passage of sound from the exterior to the interior, or between interior spaces, should be considered in building construction. The level of sound transmission that is acceptable in a building will vary considerably, depending upon the nature of the use of the building and its position. In the case of dwellings this is of particular concern where individual dwelling units are adjacent or contained within the same building enclosure. In fact, this is the case for the vast majority of dwellings in the UK. Free-standing or detached dwellings are far less common than semi-detached and terraced houses or flats. The transmission of noise between linked dwelling units can be a major problem, and all new buildings take this into account. There is also an issue associated with the transfer of sound between the exterior and the interior of the building. This can be of particular concern in locations where there is likely to be significant noise, as in the case of dwellings close to airports, for example.

Flexibility

In industrial and commercial buildings in particular, the ability of the building to cope with and respond to changing user needs has become very important. Hence the level of required future flexibility must be taken into account in the initial design of the building. This is reflected, for example, in the trend to create buildings with large open spaces that may be subdivided by the use of partitions which may be readily removed and relocated.

Aesthetics

The question of building aesthetics is subjective; however, it should be noted that in some situations the importance of the building's aesthetics is minimal, whereas in others it is of course highly important. For example, the appearance of a unit on an industrial estate is far less important than that of a city centre municipal building. The extent to which aesthetics are pursued will have an inevitable effect on the cost of the building. In the UK and other places there has been a tendency for house building to follow traditional design, as this is most readily marketable.

This summary is not a definitive list of the performance requirements of all building components in all situations; however, it is indicative of the factors, which affect the design and performance of buildings and their component parts (Figure 1.4).

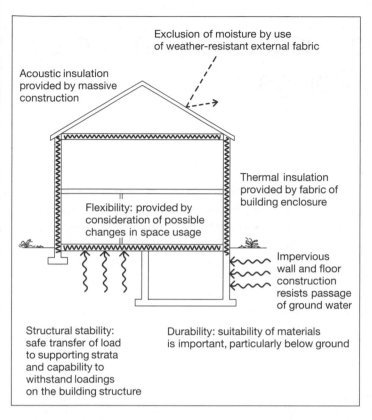

Exclusion of moisture by use of weather-resistant external fabric

Acoustic insulation provided by massive construction

Thermal insulation provided by fabric of building enclosure

Flexibility: provided by consideration of possible changes in space usage

Impervious wall and floor construction resists passage of ground water

Structural stability: safe transfer of load to supporting strata and capability to withstand loadings on the building structure

Durability: suitability of materials is important, particularly below ground

Figure 1.4 ● Performance requirements of building structure and fabric.

Reflective summary

When considering the functions of buildings, remember:

— Buildings satisfy a variety of functions to create a habitable environment: heat, light, ventilation, acoustics etc.

— They must satisfy physical requirements: structural stability, durability, aesthetics.

— Buildings are subjected to forces of different forms and from a variety of sources. In order to withstand them we must carefully select the materials, design alternatives and construction methods

Review task

List *five* performance requirements that you hope to be supplied by a dwelling and rank them in order of importance from a resident's point of view.

1.2   Forces exerted on and by buildings

Introduction

After studying this section you should be aware of the differing forces that act upon the structure of buildings. You should have developed knowledge of the origins of these forces and the nature in which they act upon the structural elements of the building. You should also have an intuitive appreciation of the relative magnitude of various forces and should be able to distinguish between the forces exerted on the building and the forces exerted by it. You should understand the terminology associated with the forces active within buildings and, given a variety of scenarios, should be able to recognise the different types of forces and appreciate their implications.

Loading forms

Overview

Building elements are subjected to loads from a variety of sources. Some of these loads are variable and are the result of applied elements, such as the weight of people and furniture. These are termed 'live' loads. Others are not variable and are the result of the self-weight of the building elements. These are termed 'dead' loads.

Forces acting upon the structural elements of buildings derive from a variety of sources and act in many different ways. However, there are a number of basic principles of structural behaviour, and these can be applied in considering the application and effect of the various forces that act upon buildings. The ways in which the structure and fabric of a building behave will depend upon their ability to cope with a range of inherent and applied loads. If the building is able to withstand the loading imposed upon it, it will remain static; in such a state it is considered to be stable. Any force acting upon a building is considered as a loading, whether it arises as a result of external factors, such as the action of wind on the building, or from the use of the building, such as the positioning of furniture, equipment or people. We must also recognise that the building itself is a source of loading simply as a result of the effect of the self-weight of the structure.

In order to withstand these forces two basic structural properties must be provided by the building. First, the component parts of the building must possess adequate strength to carry the applied loads. Second, the applied forces must be balanced in order to resist the tendency for the building to move. Thus the building must remain in equilibrium. In order to understand how these factors are achieved we must first examine the nature of the loads that act upon buildings.

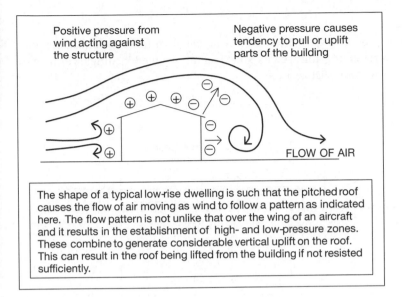

Positive pressure from
wind acting against
the structure

Negative pressure causes
tendency to pull or uplift
parts of the building

FLOW OF AIR

The shape of a typical low-rise dwelling is such that the pitched roof
causes the flow of air moving as wind to follow a pattern as indicated
here. The flow pattern is not unlike that over the wing of an aircraft
and it results in the establishment of high- and low-pressure zones.
These combine to generate considerable vertical uplift on the roof.
This can result in the roof being lifted from the building if not resisted
sufficiently.

Figure 1.5 ● Effects of wind loads on a building.

The nature of loads

The forces, or loads, applied to buildings can be considered under two generic
classifications: *dead loads* and *live loads*. Dead loads would normally include the
self-weight of the structure, including floors, walls, roofs, finishes, services and
so on. Live loads would include loads applied to the building in use, such as the
weight of people, furniture, machinery and wind loads. Such loads are normally
considered as acting positively on the building. However, in the case of wind
loads (Figure 1.5) suction zones may be created (i.e. negative forces); this effect is
often illustrated by the action of roofs being lifted from buildings in high wind
conditions. Hence buildings must be designed to cope with forces acting in a
variety of ways.

The ability of the materials used in the construction of buildings to withstand
these loads is termed 'strength'. In considering whether a building has sufficient
strength, the different types of load must be considered. Their direction is also
important: they may be oblique (at an angle) or axial (along the axis of an
element).

Stress

When subjected to forces, all structural elements tend to deform. This deformation is resisted by stresses, or internal forces within the element. The stresses
which are established in components fall into four basic categories: shear stress,
tensile stress, compressive stress and torsional stress.

Shear stress

Shear stress (Figure 1.6) is the internal force created within a structural member which resists a tendency, induced by an externally applied loading, for one part of the member to slide past another.

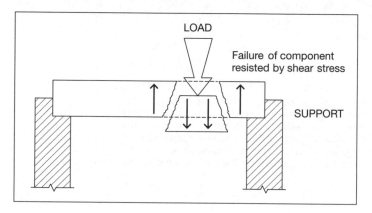

Figure 1.6 ● Shear stress.

Tensile stress

Tensile stress (Figure 1.7) is the internal force induced within an element which resists an external loading which produces a tendency to stretch the component. When such a force is applied the member is said to be in tension.

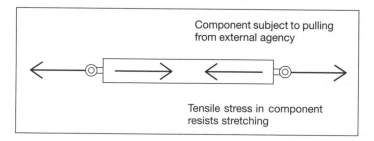

Figure 1.7 ● Tensile stress.

Compressive stress

Compressive stress (Figure 1.8) is the internal force set up within a structural component when an externally applied force produces a tendency for the member to be compressed or squashed. Such an element is said to be in compression.

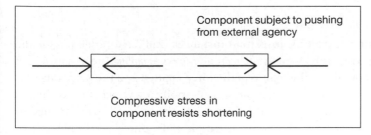

Figure 1.8 ● Compressive stress.

Torsional stress

Torsional stress (Figure 1.9) is the internal force created within a structural element which resists an externally applied loading which would cause the element to twist.

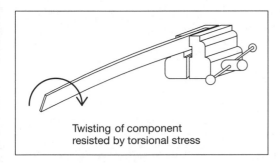

Figure 1.9 ● Torsional stress.

Strain

The effect of a tensile or compressive stress on an element is to induce an increase or decrease in the length of the element. The magnitude of such a change in length depends upon the length of the unit, the loading applied and the stiffness of the material. The relationship between this change in length and the original length of the component gives a measure of *strain* (denoted *e*):

$$e = \frac{l}{L}$$

where l = change in length and L = original length.

This effect is also evident in materials subject to shear stress, although the deformation induced in such cases tends to distort the element into a parallelogram shape.

The relationship between stress and strain (subject to loading limits) is directly proportional and is a measure of the material stiffness. The ratio of stress/strain is known as the modulus of elasticity.

Moments

The application of a force can, in certain instances, induce a tendency for the element to rotate. The term given to such a tendency is *moment*. The magnitude of such a moment depends on the extent of the force applied and the perpendicular distance between the point of rotation and the point at which the loading is applied. As a result of the effects of leverage, relatively small loads applied at considerable distances from the point of action can induce rotational forces. Moments upon structures must be in equilibrium in order for the structure to remain stable, i.e. clockwise moments (+) must be equalled by anticlockwise moments (–). The magnitude of a moment is the product of the force applied and the distance from the point of action at which it is applied (the lever arm) and is expressed in Newton millimetres (Figure 1.10).

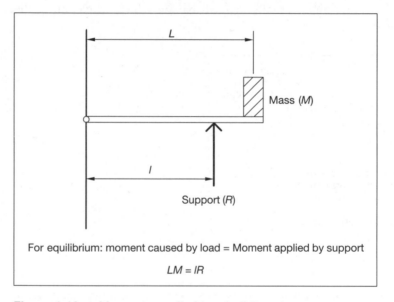

Figure 1.10 ● Moments applied to a building element.

Review task

In as few words as possible distinguish between the following forms of stress:

1. Tensile

2. Torsional

3. Shear

1.3 Structural behaviour of elements

Introduction

After studying this section you should be aware of the implications of the loads applied to structural building elements. You should understand the terminology associated with the structural behaviour of buildings and the elements within them. In addition, you should appreciate the implications of the structural performance upon the selection of materials.

Included in this section are the following areas:

● The nature of forces acting on buildings

● The nature of building components

The nature of forces acting on buildings

Overview

The effects of the types of loads or forces exerted on a building depend on the way in which those forces are applied. Maintaining the integrity and structural stability of a building relies on its ability to withstand inherent and applied loads without suffering movement or deformation. Nevertheless, it is possible to allow for a limited amount of movement or deformation within the building design, as is common in mining areas, for example. Resistance to movement and deformation results from an effective initial design of the structure as a unit and the ability of materials used for individual components to perform adequately.

Limited movement, of certain types, is inevitable in all structures and must be accommodated to prevent the occurrence of serious structural defects. The effects of thermal and moisture-induced changes in building materials can be substantial, producing cyclical variations in the size of components. This dictates the inclusion of specific movement accommodation details, particularly when dealing with elements of great size, such as solid floors of large area. Additionally, the period shortly following the erection of a building often results in minor consolidation of the ground upon which it is located; however, this will generally be very minor in nature. These forms of movement and deformation are acceptable; other forms, however, must be avoided. Their nature and extent depend upon the nature and direction of the applied forces. Three main categories of applied forces combine to give rise to all types of building movement.

Vertical forces

Vertically applied forces, such as the dead loading of the building structure and some live loads, act to give rise to a tendency for the structure to move in a downward direction, i.e. to sink into the ground. The extent of any such movement depends upon the ability of the building to spread the building loads over a sufficient area to ensure stability on ground of a given loadbearing capacity. The loadbearing capacities of different soil types vary considerably; the function of foundations to buildings is to ensure that the loading of the structure does not exceed the bearing capacity of the ground. In most instances the bearing capacity of the ground, normally expressed in kN/m², is very much less than the pressures likely to be exerted by the building structure if placed directly onto the ground. The pressure is reduced by utilising foundations to increase the interface area between the building and the ground, thus reducing the pressure applied to the ground (Figure 1.11).

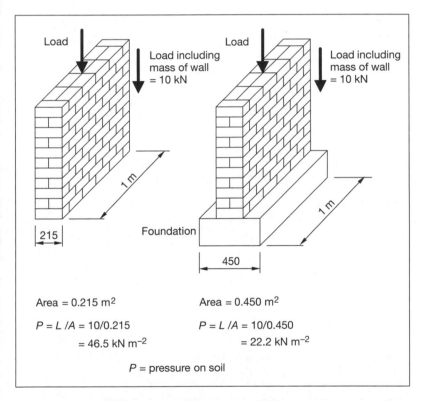

Figure 1.11 ● Reduction of pressure applied to the ground resulting from use of foundations.

The need to withstand such vertical loads is not exclusive to the lower elements of the building structure, although such loads are greater in magnitude at the lower sections due to the effects of accumulated loads from the structure. All structural components must be of sufficient size and strength to carry the loads imposed upon them without failure or deformation. Columns and walls, often carrying the loads of floors, roofs and so on from above, must resist the tendency to buckle or to be crushed by the forces exerted. The way in which columns and walls perform under the effects of vertical loads depends on the 'slenderness ratio' of the component (Figure 1.12). In simple terms, long, slender units will tend to buckle easily, while short, broad units will resist such tendencies. In long,

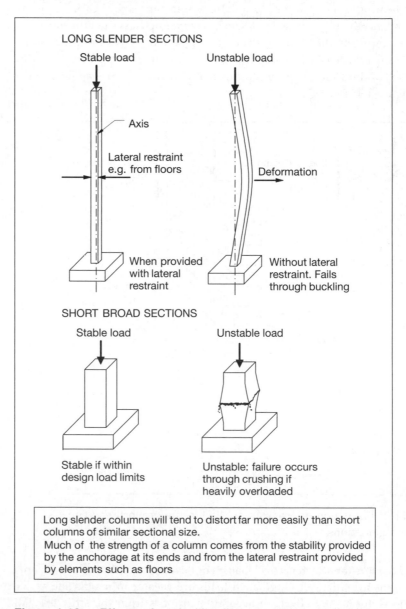

Figure 1.12 ● Effects of vertical loading on columns and walls.

thin components the risk of buckling can be greatly reduced by incorporating bracing to prevent sideways movement; this is termed 'lateral restraint'.

If overloaded significantly, even short, broad sections may be subject to failure; in such instances the mode of failure tends to be crushing of the unit, although this is comparatively rare.

Horizontal components, such as floors and beams, must also be capable of performing effectively while withstanding vertically applied loads (Figure 1.13). This is ensured by the use of materials of sufficient strength, designed in an appropriate manner, with sufficient support to maintain stability. Heavy loads on such components may give rise to deflection, resulting from the establishment of

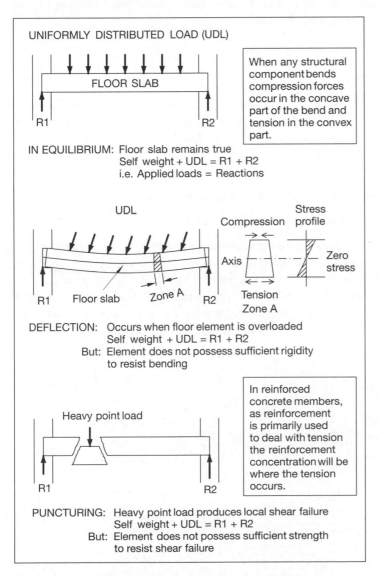

Figure 1.13 ● Vertical forces on horizontal building elements.

moments, or in extreme cases puncturing of the component, resulting from excessive shear at a specific point. When subjected to deflection, beam and floor sections are forced into compression at the upper regions and tension at the lower regions. This may limit the design feasibility of some materials, such as concrete, for example, which performs well in compression, but not in tension. Hence the use of composite units is common, such as concrete reinforced in the tension zones with steel.

As shown in Figure 1.5, illustrating the effects of wind loads, the vertical forces applied to buildings may be in an upward direction. These must also be resisted, usually by making the best use of the mass of the building. Upward loads may also be generated from the ground, in zones of shrinkable clay or those which are prone to the actions of frost, for example. The upward force exerted by the ground in such cases is termed 'heave'.

Horizontal forces

Horizontal forces acting on buildings derive from many sources and it is difficult to generalise upon their origins and effects. Typically, however, such loads may be exerted by sub-soil pressure, as in the case of basement walls, wind or physical loading on the building. The effects of such forces are normally manifested in one of two ways:

● Overturning, or rotation of the building or its components.

● Horizontal movement, or sliding of the structure.

These forms of movement are highly undesirable and must be avoided by careful building design. The nature of the foundations and the level of lateral restraint or buttressing incorporated into the building design are fundamental to the prevention of such modes of failure. Additionally, particularly in framed structures, the use of bracing to prevent progressive deformation or collapse is essential; this could be described as resistance of the 'domino effect' (Figure 1.14).

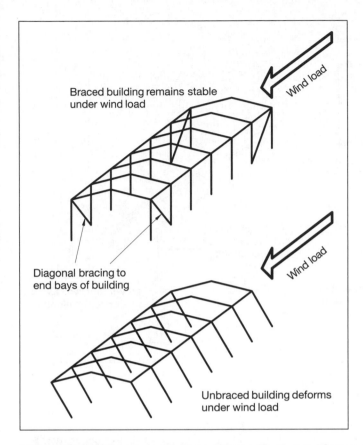

Figure 1.14 ● Resistance to the effects of horizontal forces on buildings.

Oblique forces

In some areas of building structures the application of forces applied at an inclination is common (Figure 1.15). This is generally the case where pitched roofs are supported on walls. The effects of such forces produce a combination of vertically and horizontally applied loads at the point of support. These effects are resisted by the incorporation of buttressing and/or lateral restraint details. The horizontal effects of these loads are sometimes ignored, with disastrous effects.

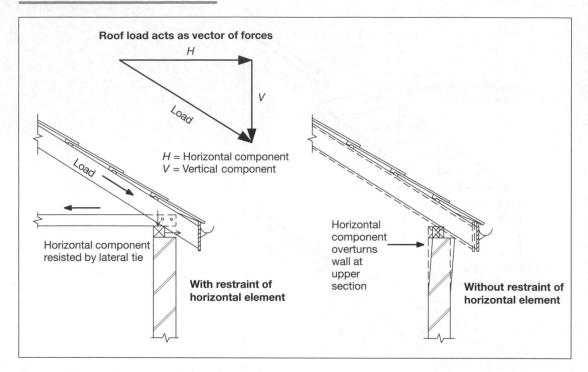

Roof load acts as vector of forces

H = Horizontal component
V = Vertical component

Load

Horizontal component resisted by lateral tie

With restraint of horizontal element

Horizontal component overturns wall at upper section

Without restraint of horizontal element

Figure 1.15 ● Effects of oblique loads on buildings.

Reflective summary

When considering the structural behaviour of building elements, remember:

— The direction of the applied loading is important in dictating the effect upon the building element.

— Failure of building elements can occur in a variety of ways, such as:
  • buckling of slender columns
  • bending of beams and slabs
  • shear at support points
  • crushing of localised areas

— Individual structural elements can act together to create a stronger form. Note the importance of lateral restraint and bracing.

Review task

Explain the value of foundations in dissipating the forces experienced by a wall.

The influence of shape – building components

This section is included to extend in a brief way the earlier material concerning the forces experienced by the components of a building. The bulk of the forces experienced by a house would be compression and tension. These tend to translate directly into the use of certain materials suited to these forces – we know that concrete, for example, is excellent in resisting compression (squashing) and that reinforcement steel is used to counteract tension (stretching) because of its elasticity. At this stage it may be useful also to consider why the components used in housing are not only of a certain material but also of a certain shape.

We can use the example of a ruler to explain the value of placing material in direct opposition to the forces that they will experience. If the ruler is laid flat and loaded centrally it will bend with relative ease (Figure 1.16).

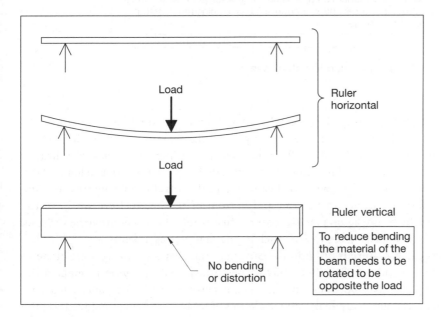

Figure 1.16 ● Placing material opposite the loads to be carried.

It will also be seen that if we now rotate the ruler through 90° and load it again, the resistance to bending is dramatically improved, even though its material content is exactly the same. The reason for this is that the materials have been placed directly in opposition to the loads to be carried.

This same effect has led to the development of certain shapes of components, such as steel beams. When we think of steel, the **I** section generally comes to mind. If we examine the forces experienced by a beam spanning a gap, we know that there is a tendency to bend in 'smile' fashion. Earlier in this chapter we discussed how this sagging leads to maximum compression at the top of beams and maximum tension at the bottom.

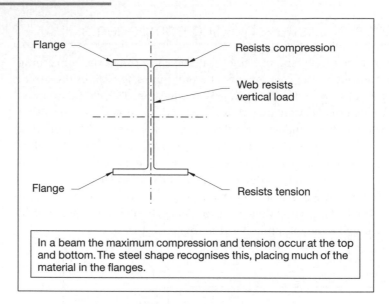

In a beam the maximum compression and tension occur at the top and bottom. The steel shape recognises this, placing much of the material in the flanges.

Figure 1.17 ● The I section steel beam.

If we now look at the **I** shape which has evolved for steel beams, Figure 1.17 shows how the beam has been arranged to place material where it is really needed. The *web* of the beam (like our ruler) is vertical and therefore directly opposes the direction of bending, providing efficiency in resistance to loads. Also, we have just said that when a beam bends the maximum compression and maximum tension are in the top and bottom of the beam. Here we have the *flanges* of the beam, again placing material just where the forces are to be resisted. This makes the **I** section a very efficient shape to use as a beam.

Corrugated materials attempt to place material closer to the vertical plane to counteract bending. The effect may be best illustrated by trying to make a flat piece of paper span between your fingers: it sags easily and the paper collapses.

However, if you were to introduce a series of folds, as shown in Figure 1.18, the reorganisation of the material and the movement of material towards the vertical helps the paper to span the gap successfully.

This principle is found in corrugated roof sheeting and in materials such as wall cladding, which is used extensively on light industrial and industrial premises.

Review task

Account for the popular sectional shape provided for steel beams.

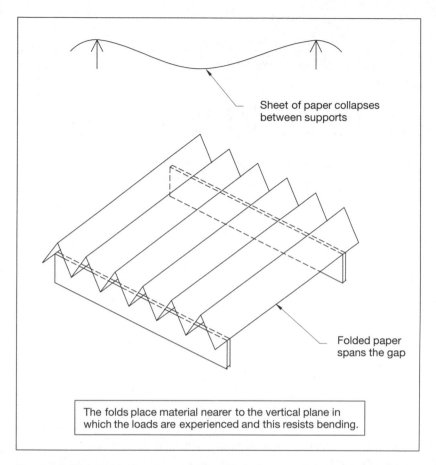

Sheet of paper collapses
between supports

Folded paper
spans the gap

The folds place material nearer to the vertical plane in
which the loads are experienced and this resists bending.

Figure 1.18 Introducing corrugations to help materials resist bending.

Reflective summary

With reference to the shape of building components, remember:

— When assessing the performance of a component we tend to examine the shape around two axes – these divide the centre of the shape in both directions.

— When a component is fixed horizontally the main issues tend to be bending tension and compression, twisting torsion, or buckling.

— When a component is fixed vertically the main issues tend to be strain-related shortening and buckling related to the slenderness of the component.

— With horizontally located components, loadings are sometimes measured around a particular point; if loads are impressed on either side of the point they may tend to counteract each other in an effect called moments.

chapter two

Preparing to build and the building process

 Aims

After studying this chapter you should be able to:

- Appreciate the criteria involved with the selection of a site
- Describe the influence of site investigation on project viability
- Discuss links between the site investigation and foundation design
- Describe in outline the application of Statutory Control to the building process
- Appreciate the extent of utility services and general infrastructure required by a development
- Outline the preparatory processes that precede formation of the building

This chapter contains the following sections:

Hot links

- Building Regulations Approved Document C: Site preparation and resistance to moisture
- BS 5930: Code of practice for site investigations
- BS 5964: Building setting out and measurement
- BS 8103: Structural design of low-rise buildings
- BRE Digests related to site investigation: 318, 348, 381, 383, 411, 412, 427
- BS 10175: Investigation of potentially contaminated sites. Code of practice (formerly DD 175)

2.1 Selection of sites for building

Introduction

After studying this section you should be able to discuss the general issues which may be examined before selecting a particular site for development. You should appreciate the physical, environmental and financial influences on site selection. You should also be able to consider the construction of dwellings in the wider context of the development process with regard to statutory restrictions. In addition you should be aware of the general implications of the availability and proximity of utility services and associated infrastructure.

Overview

There are many reasons for selecting a site for a new residential development. Typically these include:

● the local demand for housing (which can be actual demand or demand envisaged following consideration of the general growth of the area)

● the proximity of established infrastructure (in the form of roads and services such as sewers)

● the cost of the land

● the quality of land and the effect of this on preparation for use and consequential foundation expense

● the potential for profit

The decision to select a particular site is generally economic, and the developer will undertake a calculation to assess the likely financial viability of the project. This may be the Developer's Equation as outlined below. Remember that if most of the ingredients of the Developer's Equation are known, the equation can be rearranged to find out the maximum value of the missing ingredient:

Developer's Equation

Income – Outlay = Profit
Income – Profit = Outlay
Income – Profit – Outlay on all items except land = Land cost

The last line illustrates that from the basic Developer's Equation we can carry out a residual calculation, looking for the residue that we could afford to pay in this example for the land while still achieving the level of profitability needed.

The local demand for housing will have a marked influence on the profitability element of the Developer's Equation, in that it will suggest the plot area which tends to be demanded by the locality. This in turn dictates the number of units that can be built on a particular site and the price that may be charged for them. One of the biggest expenses with any new development is the outlay on infrastructure, the shared facilities to be provided – for example, the roads, sewers, footpaths, electricity, gas and water supplies. Expense on this item will be influenced by the extent of these items already in the locality but also by the costly general nature of essential features like roads through the development. Infrastructure costs are always viewed with some interest, as they generally relate to items of work to be completed or partly executed before building commences on the individual properties. Some time will therefore expire before a chance exists to recover these extremely expensive costs.

The quality of the land in question has always been seen to have a correlation with the nature of the foundations to be provided. The weaker the ground in terms of bearing capacity, the more expensive the foundation solution. Many of the large housebuilders in the UK, such as Redrow, Barratt and Wimpey, have a range of house types that they will build in different locations. Although these house types will be the same from locality to locality, the foundation solution hidden in the ground will vary to suit the conditions of that site. On good ground, variations of simple and relatively cheap strip footings will be provided, while on poor ground the solution may have to be expensive piling. Another issue of growing significance is the development of contaminated land. Here health is the predominant factor and the site will have to be cleansed appropriately; but this of course means an extra development expense, which will in turn affect profit margins. Anything which increases the outlay side of the Developer's Equation has an immediate effect on profit.

Reflective summary

When selecting a new housing site, consider:

— demand for property

— the quality of ground

— asking price for the property

— available services (roads, sewers etc.)

Remember the basic Developer's Equation:

Income – Outlay = Profit

Focus on the sensitive ingredients of the outlay side of the equation – the ingredients which cost the most – land cost, infrastructure cost, property build costs. Small changes in these items may do dramatic things to profitability.

2.2   Site investigation

Introduction

After studying this section you should appreciate the timing of the site investigation in the overall processes of construction. You should also appreciate the significance imposed by the findings of the process in terms of material selection, foundation design and overall building form. In addition, you should appreciate the range and scope of data that may typically be generated during the desktop study and the on-site investigation process.

Overview

The process of site investigation occurs early in the development of a new project and even before the purchase of the land. This process will reveal a considerable amount of information which often has a major influence on the way in which the building is put together. One of the greatest influences is of course on the foundations to the property: generally, the weaker the ground the more expensive the foundation solution.

When the feasibility of the project is examined the construction detail which arises following the site investigation is usually of great significance. Site investigation is undertaken during the early stages of project development. The Royal Institute of British Architects (RIBA) devised many years ago their 'Plan of Work', which breaks the development process into a series of phases. The earliest of these phases are Inception and Feasibility, which represent the client having the initial idea of what they want in terms of a building and the cost assessment to ensure that they can afford to pay for the structure.

We continue through the phases to project Completion and appraisal Feedback. The site investigation happens before the land is purchased during the Inception and Feasibility stages.

The purpose of an investigation may be summarised as follows

- to assess the ground's composition and characteristics

- to ensure that a foundation is chosen which is compatible with the load to be carried and the strength of the ground

- to ensure safety, efficiency and economy in the design of the building

A site investigation is a vital part of any new development. Unless you appreciate the ground conditions and are able to select your materials and design to suit the ground, the possibility of financial loss is high.

Nature of the survey

There are various forms that the site investigation can take, and these range from desktop studies and examination of existing records to reconnaissance by walking over the site and detailed, extensive sample removal exercises.

The desktop study can supply useful background information on the site, such as may be obtained from maps and historical records about the site. BRE Digest 318 outlines the procedures for undertaking such an exercise and refers to a number of areas for consideration:

- topography, vegetation and drainage

- ground conditions

- the proposed structure

Table 2.1 outlines some of the questions that may be asked of these areas.

Table 2.1 ● Typical site investigation questions.

Topography, vegetation and drainage	Does the ground slope, and if so to what angle? Are there any natural water areas on site (ponds, streams etc.)? Are there trees or hedges?
Ground condition	What strata exist in the ground? Are these strata typically associated with problems (peat layers, shrinkable clay etc.)? Is ground strength information available? Is there any ground instability or subterranean activity likely to cause instability (e.g. coal mines)?
The proposed structure	What area will the building cover? What foundation loading is anticipated? Might the soil create differential movement?

You need to recognise, however, the value of actually visiting the site, and even a topographical inspection can be far more valuable than extensive studies conducted in the office. The topography is effectively what you see from ground level: how the land lies, the nature of vegetation and plant growth, the feel of the soil (is it waterlogged for example?), buildings and natural features.

You may insist on or prefer to select a full-blown investigation, from which extensive quantities of data may emerge. The more you know about the site, the less any uncertainty about design and performance matters. The size and shape of the site and the proposed size and shape of the building on that site will generally be most influential in the methodology adopted during the undertaking of a site investigation. What we will attempt to do by the end of the exercise is to compile a representative summary of the features, characteristics and qualities of the site.

Method of extracting information

The ways in which we obtain information concerning the soil are quite wide varied. A traditional technique is to remove samples of ground for site and laboratory analysis by use of a sampling rig and an open drive sample tube.

The samples extracted in this way may be either *disturbed*, where the drilling extraction process breaks down the natural state of the ground because of the auger drill bit used, or *undisturbed*, where the sample taken shows the state of the ground just as it is. Hollow cylindrical tubes with a bottom cutting edge are driven into the ground and take a core sample, as shown in Figure 2.1.

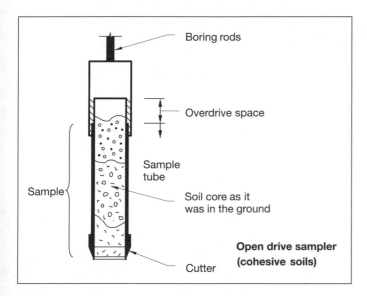

Figure 2.1 ● An open drive sample tube.

When samples are taken, a borehole log (chart) is used to summarise the findings at different depths in the ground.

In both of the techniques just discussed material samples are removed, but it is possible to obtain information regarding certain features of the ground, such as strength, without removing samples at all (Figure 2.2).

The resistance to rotation under the torque pressures experienced by driving the vanes of the deep vane machine into the ground reflects compressive strength. Seismic pulses generated by firing a charge may be used to cause shock waves to bounce back off the various strata in the ground and provide a visual picture of the soil layers present.

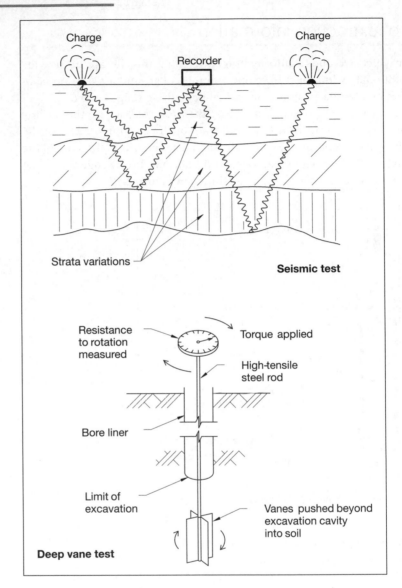

Figure 2.2 ● Deep vane and seismic methods of ground assessment.

Data generated by a site investigation

A site investigation may provide information concerning:

- the nature of the soil

- the thickness of the layers of different types of soil at the test location

- the strength of the soil

- the existence of contaminants in the soil

The construction of a new housing development will broadly involve two stages: the *pre-contract* stage and the *post-contract* stage. The former represents all the activities that take place before the legal construction contract is signed (e.g. the JCT Contract) and the latter the activities after the contract is signed. As the discovery of a water table during the site investigation takes place early in the development of the scheme this is a pre-contract discovery. Later, when construction commences on-site, the water table level will be read again to see whether it has fluctuated, primarily in order that the contractor can be paid an equitable rate for the extent of the excavation in water.

Sometimes there will be existing underground services on the site, such as water mains, sewers and electric power cables. These often have to be re-routed to suit the new development, and awareness of their location is an obvious advantage before excavations into the ground commence.

Contaminated land

Many sites now developed for housing have been previously used, and in such circumstances are likely to be contaminated. The forms that contaminants take are extensive and include:

- chemicals – processing chemicals in particular

- heavy metals, such as mercury and lead

- fibrous materials linked to respiratory problems, such as asbestos

- explosives

- nuclear waste

- natural radioactivity, such as caused by radon gas

- landfill gases, such as methane

- liquids, such as petroleum

This list can be easily extended.

The fact that many sites have contamination problems is recognised by the Building Regulations in Approved Document C, where clause C2 makes specific reference to Dangerous and Offensive Substances. C2 concerns the need to avoid danger to health caused by substances found on or in the ground which is to be covered by the building. Part C of the regulations also recognises the sensitivity of developments in terms of the use of the site. For example, a car park or hard-standing would not be very sensitive when compared with a housing develop-ment. In the event of a certain contaminant of an equal concentration existing on both of these types of site the degree of corrective work might be quite different. The name given to remedying contaminated land is *remediation*.

As investigating contamination is potentially more important to health than ordinary site investigations the approach taken in the evaluation of the site might

Ground contamination is now a very big issue. Where contaminants are found they are often removed at great expense for safety. Only licensed tips may be used for disposal, and these charge a rate per tonne for accepting the material.

be quite different. There is a British Standards Institution reference which may be reviewed in this area, namely BS 10175. The fact that this standard was in existence as a Draft for Development (DD 175) from the mid-1980s and only achieved full BS status in 2001 is probably a reflection of the difficulty of compiling a definitive approach to researching contamination problems.

Review task

Name *five* typical results that you would expect to emerge from a site investigation and rank these into importance, justifying your ranking.

Reflective summary

With reference to site investigation, remember:

— As a process, this happens at the earliest opportunity (project feasibility stage).

— It is undertaken to establish:
  • the type of ground
  • the choice of foundation
  • the presence of contaminants (including water)

— Investigation may involve taking samples for analysis, but there are ways of provide information without taking samples.

— Foundation design evolves around three criteria:
  • the load from the building
  • the strength of the soil
  • the way in which load is spread between the foundation and the soil

— Corrective work to contaminated land is termed *remediation*.

— Remediation options tend to be:
  • remove
  • seal to isolate
  • neutralise

2.3   Overview of statutory control of building

Introduction

After studying this section you should be able to appreciate the evolutionary development of building control through public health and other associated legislation. You should also be able to outline the basic process of obtaining formal approval to build and how control extends to the building process.

Overview

The application of controls over the building process is a relatively new concept. Prior to the first national set of Building Regulations in 1965, control over the building process was limited. The first real major realisation of need for control probably came in the aftermath of the Great Fire of London in 1666. The rate of spread of the fire itself was a major factor in the disaster and this was a consequence of the high density of building, with few open spaces, coupled with the combustible nature of the building materials of the time.

Following the fire, control regulations were issued which were applicable to London itself.

A main feature of the development of control in the rest of England was the various Public Health Acts (PHA), and probably the most notable of these was the PHA 1875. This had three main focuses: structural stability, dampness and sanitation. Following this Act, a set of Model Bye Laws was issued in 1877 as a guide for local authorities, who were delegated the responsibility for setting and enforcing minimum standards of construction. The concerns of the bye laws were primarily health and safety, and this set of guidance controls largely followed the contents of the Public Health Act of two years earlier.

Following the limited progress in the 19th century, legislation concerning construction was limited and mainly in the area of public health, e.g. the Public Health Act 1936. By the 1950s many local authorities were issuing bye laws peculiar to their locality, and this made life difficult for the construction professional, in that laws varied from area to area. Because of the need for consistency, the National Bye Laws were established in 1952. Following these, items of significance include the Public Health Act 1961 and the first national set of Building Regulations in 1965.

The aim of the Building Regulations was to set what are considered to be the minimum standards that are acceptable in construction. Despite the considerable step forward in national construction standards as a result of these regulations,

Legislation concerning construction has been slow to develop in the UK. Our first national set of Building Regulations did not exist until 1965.

some considerable difficulty was being experienced in ensuring that they were enforced. Consequently, in 1972 the Government established the Local Government Act, which clearly set the responsibility of Building Regulation enforcement with the local authorities, and this in turn forced these authorities to employ personnel specifically for this purpose.

Since then, enforcement has been carefully controlled, and this is still the situation today. Following the first set of Building Regulations, refinements were forthcoming which were issued initially as amendments and eventually incorporated into the body of the regulations with the issue of the Regulations 1972, 1976, 1985 and 1991.

In 1985 the format layout of the regulations changed substantially to the A4 format still used today. As in the past, the regulations tend to divide the building into a number of logical sections: Structure, Fire, Ventilation, Stairs etc. Since 1985, each of these sections has been enhanced by the use of an Approved Document. These explain the application of the regulations in detail and contain the appropriate British Standards that apply. Section 3 of the Building Regulations lays down the procedure to be followed to obtain formal approval to build, and contains sections such as Notices and Plans, Control of Building Work, and Relaxation of Requirements.

When a person wishes to obtain formal approval to build, there are broadly two areas of concern: compliance with the Building Regulations in terms of design and material content, and the suitability of the building for the location and the piece of land in question. The latter area draws in the Town and Country Planning Acts, which govern the use of land throughout the UK. Land is classified for different uses (for example residential use or agricultural use), and these pieces of legislation restrict the building to forms designated as suitable for the particular site.

Typically planning permission may be required if you want to:

- extend a flat externally

- create self-contained accommodation from part of an existing house

- divide off part of a house for business purposes

- erect something that may restrict the view of road users (e.g. a fence)

- build in a way which was not included in the original Planning Permission for the house

- widen access or supply access to a road

Minor changes to houses may be undertaken without the need to apply for planning permission under *Permitted Development Rights*; for example, where the proposed extension has a volume which is less than 15% of the original house volume (calculated on *external* measurements) or 70 m^3, whichever is the greater. The situation can, however, be complicated if certain conditions apply, such as the property being located in a conservation area, or where other extensions have already been added.

Planning permission may also be required for putting up certain fences, walls or gates, or forming patios, paths and driveways.

Other forms of approval may also be needed in connection with contemplated works:

- listed building consent

- conservation area consent

- where tree preservation orders exist

A major reference for the safety of persons associated with the building process is the Health & Safety at Work Act 1974, which applies to the site investigation process as well as the construction phases of the project. Since the issue of the Building Regulations 1985 there has been a significant change in legislation concerning health and safety, and also environmental issues. The Management of Health & Safety Regulations 1992, which apply to firms with five or more employees, require the firm to adopt a formal approach to safety. This generally requires the establishment of a Safety Management System requiring consideration of methods of induction, risk assessment, method statements, consultation and audits of performance.

The Construction (Design & Management) Regulations 1994 (CDM) (effective from 31 March 1995) impose safety issues on contractors, employees and clients. Health and safety on site is now a critical part of most building works.

Brief summary of CDM needs

- The regulations apply when a job is to last more than 30 days or where five or more persons will be working on site at any one time.

- They share responsibility for health and safety between the client, designer and contractor.

- They suggest the need for the process of safety management to be considered as the design develops, to be carried over to the site, and then to be applied during the maintenance phases of the building.

- They imply that contractors are to take greater control of sites and greater responsibility for any failures in health and safety management.

- The contractor is to establish a Health and Safety Plan.

- The client is to appoint the Planning Supervisor (who has specific responsibilities for day-to-day health and safety matters on site) and the main contractor (referred to as the Principal Contractor).

Under this relatively new legislation the client has very specific responsibilities to check the competency of the main contributors to the project, namely the Planning Supervisor, the Design Team and the Principal Contractor. This means that before a person is selected (usually on a fee bid basis), the client has to check them out for suitability. Forms have been devised for this purpose which ask many questions of the party concerned in respect of previous experience in the areas of building and in safety issues. These forms are typically titled Pre-Qualification Questionnaire for Planning Supervisor, Design Team, or Principal Contractor. It should be stressed that these measures to be taken by a client are to fulfil a statutory duty, and are not therefore to be regarded as superficial.

The Health and Safety Plan is created by the Planning Supervisor in collaboration with the Principal Contractor. Allied to this, the Planning Supervisor will establish and maintain a Health and Safety File on site which will be passed to the client for later use during work on the building.

The Environmental Protection Act 1990 (EPA) and the Environment Act 1995 have had a major impact on procedures on site and also in respect of legal responsibilities related to site pollution. The EPA has also dealt with the issue of hazardous waste disposal and has established the present Landfill Tax system which provides for dangerous waste material to be handled by licensed tips. As there is a charge per tonne for disposal of the hazardous waste this may produce a considerable expense, which could even affect the viability of projects. Remember that, in terms of the Developer's Equation, if there is an increase in development costs this has a direct influence on profit.

Reflective summary

With reference to Statutory Control, remember:

— This is a process only recently applied in the history of building.

— The first national set of Building Regulations was published in 1965.

— Formal approval to build generally involves two processes – Building Regulation approval and Planning Permission.

— Health and safety are now important issues.

— Major references for health and safety include:
  • the CDM regulations
  • the COSHH (Control of Substances Hazardous to Health) regulations
  • the Health & Safety at Work Acts

— 'green' issues are now important

— Major references for green issues include:
  • the Environmental Protection Act 1990
  • the Environment Act 1995

 ## Review task

What *two* processes are normally undertaken when seeking formal approval to build from a local authority ?

What are the CDM regulations and when do these apply?

2.4 Overview of utilities and infrastructure

Introduction

After studying this section you should be able to explain the content and significance of infrastructure in the development of dwellings. You should also be aware of the entry details of utility services to individual properties.

Overview

Utility services supplied to a residential development relate to the public utility services of water, electricity, gas and sewers. The term 'infrastructure' also includes items such as roads, footpaths and street lighting. These items represent early expenditure on the project, as they are installed or completed before work really commences on individual house units. The extensive cost associated with them is generally divided among the house units when setting retail prices.

Cold water supply

It is a requirement of the Water Act that every dwelling should be provided with a drinking water supply. On its way to a house the water passes through various processes and often along extensive pipelines. Figure 2.5 shows this route and indicates the pressures needed to overcome resistances in the pipe and fluctuations in demand, ensuring that sufficient pressure is available for correct delivery. The water provided may come from a variety of sources, including reservoirs and underground wells.

The water main supplying residential developments is normally located in the public footpath outside the boundary of the house units. At this location a water company stopcock is normally positioned to allow the water supply to the individual house to be cut off without the need to enter the boundary of the property. From this point the water pipe supplying the house is termed the cold water service pipe (Figure 2.6). As shown in the illustration, this service pipe is buried some distance in the ground to avoid damage and prevent freezing in cold weather. In the UK the ground rarely freezes beyond 600 mm depth so at 1 m depth this pipe should be safe.

The service pipe was traditionally made of lead, but as we now appreciate that lead may dissolve into the water and affect health, the pipe is now made of high-

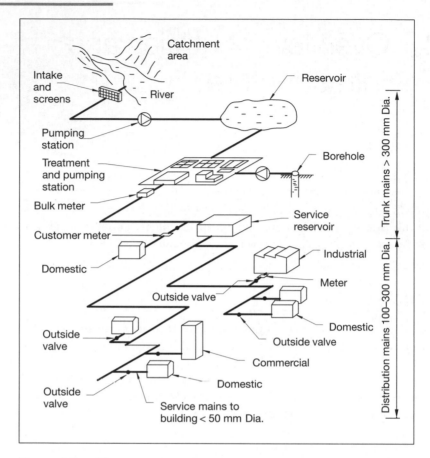

Figure 2.5 ● Water supply national distribution.

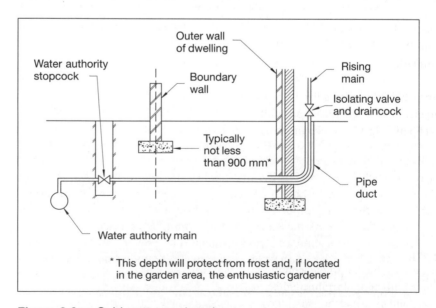

Figure 2.6 ● Cold water service pipe.

density polythene. To assist in identification on site this pipe is bright mid-blue in colour. As the pipe is flexible it will assist entry to the property if a duct of drain pipe material or similar is used through the external wall and extended to the top of the ground floor to allow the pipe to be threaded through.

Once this pipe emerges beyond floor level a stopcock is used to allow the occupier to close down the cold water supply in the event of a pipe burst or while undergoing maintenance work. On leaving the stopcock this cold water supply pipe is referred to as the *rising main* as it moves up through the property, generally terminating at the cold water storage tank.

Electricity supply

As with the supply of water, an established delivery network is the means for conveying electricity supplies to residential developments. Again, as with the water supply, resistance has to be overcome and sufficient capacity provided to ensure adequate supplies to the consumer. This time the resistance is, of course, electrical resistance rather than friction.

To ensure that the correct strength of supply is provided to the householder, the National Grid for distribution has to carry some extremely large voltages, as shown in the illustration. As we get nearer to the point of use a series of reductions in voltage is ensured by the use of transformers. In the footpath to a residential development we will generally have a three-phase four-wire supply: three live wires and one neutral. Between each of the live wires the voltage potential is now 415 V and between any of the live wires and the neutral wire 240 V. This means that to tap into the cable in the footpath outside the boundary to the house we need to connect to one live (phase) and the neutral to connect the property (Figure 2.7). This 240 V supply is termed single phase, as only one live wire is used.

The underground wires are wrapped in protective covers as they are brought to the house. Modern housing has a meter box on the outside wall, accessible from outside the premises for meter reading purposes and similar to those illustrated later for incoming gas supplies.

Gas supply

Gas was previously generated by processing coal and was referred to as 'town gas'. This was not a very environmentally friendly fuel because of the carbon placed in the atmosphere during production. However, most of the gas consumed in the UK is now natural gas, methane from natural tapped pockets buried below ground. This natural gas has a much higher calorific value (heat produced per unit), but requires more air to assist in the combustion process than its old rival. In terms of national distribution (Figure 2.8) there is now an established pipework network and, similar to moving water through pipes, the gas requires significant pressures to ensure that a constant supply is available.

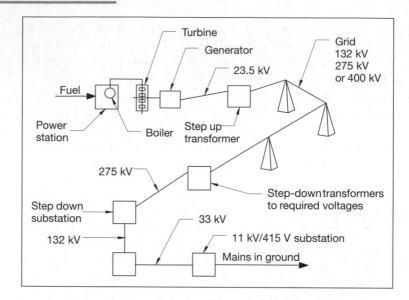

Figure 2.7 ● House and tapping into a three-phase supply.

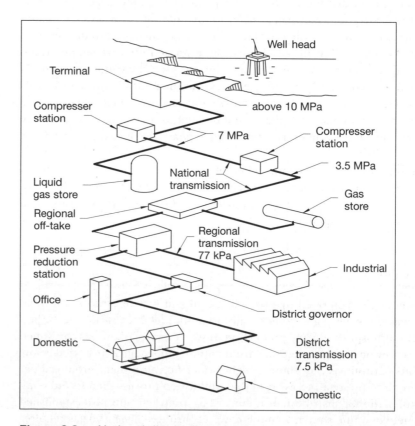

Figure 2.8 ● National distribution of gas.

High-pressure supplies need, of course, to be reduced as they move towards the final consumer, and even the house gas meter has its own pressure governor fixed to the inward connection of the gas meter.

Supplies of gas tend to be conveyed in high-density plastic pipes, as with the water supply, but this time are coloured yellow for identification purposes. The supply main is often in the pathway or road beyond the house boundary, and the supply is brought in below ground. On modern house developments a meter box is typically used of the same type as for the incoming electricity supply. Figure 2.9 shows a common way to bring the supply into the premises, and ducts are often used as penetration of the wall is achieved to protect the supply from damage.

Having services of different types in close proximity as they are routed to a development may be an advantage, but it can create some difficulties; damage when gaining access is not uncommon.

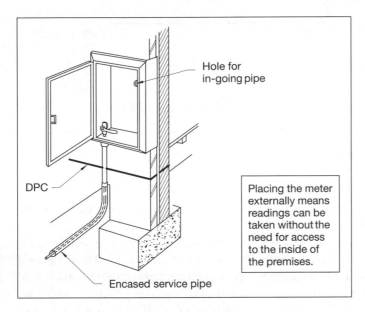

Hole for in-going pipe

DPC

Placing the meter externally means readings can be taken without the need for access to the inside of the premises.

Encased service pipe

Figure 2.9 ● External gas meter box.

Drain connections

Below ground drainage is provided to move waste water from the property, and pick-up points for this are generally located around the outer perimeter of the house. Many of these drain runs begin with a gully – for example where rain-water discharges from downpipes to the drain or where waste pipes leave the property containing discharges from sanitary appliances, such as kitchen sinks, baths and washbasins. Figure 2.10 shows a drainage layout typically used. Occasionally we pick up the discharges from an internal ground floor toilet (WC) which is inside the external walls of the property, and such connections require the drain pipes to be brought in and set into the ground floor long before the toilet itself is positioned.

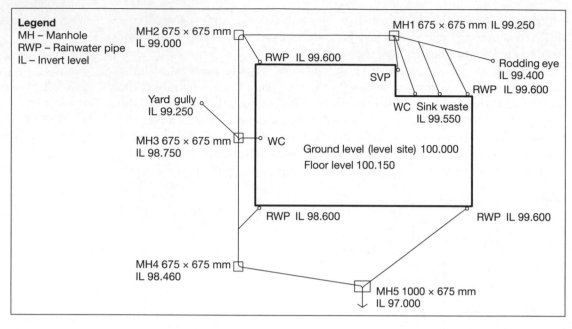

Figure 2.10 ● Combined drainage system.

In older properties the drainage systems for foul water and surface or rainwater were combined. This resulted in excessive quantities of water being treated at the sewage treatment plant. Newer systems separate rainwater and foul water to reduce the amount of water that must be treated

Drains are more often than not connected to a sewer which will carry the discharges to a treatment plant.

Water discharges from housing tend to be divided into two types: surface water discharges and foul discharges. Surface water is rainwater collected from the roof of the property, which by its nature needs no treatment as such. By contrast, foul discharges are those which originate at a sanitary appliance (bath, basin, sink, shower or toilet), and clearly these need treatment at a treatment plant. Recognising the benefit of separating the rainwater from the foul water in terms of the total volume of material requiring treatment it is best that a *separate system* of drainage is employed. Here all the rainwater collected goes into one set of drain pipes and all the foul water into another set of drain pipes. Each of these pipe systems then discharges into a separate sewer, one for rainwater and another for the foul water.

Some new developments connect to existing sewers. Where this is the case and where only one sewer exists both rainwater and foul water will be discharged into this one sewer. Here drains surrounding the building mix rainwater and foul water together and are referred to as a *combined system* as shown in Figure 2.10.

In Figure 2.10 the designation IL means 'Invert Level'. This is the lowest point on the interior bore of the pipe measured at any location in the drainage system. Smaller values of invert level indicate that the pipe is getting deeper into the ground as the dimensions draw closer to the base level of 0.00 m, which is the reference level from which all heights are measured.

Case study

Installation of drainage services at an early stage of construction

The connections for sanitary appliances must be catered for early in the construction sequence. Here we see the soil pipe for a WC passing through the ground floor and external wall below ground level. The connections to the pipe will be made later.

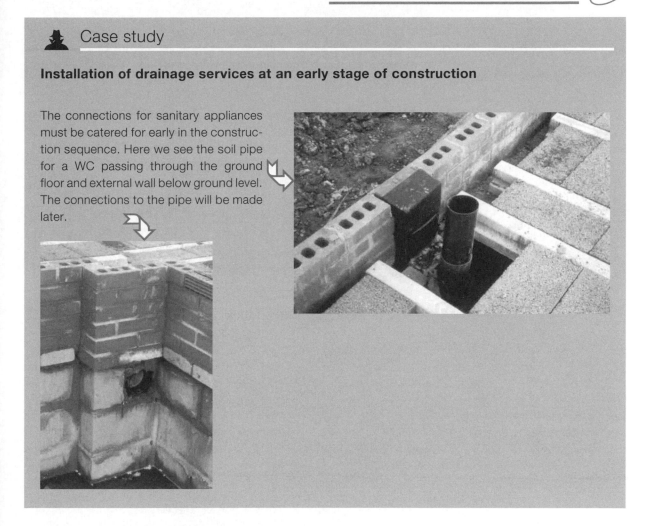

Shared access, roads and footpaths

Infrastructure items include shared facilities, such as those provided for access. Roads to residential developments are generally partly formed for access during the construction operations and only finished at the very end of the project. The sewers are located below the various layers of material used for the body of the road. Where the development has two sewers – surface water and foul water – the rainwater collected by the road drainage will generally discharge into the surface water sewer. The only compromise to this is the *partially separate system*, where rainwater from roads is collected by the foul sewer and only rainwater from house roofs goes into the surface water sewer.

Excavation for the road will suit the prevailing ground levels and slopes. Many access roads are cambered and slope from the centre of the carriageway to the kerbs on each side. Others slope in one direction only for directing rainwater off the surface, and this of course means road gully locations to one side of the carriageway only. Kerbs set in concrete to the edges of the road locate its boundary during the laying of the materials for the road body. These have shapes which comply with BS 7263.

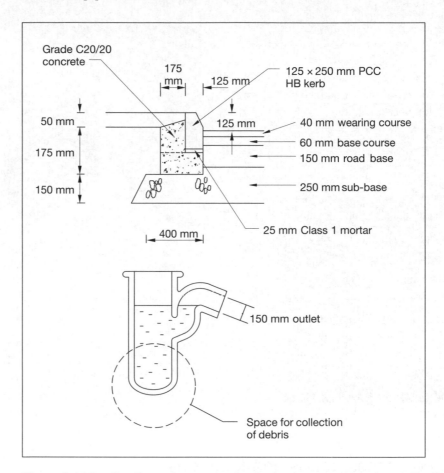

Figure 2.11 Section through an example of a road pavement and a road gully.

Tarmacadam is the standard surface for road pavements. Figure 2.11 illustrates that this material tends to be applied in layers with a base course underlying a wearing course. Footpaths may also be laid in tarmac on a hardcore (stone) base (Figure 2.12).

Various alternative forms of footpath are illustrated in Figure 2.13.

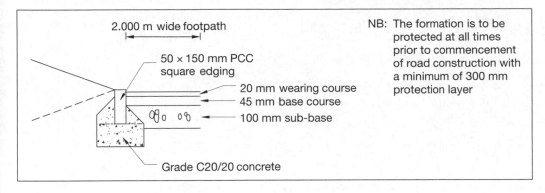

NB: The formation is to be protected at all times prior to commencement of road construction with a minimum of 300 mm protection layer

2.000 m wide footpath

50 × 150 mm PCC square edging

20 mm wearing course

45 mm base course

100 mm sub-base

Grade C20/20 concrete

Figure 2.12 Section through a tarmacadam footpath.

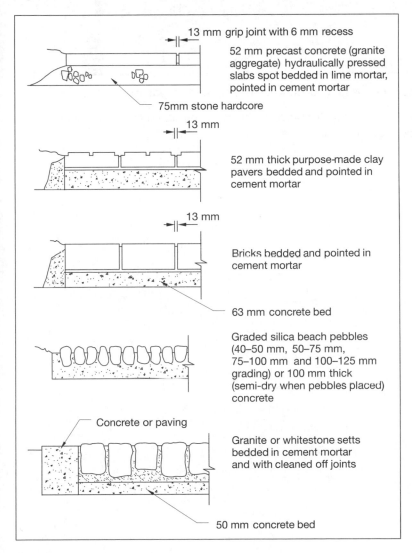

13 mm grip joint with 6 mm recess

52 mm precast concrete (granite aggregate) hydraulically pressed slabs spot bedded in lime mortar, pointed in cement mortar

75mm stone hardcore

13 mm

52 mm thick purpose-made clay pavers bedded and pointed in cement mortar

13 mm

Bricks bedded and pointed in cement mortar

63 mm concrete bed

Graded silica beach pebbles (40–50 mm, 50–75 mm, 75–100 mm and 100–125 mm grading) or 100 mm thick (semi-dry when pebbles placed) concrete

Concrete or paving

Granite or whitestone setts bedded in cement mortar and with cleaned off joints

50 mm concrete bed

Figure 2.13 External paving details.

Reflective summary

With reference to utility services and infrastructure, remember:

— Infrastructure can be regarded as items which will be shared by the houses of the development: *roads*, *footpaths*, *sewers*, and incoming services such as *water*, *electricity* and *gas*.

— Connections to incoming service supplies must be considered early in the building process.

— There tends to be a set position of one service relative to another, and colour coding the services helps identification.

Review task

What colours are used to identify gas pipes and cold water pipes?

How does the type of material carried by below-ground drain pipes lead to a classification system for the pipes?

2.5   Preparing the site for use

Introduction

After studying this section you should be able to appreciate the typical stages that occur when excavation is undertaken for a property. You should also understand the content and significance of Part C of the Building Regulations and be able to identify some of the works which may be used to improve the quality of the site, either permanently or temporarily.

Overview

On sites where contamination is not an issue there will be other preparatory works to do before the building can commence, and this is also recognised by Building Regulations Part C. Clause C1 refers to the need to have the ground covered by the building reasonably free of vegetable matter. This will mean stripping the site of growing vegetation, but also it will necessitate the removal of topsoil.

As more land is consumed for building there is a drive to preserve green field sites in favour of brown field sites. As a result, developments on land that was previously seen as contaminated or derelict are becoming more common. Hence the technology of contamination remediation is advancing rapidly.

Most sites in the UK will naturally have a layer of topsoil of varying thickness overlying the ground strata below. This topsoil layer is aerated and loamy and ideal for the growth of plant life and grass. We would not want plants to be growing below the building, but another important reason for the removal of topsoil is the fact that it is of little if any bearing strength. If we placed the structure directly onto this layer it would sink. The thickness of the topsoil layer will be one of the features provided by the site investigation process, and typically we would expect 150–300 mm. Once removed, the normal procedure would be to store the soil on site in spoil heaps for later reuse for planting and grassed areas.

When we start to excavate the topsoil we will be usually commencing at Original Ground Level, and when we have finished we are at Strip Level. In the earthworks undertaken for the construction of a typical house there are a number of terms and abbreviations used to identify the various levels reached, and these ordinarily come into consideration when dealing with the excavation needed for floors. However, we will illustrate these at this stage as a preamble to the section dealing with floors.

Designers will generally specify the finished level that is needed for the internal floor of a building, and this will be by reference to the national system of levels that is used in the UK. This system uses its base level as 0.00 m, which is mean sea level at Newlyn in Cornwall. The system is referred to as Ordnance Datum. All levels of ground and buildings throughout the UK are relative to this level and give the height in metres (previously feet) above this level. In Figure 2.14 the

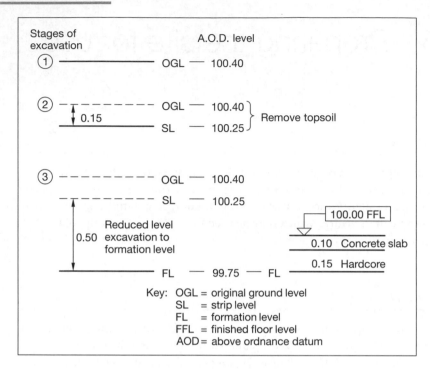

Figure 2.14 ⬤ Identifying stages in excavation.

internal Finished Floor Level (FFL) is set as a result of consideration of the general levels of the site being developed and mindful of the fact that we require the internal floor to be above outer ground level to help us protect the building from moisture entry. This is also the subject of clause C4 of the Building Regulations, Part C, which requires the floors, walls and roof to resist moisture entry.

Clause C3 of Part C of the Building Regulations refers to the possible need to apply subsoil drainage to lower ground moisture levels, protecting the fabric of the building in the ground and reducing the chance of the movement of moisture into the building. Subsoil or *land drains* are quite different from the drain pipes that we use to carry the discharges of the house's sanitary appliances, particularly in the fact that they are either porous or perforated. Clearly, with the discharges from sanitary appliances we have to use impervious pipes to contain the material as it is carried to the point of discharge.

Land drainage trenches (Figure 2.15) are generally filled with granular material rather than earth to speed the passage of water down to the collecting pipework. An illustration of the application of this type of drainage is shown in Figure 2.16. Here the house is to be placed at the foot of some sloping ground and the aim of the drainage system is to intercept water running off the face of the sloping ground during or following rainfall.

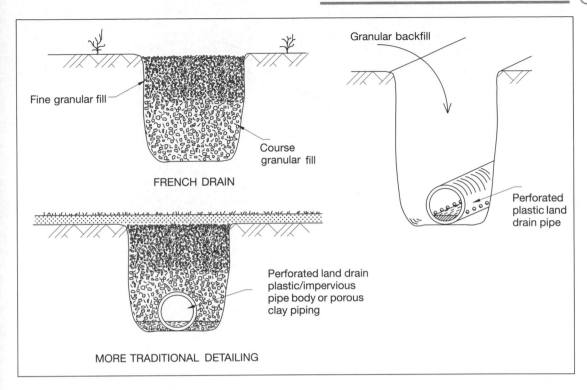

Figure 2.15 ● Land drainage trenches.

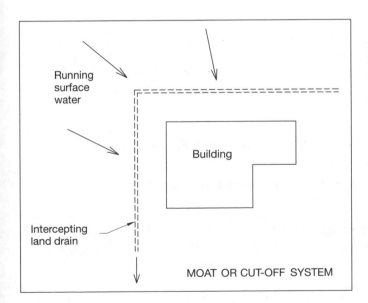

Figure 2.16 ● The moat system of land drainage.

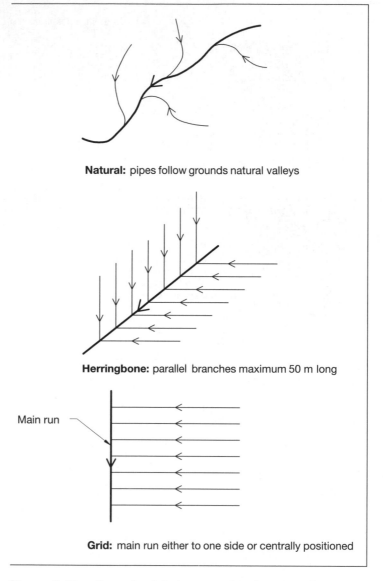

Natural: pipes follow grounds natural valleys

Herringbone: parallel branches maximum 50 m long

Main run

Grid: main run either to one side or centrally positioned

Figure 2.17 ● Some land drainage system layout options.

The pipe layout for the land drainage system may vary from one which follows the natural valleys and contours of the land (natural) to others devised to collect efficiently from the shape of the site in question. Figure 2.17 shows some of the options.

As the land drain is only to collect rainwater (surface water), there is no need to collect it for treatment. We simply need to collect it to prevent nuisance or to help improve the stability of the ground, and once collected there are therefore a number of options for disposal. Some of these options are illustrated in Figure 2.18.

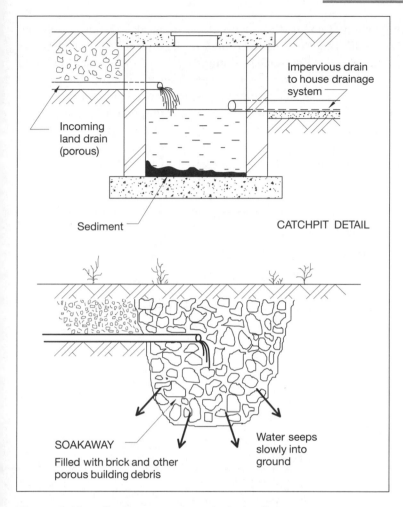

Impervious drain
to house drainage
system

Incoming
land drain
(porous)

Sediment

CATCHPIT DETAIL

SOAKAWAY

Filled with brick and other
porous building debris

Water seeps
slowly into
ground

Figure 2.18 ● Soakaway and catchpit details.

The catchpit detail is effectively a break in the pipe to allow sediment to be collected before connecting the water to the true house drainage system. Without a catchpit a serious threat exists of sediment carried by the groundwater filling the house drainage pipes and disrupting the flow.

These solutions are permanent methods of water control, but we may wish to lower the groundwater level or control water in some other way on a temporary rather than permanent basis. Water levels in the ground can be substantially reduced on a temporary basis by using the technique of dewatering. Here we surround the excavation area with well extraction points, which consist of perforated steel tubes which are connected with flexible hoses to a larger pipe that encircles the excavation site. This larger ring pipe is then connected to a pump. To sink the well pipes (generally referred to as *well points*) we force water around the horizontal ring pipe and down the well point. By doing this we jet a cavity by pressurised water allowing the pipe to be sunk to the desired level. Once this is achieved the well point is surrounded by granular material to act as a filter when the pump is reversed and the water is extracted from the ground. Figure 2.19 shows how the water level in the ground may be influenced by the technique.

If we did not wish to lower the water table level but simply protect the excavation site from water we could use some temporary steel sheet piling as an intercepting barrier to the water. When such a barrier is formed into a complete enclosure surrounding the area of the site we call it a cofferdam (Figure 2.20).

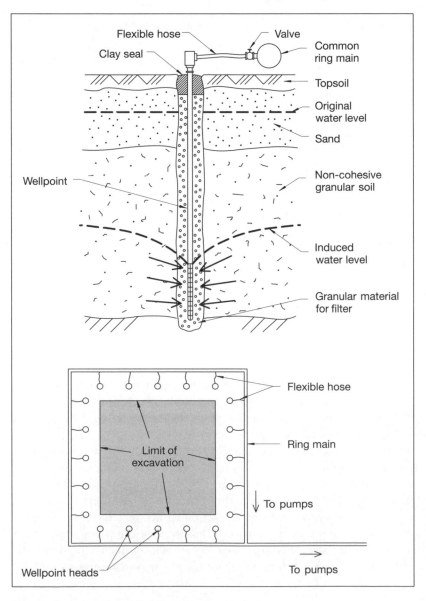

Figure 2.19 ● Well point dewatering system.

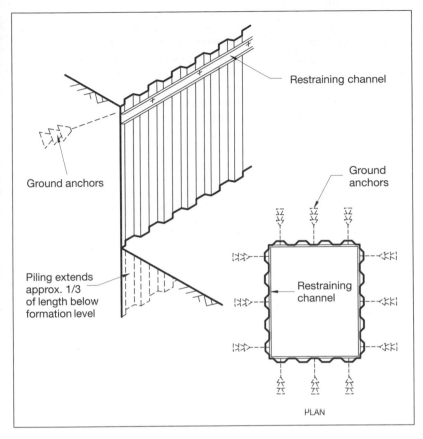

PLAN

Figure 2.20 ● Steel sheet piled cofferdam.

Reflective summary

With reference to site preparation, remember:

— Topsoil removal is essential to discourage plant growth and to remove a layer of insignificant bearing strength.

— Land drain pipes are either porous or perforated, unlike drain pipes taking the discharges from the building, which need to be impervious.

— Ground contamination is increasingly common when undertaking new housing developments because of the lack of availability of previously unused land.

Review task

Which part of the Building Regulations extensively applies to preparatory works for a new building site?

Define the abbreviations SL and FL, which are associated with the excavation works needed for the formation of a ground floor.

2.6 Methods of building

Introduction

After studying this section you should have developed an understanding of the ways in which the building process has evolved. You should also be familiar with the varying approaches to building, from the traditional to the industrialised, and you should be able to identify the key aspects of each.

Overview

Buildings are formed by the assembly of large numbers of individual elements and components, of varying size and complexity. Historically the production and assembly of these components would have taken place on-site. As discussed in Chapter 1, vernacular architecture has developed as a result of the ability to fabricate components from locally available building materials. This was dictated by limitations in the ability to transport materials and fabricated components over even modest distances. With advances in transport networks and technology, notably during the Industrial Revolution, it became possible to transport materials and components over large distances. These advances introduced not only the possibility of using non-local materials, but also of producing even sizable components away from the site. The possibility of mass producing components in a factory environment initiated a change in approach to the whole building process, with the beginnings of industrialised building.

Traditional building

As discussed earlier, building form has historically been dictated by the availability of building materials, the local climate and the lifestyle of the population. The needs of nomadic peoples to re-site their dwellings regularly imposes very different constraints on building form from those of people with a more static lifestyle. These forms of vernacular architecture could be considered to be the results of truly traditional building production. The nature of traditional building as it exists at present derives from this type of construction and the principles involved in it.

The use of traditional, labour-intensive, building crafts in the production of buildings is now restricted to the building of individually designed, 'one-off' structures or the area of specialised building refurbishment. The cost implications of such a building method are considerable, with highly trained craftsmen fabricating components on-site, although a number of pre-fabricated components

In recent years there has been a growth in the adoption of timber frame house construction. The term 'traditional' has become associated with masonry construction and, in particular, cavity wall construction of dwellings. In its true sense, however, it can be taken to refer to a process involving site manufacture of components that is highly labour-intensive.

would inevitably be used in all but very specialised cases. The nature of this method, in which most parts of the buildings are formed from a number of small parts, made to fit on-site, is inherently slow. Hence its use for large buildings, or large numbers of buildings, in today's economic climate, where time and cost are of the essence, is impractical.

There are, however, a number of advantages in the adoption of this method, in that it allows tremendous flexibility, with the potential to ensure that all parts can be adapted to ensure a good standard of fit, since all parts are 'made to fit'. This allows for flexibility both during the construction stage and throughout the life of the building. Elements of this mode of construction are still to be found in some modern building, such as house building using traditional rafter and purlin roofs. In this case the roof structure is fabricated by carpenters, on site, from straight lengths of timber. Even this type of traditional building has become rare, with increased levels of off-site fabrication.

One of the main disadvantages of traditional building using on-site fabrication and the formation of components *in situ*, is the difficulty of manufacturing components in a hostile location. The vagaries of the climate and conditions which prevail on site restrict the ability to work to fine tolerances and to fabricate elements with consistency. Although building is essentially a manufacturing process, the conditions in which it is undertaken are far removed from those in a cosseted factory environment. The disadvantages of cost, time and uniformity of standards of quality, together with difficulties in obtaining suitably skilled labour have resulted in the adoption of what has become known as 'conventional' or 'post-traditional' building.

Post-traditional building

The evolutionary nature of the building process, with the periodic introduction of new materials and new techniques, has ensured that even traditional building has developed and progressed significantly in the past. Examples of such develop-ments are the introduction of ordinary Portland cement, allowing the production of large, complex building sections by casting of concrete, and the development of reinforcing techniques using steel, allowing very strong sections to be produced. Such advances in building technology, allied with the need to mini-mise construction time and cost, resulted in the adoption of the post-traditional method of building. It must be noted, also, that this would not have been possible without the advent of developments in transport mechanisms. These have allowed non-local materials to be transported to the site and components to be produced some distance away for transportation to the site.

This form of building is a combination of traditional, labour-intensive, craft-based methods of construction, with newer techniques, utilising modern plant and materials. The use of mechanical plant is one area where post-traditional building differs greatly from traditional building. Post-traditional construction is often adopted for the erection of buildings of large scale. In such instances, the craft-based techniques of traditional building, such as plastering and joinery, are not dismissed from the construction process, but rather are aided by the use of mechanised plant. Machinery used for earth moving, lifting of elements and mixing of concrete and plaster is now essential on most building sites as a result of the magnitude of the operations being undertaken. Additionally, increased use is made of pre-fabricated components, manufactured in large numbers, in factory conditions. Hence an element of industrialisation was introduced into the construction process. The nature of the building design has not evolved to the extent of system building, where a series of standard parts may be used to produce the end product. Instead, the mass-produced components are placed and finished in a typically traditional way, using traditional crafts such as joinery and plastering. An example of this approach is the use of pre-fabricated trussed rafters for roof construction, in favour of the traditional site-fabricated rafter and purlin form of construction. It is now very unusual to find the on-site fabrication of components such as windows and doors, which can be produced more cheaply and to higher quality standards in a factory environment. Although the traditional building activities have, in essence, changed little, the scale of post-traditional building, together with the demands of cost and time effectiveness, have placed great importance on the active planning of building operations. It is this planning to ensure efficiency which is one of the main trade marks of post-traditional construction.

Rationalised and industrialised building

Rationalised building, as considered today, is the undertaking of the construction of buildings, adopting the organisational practices of manufacturing industries, as much as this is possible, with the previously described limitations of the construction industry. Such an approach to the construction process does not necessarily imply the adoption of industrialised building techniques, but is more usually based upon the organisation and planning of commonly used existing techniques. The key to the effective use of rationalised building is ensuring the continuity of all production involved in all stages of the overall construction process. This continuity relies upon the evolution of building designs to allow full integration of design and production at all stages. The aim of this process of building is to ensure cost-effective construction of often large and complex buildings, within given time parameters, while maintaining acceptable standards of quality. This requires the construction process to be, as near as possible, continuous, hence necessitating the efficient provision of all resources in the form of labour, plant, materials and information. This can, to some extent, be enhanced by the use of standardised, pre-fabricated components and effective use of mechanical plant, thus separating fabrication from assembly and reducing on-site labour costs. It will be seen that this approach is a logical evolution from post-traditional construction.

In the later part of the 20th century, notably in the 1960s, great demands were placed upon builders to construct buildings quickly and cheaply. To cope with these demands, systems of building were developed based upon the use of standard pre-fabricated components to be assembled on-site, largely removing the reliance upon traditional building techniques. Such systems attempted to introduce industrial assembly techniques to the building site. This approach is often termed 'system building'. Within this description two basic approaches exist: Open System and Closed System building.

Open systems of building, often referred to as component building, utilise a variety of factory-produced standard components, often sourced from a variety of manufacturers, to create a building of the desired type. The construction of buildings adopting this approach makes little or no use of the traditional 'cut and fit' techniques of traditional and post-traditional building. An example of such an approach is the construction of lightweight industrial buildings, which are based upon designs that utilise a selection of mass-produced components that are not exclusive to the specific building. Hence flexibility of design is maintained.

In contrast, closed systems adopt an approach which utilises a dedicated series of components, specific to the individual building and not interchangeable with components made by other manufacturers. Such a method is beneficial to the speedy and efficient erection of buildings when aided by the use of large-scale mechanical plant. These systems, however, do not allow the adaptation of the design on- or off-site. This can be very restricting, particularly during the later life of the building, when changing user needs may require flexibility in the design. Such systems have also been subject, in the past, to many problems associated with on-site quality control and lack of durability of materials. These problems arose, in part, from a lack of familiarity of the workforce with the new building techniques, the use of untried materials and the need to construct quickly, thus encouraging the short-cutting of some site practices. The occurrence of such problems and the inherent lack of flexibility in buildings of this type have resulted in the general rejection of closed systems in favour of open systems.

Accuracy in building

In traditional construction, accuracy in building was to some extent ensured by the ability to make components to fit specific spaces. This ability to be flexible in the production of elements of the building has been removed to a great extent, as many components are fabricated away from the site. The industrialised manufacture of components dictates an increased emphasis on the accuracy of component sizes in order to ensure that mismatches are reduced to a minimum on-site.

The use of factory-produced building materials and components in even small-scale post-traditional construction has resulted in some standardisation of building component dimensions. For example, the widespread use of plaster-board, which is manufactured in a range of sizes based on multiples, or modules, of 600 mm, is made more efficient if minimal cutting of panels is required. Hence room sizes based on 600 mm modules are common, thus reducing fixing time and wastage of materials on-site. Such an approach is also evident in the manufacture of components which are designed to fit into openings in brick walls, such as windows, which are manufactured in a range of sizes which correspond to multiples of whole brick sizes. This is termed a modular approach to component size. Such an approach is based on simple logic, and is of increased importance when related to the construction of larger, more complex, buildings. When dealing with larger buildings, the size and number of components which must be assembled increases substantially. The degree of accuracy with which they are assembled must be adequate to ensure that the building is erected without undue difficulty and without the risk of compromising its performance. The modularisation of such buildings is immensely beneficial in maintaining an acceptable degree of building accuracy. This is sometimes effected by the use of 'dimensional coordination'. Dimensional coordination relies on the establishment of a notional three-dimensional grid, within which the building components are assembled. The grid allows for some variation of component size, providing a zone within which the maximum and minimum allowable sizes of a given component will fit. This variation in the sizes of elements of buildings is inevitable for a variety of reasons, including:

- Some inaccuracy in manufacture is unavoidable because of the manufacturing technique. The production of a component in concrete is subject to size variation as a result of drying shrinkage following casting, together with great limitations in the manufacture of very accurate formwork.

- The high cost of producing components with great accuracy may be substantial and considered unnecessary in a given situation; hence a degree of variation in size may be accepted.

- The accuracy of location of the component, resulting from fixing variations also has some effect.

Hence building components are not designed to fit exactly into a given space or position of a given dimension. Instead, allowances are made for jointing and component linking, taking into account possible variations. For these and other reasons, including the need to allow for thermal and moisture-induced variation in size following construction, a degree of allowable variation or 'tolerance' in component size is an essential feature of modern building. The use of modular design and the allowance for tolerance, while maintaining acceptable accuracy, is of particular importance in the design and construction of system-built structures. In such buildings, ease, and consequently speed, of site assembly are of paramount importance. In such situations, the ease of assembly of the parts of the building depends upon a number of factors, including:

- the degree of accuracy with which components have been manufactured

- the degree of setting out accuracy on site

- the nature of construction and assembly methods on site

- the nature of jointing of components and the degree of tolerance which is acceptable in a given situation

The nature of the building process is such that there will be inevitable inaccuracy in site operations. Hence it is essential that components are made with this in mind. The ability to allow for site tolerances ensures that construction can progress smoothly. Without such an approach there could be problems that lead to delay in the construction sequence.

It must always be remembered that the production of components to very fine degrees of accuracy has a direct cost implication, which may not be justifiable in a given situation. For this reason, and those noted above, it is common to refer to component sizes of an acceptable range, rather than an exact dimension, this may be given in the form of a nominal dimension and an acceptable degree of variation, e.g. nominal size 1200 ± 10 mm. The degree of accuracy required depends on the exact situation of the components, but may be of particular importance where structure and services interrelate, since services are generally engineered with finer degrees of tolerance than is the building fabric.

Reflective summary

With reference to methods of building, remember

— Modern building can be classified as Traditional, Post-traditional or Rationalised.

— Traditional building tends to be more labour-intensive and more craft-based than other methods.

— The use of mechanised construction methods features heavily in the post-traditional style.

— Rationalised building involves the use of factory-produced components which may be interchangeable from a variety of suppliers (open systems), or of fixed type incapable of interchanging (closed systems).

— Accuracy is of paramount importance when dealing with the assembly of preformed factory-produced components, while labour-intensive traditional methods of building involve the site production of components made to fit the space available.

 ## Review task

What do you understand by 'system building'?

Distinguish between *open* and *closed* systems.

2.7   Building sequence

Introduction

After studying this section you should appreciate that the construction process for the completion of a building may be divided into stages or phases. You should also have an appreciation of the likely events that occur in the formation of a house and be familiar with the Plan of Work established by the Royal Institute of British Architects as a logical division of the building process.

Overview

The sequence of building may be viewed from two perspectives: the stages or phases into which the various building operations fall, or a more detailed examination of the sequence of operations involved in the construction of a specific residential unit. For the purpose of this section both of these views will be examined.

Building sequence – the phases or stages of construction

Some years ago, the Royal Institute of British Architects (RIBA) established its Plan of Work. This was to divide the entire building process into logical stages in order to consider what should be happening at each stage and what the responsibilities of the parties associated to the process should be at each stage. The typical headings of the stages produced are:

- *Inception*   first idea of the building
- *Feasibility*   cost projections
- *Outline proposals*   sketches
- *Scheme design*   some drawings
- *Detailed design*   working drawings
- *Production information*   specification etc.
- *Bill of quantities*   material needs
- *Tender action*   examine bids
- *Project planning*   programming work

- *Operations on site*   construction
- *Completion*   handover
- *Feedback*   review of success

Once these headings had been established it was possible to produce a sheet of stages for each of the parties involved with the process, so sheets outlining the duties of the Architect and the Quantity Surveyor, for example, were produced. This helped clarify the responsibilities of each person associated to the project, but also allowed better planning and evaluation of the time likely to be associated with the process.

To have stages allocated to the building process is extremely helpful for the control mechanism of cost planning. When a project is first thought of (inception), some rough outlines are given to the construction economist (often the QS) who is then asked to supply a likely contract figure with this bare minimum of information. The basis for this educated cost guesstimate is generally historic cost information stored from similar projects in the form of price per square metre of gross floor area (gfa). When a project is completed the final contract sum is divided by the gross floor area of the building (that is the floor area as measured to each floor inside the external walls and over any partitions or floor openings as if they were not there). The result is a cost per square metre.

We can take this figure, make some arithmetical adjustments for the time delay between storing the cost information and the date proposed for the new project (index-based), and then multiply the likely new building area by the cost per m^2 to arrive at the first likely cost estimate (feasibility – is this within the client's cost range?).

As the design develops and specifications are firmed up we can review the detailed specification of the new building against those of historic building and make adjustments for quality and quantity as appropriate. In this way a running likely project cost is refined as the design develops, and we should be able to ensure that the contract always falls within the purse of the client. If an overspend looks likely we would have an opportunity to reduce the specification and hence costs in a controlled and balanced way.

The way in which many construction contracts are arranged today (procurement) means that some of the details regarding the responsibilities of the professionals as listed on the Plan of Work may have changed, but the plan itself is still a useful breakdown today.

Building sequence – the stages in the construction of a house

When a house is constructed it is not possible to give an exact sequence of construction events, as activities are not always commenced as another is completed. It is common for some activities to be undertaken at the same time. For example, the electrical installation could be installed while work is undertaken to the plumbing. External landscaping and planting could be happening at the same time as a variety of other tasks.

However, it is possible to provide a broad appreciation of the typical overall activity sequence for the construction of a house.

Up to and including external wall DPC

Setting out   establishing the position of the building on the site

When setting out the building, one of the key markers is the frontage line, and from this the layout of the rest of the building develops using lines projected at right angles to show the width of the property. A theodolite, builder's square or Pythagoras' may be used to create the right angle (Figure 2.21).

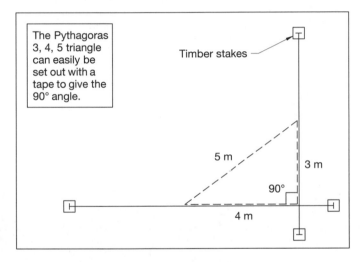

The Pythagoras 3, 4, 5 triangle can easily be set out with a tape to give the 90° angle.

Timber stakes

5 m

3 m

90°

4 m

Figure 2.21 ● Setting out a right angle.

Particularly when using strip footing foundations, we mark the position of the trenches for the excavator using profile boards (Figure 2.22). String can be stretched between these boards to represent the position of the trench and also the position of the wall.

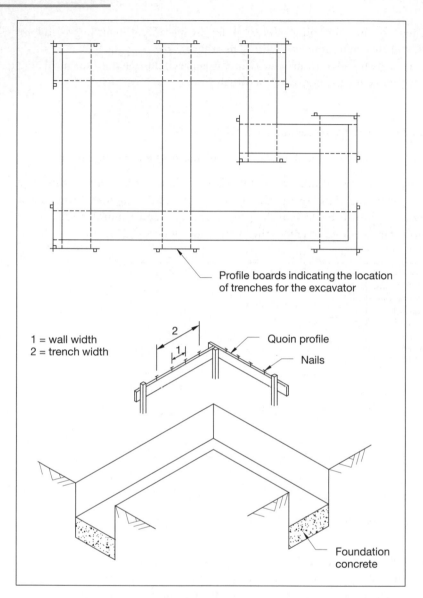

Profile boards indicating the location of trenches for the excavator

1 = wall width
2 = trench width

Quoin profile

Nails

Foundation concrete

Figure 2.22 ● The use of profile boards to mark trench positions.

Excavation	of topsoil down to formation level (point of commencing floor)
	foundation trenches (assuming strip footings)
	compaction of trench bottoms
Concrete	in strip foundations
Services	route and position incoming services (and occasionally outgoing ground floor WCs), including ducts through walls to inside floor level as needed
	install below ground drainage system

	form trench(es) for incoming water, electricity, gas, telecommunications
Brickwork/blockwork	common bricks or blocks in foundation trenches
	facing bricks to outer skin up to DPC (three courses minimum is usual)
Filling	stone hardcore to floor slab and to inner part of foundation trenches
	sand blinding to hardcore surface
	the cavity to external ground level with mortar
Membranes	damp-proof membrane (DPM) (polythene sheeting, e.g. Visqueen) turned over inner skin of external wall and any internal walls which have foundations
Insulation	possible rigid board insulation for floor slab
Concrete	to floor slab (assuming solid floor slab)

Above external wall DPC

Brickwork/blockwork	construct external wall blockwork, place insulation and attach holding ties, lay brickwork
	form openings for windows and doors, including building in lintels, cavity tie/weephole arrangements and closing cavity
	construct brickwork/blockwork to internal partitions, all to first floor level
Woodwork	fix first floor joists
	fix staircase
Brickwork/blockwork	continue with external walls and window openings
Roofing	fix wall plate above inner external wall skin
	locate and fix trussed rafter roof structure
	fix sarking felt and tile roof and flashings
Partitions	fix the first floor partition carcass (assuming that all first floor partitions are non-loadbearing studded type)
Services	provide first fix for electrical (cables in)
	provide first fix for plumbing and heating (pipes in)
Windows and external doors	fix in position
Woodwork	apply floor boarding to first floor
Finishes	apply plasterboard and *in situ* plaster finishes
	apply floor screed to ground floor (if not power floated)

Woodwork	fix skirting boards
Services	second fix electrical (lights, sockets and switches)
	second fix plumbing (sanitary appliances and connections)
	second fix heating (equipment and radiators)
	electricity company connection of supply
	commission services on completion including test of below ground drainage
Fittings	install cupboards
	fit kitchen
Painting	externally and internally
External works	landscaping, grass laying, planting, boundary fencing/walls and paths

The completion of activities such as are listed above may be charted and a time allocated to them in order to produce a programme for the works. This would allow examination of progress to ensure that completion on time is achieved. This may not be such an issue for a single property, but if the project was a residential development of sixty units the establishment of a programme would be extremely useful.

Reflective summary

With reference to the sequence of building, remember:

— It is convenient to divide the construction process into a series of stages.

— An established layout for the division of these stages is the RIBA Plan of Work.

— It is not always possible to place all construction activities into a rigid sequence, as many of them happen at the same time.

— It is common to divide the construction activities into those which occur in the ground and up to DPC level, and those which occur above DPC level.

— If we list the activities of construction and allocate a time to the completion of each activity we have then established a construction programme, and this may be used to monitor progress.

 ## Review task

Explain the purpose of the RIBA Plan of Work.

What do the first three stages of the RIBA plan involve?

2.8 Expenditure on building

Introduction

After studying this section you should gain an appreciation of the link between expenditure and time while constructing a property. You should appreciate that an *S curve* profile is the way in which we may represent expenditure commitments during the construction process.

Overview

The nature of the building industry is such that the vast majority of houses are built for profit by developers. In a relatively small number of cases the construction of dwellings is commissioned by individuals who are not driven by the developer's equation that was discussed earlier. However, most house building is speculative, and the developer's equation is the key to the viability of the project; hence the control of building costs is essential.

The expenditure profile of any construction contract is directly related to the sequence of building operations. In the case of most housing developments, the 'contract' will generally encompass the entire development, which will include several individual dwellings. There are a number of implications arising from this kind of project, relating to the fact that the completion of individual units or phases of the contract is achieved prior to completion of the entire project. It is common to see housing developments in which differing stages of the construction process are visible at one time. Indeed, it is normal for parts of the development to be occupied by purchasers while other parts are in the early stages of construction. The reason for this is related to the developer's equation and the need to generate income on the project as well as controlling expenditure.

Building costs

The total cost of a building project is made up of a number of individual elements, in addition to the cost of the materials, labour and plant used for the building itself. Aspects of setting up the site, providing insurance and so on are all elements that have a cost implication. These are often referred to as *preliminary items* and are normally included within the overall costings on the basis of a percentage addition to each costed item or as specific items identified within the project costings. It is not the purpose of this book to consider the nature of construction contracts and tendering; hence, we will not consider the basis of pricing in detail. However, it is important to understand the nature of the total project costs and the individual elements that it comprises. This was considered to some extent when the developer's equation was introduced, although the elements were not set out in detail. Since every construction project is individual, it is not possible to set out a definitive list of items of expenditure. Table 2.2 sets out the typical list of items included within the total cost of a building project from the point at which work commences on site, but this should not be considered as definitive.

Table 2.2 ● Items included in cost of building project.

Item	Description	Phasing
Statutory and other fees	Costs associated with inspection of the works in progress, insurances and guarantees such as NHBC	Various stages within the project
Insurances	Public and employer's liability insurance, together with insurances for equipment, plant and buildings paid by the contractor and subcontractors	Normally paid at the outset of the project
Utilities connections	Costs of connecting to gas, electric, water, drainage and other utility services	During the early stages of the project
Temporary works	Protective hoardings, scaffolding, fencing, temporary supplies of power, water etc.	At the early stages of the project
Accommodation and facilities	Site accommodation for offices, canteen facilities, toilets, secure storage of plant and equipment etc.	At the outset of the project
Plant hire	Hire of specific items of plant and equipment, such as excavators and hoists	Throughout the project
Infrastructure	Roads, access and services installation	At the early stages of the project
Labour	Costs of skilled and unskilled labour to undertake the work, including supervision costs	Throughout the project
Plant	Costs of purchase, hire or depreciation of existing plant involved in the works	Throughout the project
Materials	Costs of materials and components used in the building process	Throughout the project
Making good	Costs associated with removal of temporary works and making good damage to any areas affected by the works outside the boundaries of the site	At the end of the project

Expenditure profile

As previously stated, the majority of house building projects include several dwellings. However, in order to understand the totality of the project we must first consider the expenditure profile relating to an individual house.

The preceding section considered the process of building and set out in some detail the typical sequence of operations involved in the construction of a dwelling. Each of these operations has a cost attributed to it that will be made up of three components: materials, plant and labour. The materials are the raw materials (such as timber, sand and cement) and the manufactured components (such as windows, lintels and roof trusses) that are required to facilitate the construction of the building. 'Plant' is the term used for mechanical tools and vehicles, such as lifting equipment and dumper trucks used to assist the construction process. Labour is the human resource in the form of skilled and unskilled tradespeople taking part in the construction process. Each of these has a direct cost that can be calculated for any element of the project.

By applying these costs to each activity within the construction sequence we are able to build up an expenditure profile that illustrates the cost of the project at any given point. When expressed in terms of a cumulative cost profile, i.e. the total cost of all elements up to any given point, this produces a curve which is referred to as a 'lazy S' (Figure 2.23).

The profile of the curve arises as a consequence of the fact that the expenditure accelerates at the beginning, achieves a consistent level in the middle and decelerates at the end of the project. This is because there is a period at the beginning of the project during which the site is established and preparation works are under way. This results in modest outlay initially, before expenditure on

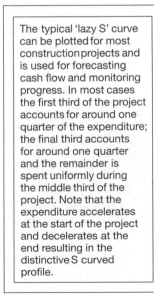

The typical 'lazy S' curve can be plotted for most construction projects and is used for forecasting cash flow and monitoring progress. In most cases the first third of the project accounts for around one quarter of the expenditure; the final third accounts for around one quarter and the remainder is spent uniformly during the middle third of the project. Note that the expenditure accelerates at the start of the project and decelerates at the end resulting in the distinctive S curved profile.

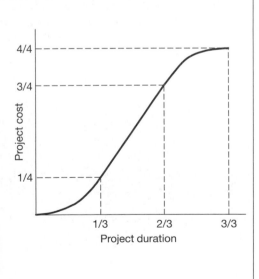

Figure 2.23 ● Plotted project expenditure – the S curve.

materials and assembly begins. Once the preparatory period has been completed, expenditure on plant, labour and materials remains fairly constant until the later stages. At this point, items of finishing and tidying are undertaken. These take time, but are not costly in terms of materials etc. Although each project is individual, some generic models of expenditure have been developed. One of the most common is the quarter:third model. In this, the expenditure is anticipated on the basis that one quarter of the cost will be attributable to the first third of the project period, one quarter to the final third and the remainder spent uniformly in the period between.

Financing the building process

One of the factors that affects the profitability of any building project is the cost of financing the process. In most cases, the house builder will need to borrow money to fund the project in advance of receiving payment for the dwellings. The cost of borrowing relatively large amounts of money can be significant and this must be taken into account by the builder as part of the developer's equation. It would normally be the intention that such borrowings were of as short a duration as possible, to reduce the interest payments that must be made. This is one reason why building projects often have phased completion of dwellings. If some dwellings are available for early sale, the profit made can be used to reduce borrowings or to fund the later phases of the development directly. It is not uncommon to see large housing developments completed in increments, such that houses in one phase may be at foundation level while others have already been sold and occupied.

It is not the intention of this text to consider in detail the funding and management of the construction process. However, these factors must always be borne in mind, since construction is a business and, like any other business, it is driven by profit.

Reflective summary

With reference to expenditure on building, remember:

— The key issue tends to be outlay over time, which when represented in graph form inevitably forms an 'S' profile.

— Examination of the S curve shows the intensity of expenditure that is likely to be experienced at different times, and peak times can be easily recognised.

Review task

What do we typically use to visually represent the expenditure outlay on a building as it develops on site?

What would variations in this shape suggest?

part two

Building substructure

chapter three

Foundations

Aims

After studying this chapter you should be able to:

- Identify the various elements that comprise the substructure of a dwelling
- Appreciate the interaction between the various elements and the implication of selection of specific design alternatives
- Relate the selection of individual options to building form, ground conditions and construction process
- Appreciate the criteria upon which selection of alternatives is based

This section contains the following sections:

3.1   Foundations

3.2   Functions of foundations and selection criteria

3.3   Types of foundation

Hot links

- Building Regulations Approved Document A, Structure
- BS 5997: Guide to British Standard codes of practice for building services
- BS 6515: Specification for polyethylene damp-proof courses for masonry
- BS 8110: Structural use of concrete
- BS 8215: Code of practice for design and installation of damp-proof courses in masonry construction
- BS 8301: Code of practice for building drainage

3.1   Foundations

Introduction

After studying this unit you should be able to distinguish between the various foundation options available for use in low-rise construction. You should have developed an appreciation of the functional requirements of foundations and the implications of soil type upon their selection. In addition, you should have developed a detailed understanding of the construction detail and sequence of operations associated with each of the forms in common use. You should be able to evaluate a variety of scenarios and make valid selections of foundation type based upon a detailed understanding of the issues involved.

This section includes the following topics:

● Soils and their characteristics

● Functions of foundations and selection criteria

● Foundation options for low-rise construction

● Shallow foundation forms

● Deep foundation forms

Soils and their characteristics

Overview

The stability and integrity of any structure depends upon its ability to transfer loads to the ground which supports it. The function of foundations is to ensure the effective and safe transfer of such loadings, acting upon the supporting ground while preventing overstressing of the soil. The nature of the structure, its foundations and the soil onto which they bear dictate the ways in which this function is achieved. It is inevitable that in the period shortly after the construction of a building some consolidation of the soil takes place. Minor initial settlement is, therefore, to be expected; but more serious movement must be avoided, in particular that which is uneven and which may result in differential settlement, causing cracking and deformation of the building. The specific design of a foundation depends upon the structure, the way in which its loads are delivered to the foundation and the loadbearing characteristics of the soil type. It is logical, therefore, in considering the performance requirements and design of foundations, to first consider the various soil types and their individual properties.

Before attempting to study this section carry out the following exercise.

Review task

On the basis of your general knowledge try to identify the different types of soil that could form a base for the construction of low-rise buildings. Attempt to rank the various types in order of strength.

Reconsider the exercise after studying this section.

Soil types

In practice, there is an infinite variety of soil compositions; however, these can be broadly categorised into five generic types in addition to solid rock, although these can be further subdivided into a large number of specific descriptions. Since the properties of soils depend upon the size of the particles from which they are comprised, the system of classification often used is based upon particle type and size. In addition to solid rock, the five categories are gravels, sands, silts, clays and peats (Table 3.1; Figure 3.1).

Table 3.1 ● Bearing capacity of different soil types.

	Rock	Gravel	Sand	Silt	Clay
Bearing capacity kN/m²	800+	Up to 600+	Up to 300+	Up to 75	75–300
Particle range (mm)	N/A	2+	0.06–2	0.002–0.06	<0.002

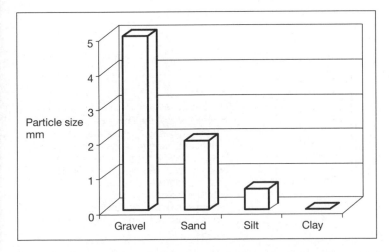

Figure 3.1 ● Typical particle size (upper limits) for various soil types.

Soils and particle size

The size of soil particles has an influence on the level of cohesion displayed by the ground. Smaller particles tend to be characteristic of soils with high levels of cohesion. Conversely, soils with low levels of cohesion tend to be made up from particles of greater size.

Identifying soil types

The procedures adopted for identifying the various soils on site are set out in BS 8004, 8103 and 1377. It is clear that the size of particles making up the soil has an effect upon the strength and cohesion of the ground. These factors directly affect the ability of the ground to provide an appropriate supporting medium for foundations to low rise buildings. As a general rule the level of cohesion of the soil increases as the size of particles decreases.

As discussed in Section 2.2, concerning site investigation, the process of identifying soil types on-site is relatively simple. Building Research Establishment Digest 64 sets out some of the salient characteristics of the various types and attempts to identify some of the potential problems associated with each.

Rock

Solid rock provides a sound base upon which to build, as a result of its very high loadbearing characteristics. Typically, the safe loadbearing capacity of sedimentary rock, such as sandstone and limestone, is approximately 10 times that of a clay soil, with igneous rocks, such as granite, having capacities 20–30 times that of clays. These high loadbearing capabilities suggest that solid rock is an excellent base upon which to build. However, there are also great disadvantages, resulting from the difficulty in excavating and levelling the sub-strata. This presents a considerable cost implication in building on such sub-strata. An additional problem, manifested in some sedimentary rocks, is that posed by the presence of inherent weak zones, created as a result of fault lines in the rock, together with the presence of slip planes between adjacent layers of differing composition. In such circumstances the use of ground securing anchors (Figure 3.2) is possible to alleviate the problem of instability.

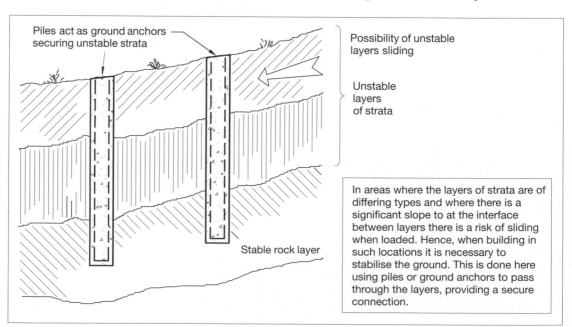

Figure 3.2 ● Use of ground anchors to secure unstable rock layers.

Cohesive and cohesionless soils

From the point of view of the process of construction, the nature of the soil is potentially important for reasons other than its loadbearing capacity. When excavating for the placement of foundations, the extent to which the soil is self-supporting, or conversely, the extent to which it requires temporary support, is also important. The need to provide temporary support to excavations has implications in terms of the speed of construction and the cost. In general terms, the more cohesive the soil the greater its ability to support itself during the process of excavation. Thus the degree to which trench side support is necessary depends on the degree of cohesion of the soil as well as the proposed depth of the excavation.

Gravels and sands

Gravels and sands are often grouped together and considered under the broad heading of coarse-grained cohesionless soils. The particles forming these soil types, ranging in size from 0.06 mm upwards, show little or no cohesion; hence, if unrestrained, they tend to move independently of each other when loaded. This property can result in many problems if not addressed; however, if treated properly these forms of soil can provide an adequate building base. When initially loaded some consolidation is likely to occur, which may pose problems in relation to the connection of services and so on. The voids present between individual particles are relatively large, but represent a low proportion of the total volume. The presence of such voids results in the soils being permeable; hence water is not held in the ground for long periods.

Silts and clays

These types of soil are generally considered within the broad category of fine-grained cohesive soils. The small size of the particles making up these forms of soil, with a high proportion of small voids between particles, causes the tendency of clays and silts to display considerable variation in volume when subject to changing moisture content. This results in drying shrinkage in dry weather and swelling and heave in wet weather (Figure 3.3). The nature of the soil is such that moisture is retained for considerable periods, due to low permeability. Such soil types may also be compressible when loaded, especially at shallow depths. However, at suitable depths, below the region which is likely to be affected by moisture variation (normally 1 m or deeper), satisfactory bearing is normally found. The effects of trees, particularly those which have been felled recently, can be significant, as they affect the amount of water which is removed from the ground. A further problem which is sometimes present in areas of clay soil is that posed by the aggressive actions of soluble sulphates in the soil upon ordinary Portland cement, which may necessitate the use of sulphate-resisting cements in some areas.

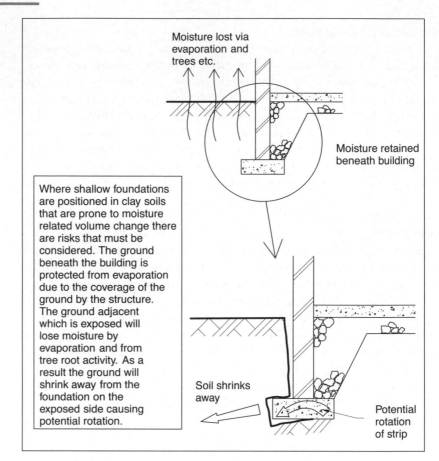

Moisture lost via evaporation and trees etc.

Moisture retained beneath building

Where shallow foundations are positioned in clay soils that are prone to moisture related volume change there are risks that must be considered. The ground beneath the building is protected from evaporation due to the coverage of the ground by the structure. The ground adjacent which is exposed will lose moisture by evaporation and from tree root activity. As a result the ground will shrink away from the foundation on the exposed side causing potential rotation.

Soil shrinks away

Potential rotation of strip

Figure 3.3 ● Ground moisture and foundation stability.

Peat and organic soils

Soils which contain large amounts of organic material are generally subject to considerable compression when loaded, and are subject to changing volume resulting from the decay of the organic matter. Hence they are generally unsuitable for building. For these reasons, top soil is removed prior to building, and excavation will normally take place to remove soil with a considerable quantity of organic matter present.

Table 3.2 shows the typical loadbearing capacity of various soil types.

Table 3.2 ● Typical safe bearing capacity of various ground conditions/soil types.

Soil type		Typical safe bearing capacity (kN/m^2)
Rock		
Igneous		10 000
Limestone/strong sandstone		4 000
Slate		3 000
Shale		2 000
Cohesionless soils		
Gravel/Sand	Dense	> 600
	Medium	200–600
	Loose	< 200
Sand	Compact	> 300
	Medium	100–300
	Loose	< 100
Cohesive soils		
Clay	Very stiff/stiff	150–600
	Firm	75–150
	Soft/silt	< 75
Peat and fill		N/A

The range in bearing capacity between soil types is obviously considerable. However, it must also be noted that ranges within soils of a given type can be great; hence the term 'Typical safe bearing capacity' is used.

Note: this is a measure of pressure that the soil can withstand:

Pressure = Force/Area

The area of contact with the ground can be varied by appropriate foundation design.

Trees and their effects

As mentioned previously, the effects of the presence of trees in close proximity to the foundations of the building can be damaging to the structure of the building (Figure 3.4). This is particularly the case in areas of clay, which are prone to considerable changes in volume as a result of changes in water content. This is linked strongly to the presence of trees. The extent to which mature trees extract water from the ground is considerable, and naturally this increases with the growth of the tree. This results in shrinkage of clay soils and is particularly noticeable in periods of dry weather, when the moisture is not replenished by rainfall. The consequence of this removal of moisture and the resulting shrinkage of the soil is that the foundations suffer from subsidence as the ground beneath them shrinks away. The effect is often one of rotation of the foundation rather than simple subsidence, as the area of soil beneath the building maintains a more stable moisture level. This is because the presence of the building prevents moisture loss form the ground by evaporation.

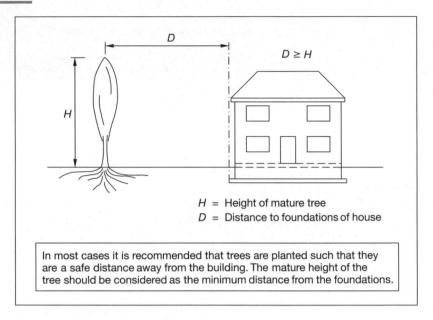

H = Height of mature tree
D = Distance to foundations of house

In most cases it is recommended that trees are planted such that they are a safe distance away from the building. The mature height of the tree should be considered as the minimum distance from the foundations.

Figure 3.4 ● Proximity of trees.

Problems occur not only because of the presence of trees, but also as a consequence of their removal. In areas where there have been established mature trees, the ground water level maintains a reasonable degree of equilibrium. The moisture level is regularised by the action of evaporation from the surface of the ground and moisture drawn by the trees. If the trees are then removed, the balance changes. In such circumstances the ground will retain more moisture than usual and in clay soils this will result in swelling of the ground. The swelling, in turn, causes uplift or 'heave' to buildings in close proximity. The effects of heave are similar to those of subsidence, but in reverse.

BS 5837:1991 sets out recommendations for dealing with trees close to buildings. The effect of a tree's presence varies with species of tree and with soil type and characteristics.

 ## Review task

A link has been noted between the soil type, its bearing capacity (pressure) and the loads from a building.

— How can this relationship be reflected by foundation design?

— What are the implications of foundation depth in terms of loadbearing capacity?

🗜 Case study

The site selected here is close to the industrial zone of a major city. The site has been built on in the past, but has since been cleared. This is known as a 'brown field site'. The ground here consists of areas of fill where demolition has occurred. This has poor loadbearing capacity and is in need of consolidation. The consolidation is effected by driving aggregate into holes formed by a displacement driver. The action of forcing the extra volume into the ground increases its density and hence its strength.

On the same site, areas of rock must be excavated using mechanical plant to allow for the provision of drainage below ground.

Review task

From the following list select the key features of cohesive and cohesionless soils:

— high proportion of voids between soil particles

— compressible

— high permeability

— low permeability

— variable volume with change in moisture content

— able to support itself during excavation

Contaminated ground

The risk of the presence of certain forms of contamination in the ground can be of great significance to the process of construction. Although it is not possible to consider this complex issue in depth within this book, it is useful to consider the topic in overview. Contaminants that are likely to be found in the ground can pose problems in the form of potential risk to health or as aggressive substances to the materials used in construction. The Building Regulations define a contaminant as:

> 'any substance which is or could become toxic, corrosive, explosive flammable or radioactive and likely to be a danger to health & safety'

Site investigation will be necessary to identify the nature and extent of contamination. This may have direct consequences for the viability of the proposed building project, and the requirements for remediation may be onerous. The Environmental Protection Act and Environment Act impose a responsibility for remedial action to negate the potential risks associated with land contamination. This can have very great consequences in terms of cost and time.

The main options available for treatment of the problem of contaminated ground are:

● removal of the contaminated material to another location, normally a licensed site

● provision of an impervious layer between the contamination and the ground surface, often termed 'cover technology'

● biological or physical remediation to neutralise or remove the contaminant

The types of contaminant typically found on sites that may be intended for building projects are set out in Table 3.3.

Table 3.3 ● Possible contamination risks on building sites.

Contaminant	Signs	Typical action
Metals	Affected vegetation Surface materials	Extraction of contaminated matter or cover technology
Organic compounds	Affected vegetation Surface materials	Biological remediation, extraction of affected matter or cover technology
Oil/tar	Surface materials	Extraction of affected matter
Asbestos/fibres	Surface materials	Extraction of affected matter or cover technology
Combustible materials	Surface materials Fumes/odours	Cover technology with venting facility or extraction of affected matter
Gases (Methane/ CO_2)	Fumes/odours	Barrier or cover technology
Refuse/waste	Surface materials Fumes/odours	Extraction of affected matter or cover technology

Reflective summary

With reference to soils and their characteristics, remember:

— Apart from rock, soils tend to be classified as cohesive or cohesionless (non-cohesive).

— Even rock can be unstable if its strata layers are shaped to encourage slipping under load.

— Bearing capacity in kN/m^2 is how we reflect a soil's ability to carry load.

— Changes in soil moisture content caused by trees or the prevailing weather may cause swelling or shrinkage in cohesive soils.

— Contamination of soils is now common – recognise the legal obligations that apply on discovery.

3.2   Functions of foundations and selection criteria

Introduction

After studying this section you should have developed an understanding of the nature and functions of foundations for low rise construction. You should understand the implications of loading and ground conditions upon the selection of foundations. In addition, you should be able to identify and evaluate the factors that affect their choice and be able to select appropriate foundation solutions in a variety of scenarios. As well as being aware of the merits and limitations of the various options, you should have an appreciation of the typical sequence of operations involved with their formation.

Overview

The foundations of a building form the interface between the structure and the ground which supports it. The primary function of the foundations is to transmit the building loads safely to the supporting strata, spreading them over a sufficient area to ensure that the safe loadbearing capacity of the soil is not exceeded. In addition, it must be ensured that the pressure on the ground at all points below the foundation is equal, in order to prevent differential movement or rotation. It is normal, therefore, to attempt to ensure that the centre of gravity of the loadings is located at the centre of the foundation area.

Functions of foundations

As previously noted, the primary functional requirement of a foundation is to transfer the loads from the building to the ground to ensure the stability of the structure (Figure 3.5). In order to achieve this, a number of performance requirements must be achieved. These aspects of the performance of foundations are satisfied in different ways by differing foundation solutions. However, they are all essentially similar in the end result that is desired: to provide a stable durable base for the construction of the dwelling.

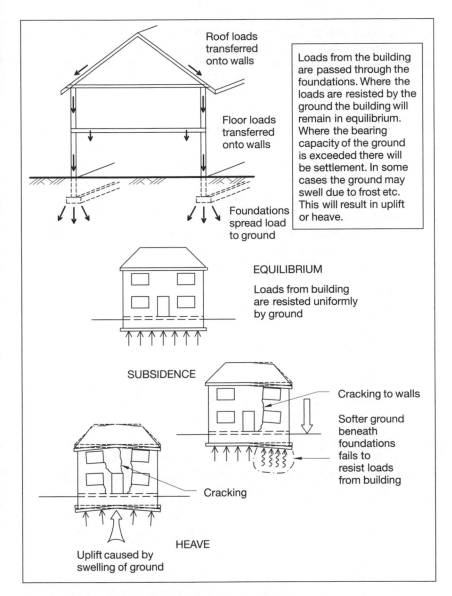

Loads from the building are passed through the foundations. Where the loads are resisted by the ground the building will remain in equilibrium. Where the bearing capacity of the ground is exceeded there will be settlement. In some cases the ground may swell due to frost etc. This will result in uplift or heave.

Roof loads transferred onto walls

Floor loads transferred onto walls

Foundations spread load to ground

EQUILIBRIUM

Loads from building are resisted uniformly by ground

SUBSIDENCE

Cracking to walls

Softer ground beneath foundations fails to resist loads from building

Cracking

HEAVE

Uplift caused by swelling of ground

Figure 3.5 ● Load transfer through foundations.

The following summarises the main aspects of foundation performance.

● The foundation must possess sufficient strength and rigidity to ensure that it is capable of withstanding the loadings imposed upon it without bending or suffering shear failure at the point of loading.

● It must be capable of withstanding the forces exerted by the ground, and must resist the tendency to move under such loads as those exerted by volume changes in the ground caused by frost and moisture action etc. This is, in part, achieved by ensuring that the foundation is set at a sufficient depth below ground level, normally at least 1 metre.

● It must be inert, and not react with elements within the ground, such as soluble sulphates, which may degrade the material from which the foundation is formed.

Selection criteria

The basis for the selection of foundations is quite straightforward. It is important to remember that the performance of foundations is based on an interface between the loadings from the building and the supporting ground or strata. The nature and conditions of each of these may vary, and it is primarily as a result of these variations that some foundation solutions are more appropriate in certain circumstances than others. In all cases, however, the most economical solution will be selected, provided that it satisfies the performance requirements.

Factors related to ground conditions

In most cases the nature of the ground upon which dwellings are constructed is reasonably stable, level and of uniform composition. It is generally the case that the ground close to the surface is capable of supporting the relatively light loadings resulting from the construction of a dwelling. Thus, shallow forms of foundation are generally adopted. In some instances this is not the case, and the foundation solutions must be selected accordingly. The specific factors related to the nature of the ground that affect foundation selection are as follows:

● *Bearing capacity of the ground*: In Section 3.1 we considered the variability of soils and the degree to which their ability to carry loads differs. This is one of the key elements in the selection of appropriate foundations for all types of building.

● *Depth of good strata*: Although the site upon which the dwelling is to be constructed may provide ground of appropriate bearing strength, this may be at a considerable depth below the surface. In these circumstances the use of a shallow foundation form is unlikely to be efficient or cost-effective, and the adoption of a deeper foundation such as piles would be considered.

Brown field sites are sites that have been built on in the past and which have been cleared to provide the base for a new construction operation. Many such sites are located in urban areas, where virgin sites are unavailable. The need to conserve green field sites has increased the emphasis on reusing existing building land in this sustainable way.

● *Composition of the ground*: Ideally the construction of houses takes place on sites with uniform, stable ground conditions. As more and more sites have been utilised in recent years the supply of these ideal sites has diminished. Hence it is becoming increasingly the case that sites for the construction of dwellings are less than ideal. The increasing trend to build on 'brown field sites', driven by the need to develop in a more sustainable way, has led to greater variability in ground composition. It is not uncommon to find houses being constructed on sites that feature areas made up of filled ground. Sites with lower than ideal bearing capacities may also be considered. These circumstances generally make the use of a traditional strip foundation unviable.

● *Ground level and gradients*: It is quite rare for building sites to be truly flat and level. In most cases, however, the slight irregularities and changes in level of the ground do not pose significant problems. In cases where the variation in level is more extensive the design of the foundation will be affected. Several factors are significant in this scenario. Firstly, there is the need to provide a level base from which to build; this results in the need to step the foundation along the slope. Secondly, there is the potential for the entire structure to slide down the slope as a result of the action of gravity. In addition, there is the need to consider the implications of embedding parts of the building below ground level and/or creating deep sub-floor voids.

There are several potential design solutions to facilitate the construction of buildings on sloping ground (Figure 3.6). Each has merits and disadvantages. The first option is to provide a level foundation that cuts into the ground. This results

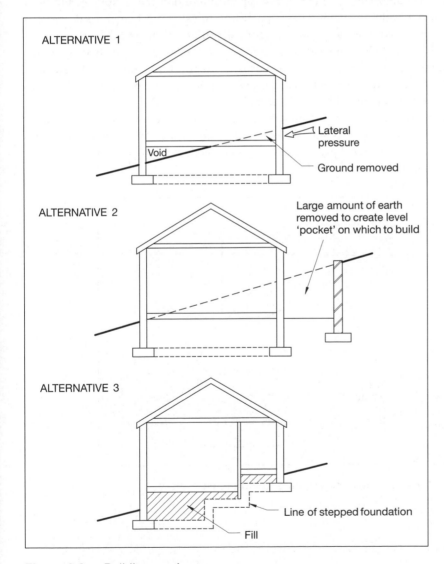

Figure 3.6 ● Building on slopes.

in the need to excavate a pocket in the ground at the upper end of the building, while creating a deep sub-floor void at the lower end. A factor that must be taken into account here is the degree to which lateral loading will be applied to the walls of the building, where the ground level is high relative to the ground floor of the building. There is potential for the lateral load to cause deformation if it is of sufficient magnitude.

One way of avoiding this is to adopt the second available option, which relies on the excavation of a pocket in the sloping ground and the formation of a retaining wall to protect the structural wall of the building. One of the implications of adopting either of these approaches is that the water that will run down the slope must be dealt with if penetration to the interior is not to be a problem.

The third approach is to create a stepped foundation that results in the floor level of the building changing as it passes up the slope. A benefit of this is that there is no need to excavate an excessive depth of soil. In addition, the level of lateral load applied to the walls is minimised. However, where such an approach is adopted, care must be taken to ensure that the foundation is of sufficient strength at the step to avoid fracture. This requires the incorporation of a sufficient overlap as detailed in the diagram below.

When the ground slopes it may make economic sense to step the foundation rather than have excessively deep trenches and excessively deep foundation brickwork. Figure 3.7 shows the dimensional needs at a step for compliance with Building Regulations.

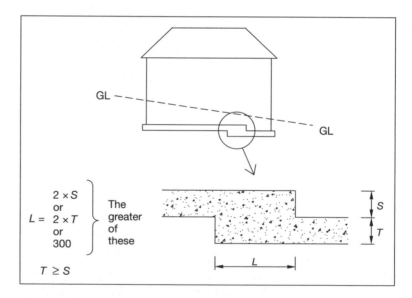

Figure 3.7 ● Steps in strip footing foundations.

Factors relating to loads from the building

The form and type of the building to be erected dictate the nature of the loadings that are directed to the foundations as well as their magnitude. In the case of low-rise housing the extent of the loading is relatively modest. This is one of the reasons for the widespread use of shallow foundations. As loads increase the need to provide deeper foundation solutions increases also. This is because the strata at a greater depth are more highly compacted, and generally, therefore, have the ability to withstand higher loads. By contrast, the strata close to the surface are generally less well compacted and less able to withstand loading.

Reflective summary

With reference to the function and selection of foundations, remember

— The function is to primarily perform with safety, efficiency and economy.

— Loads on foundations may arise from ground movements as well as from building loads.

— Foundations need to be resistant to chemical contaminants in the ground, such as sulphates.

— Bearing capacity in kN/m^2 is the measurement of soil strength.

— Construction on sloping sites needs special consideration in order to ensure building stability.

— One of the key functions of a foundation is to spread the building load in a way which suits the ground.

3.3 Types of foundation

The nature of the foundation that is appropriate in a particular situation depends on a number of factors. The extent of the loading and the way in which it is applied to the foundation dictates the design, together with the nature of the supporting strata. Point loads on level sites are, for example, treated in a very different manner from uniformly distributed loads on sloping sites. Most forms of foundation are formed from concrete, either reinforced or unreinforced, although other forms, such as steel grillage foundations, are sometimes used in very specific circumstances.

In general, the foundation solutions available for the construction of dwellings are restricted to simple forms; these are normally defined within the classifications of shallow foundations and deep foundations.

Review task

With your present knowledge, and before you read this section, see how many different foundation forms you can mention.

Shallow foundations forms

Introduction

After studying this section you should have developed an understanding of the nature and functions of shallow foundations for low-rise construction. You should understand the nature and construction form of shallow foundations. In addition, you should be able to identify and evaluate the factors that affect their choice.

Overview

The nature of the construction form of houses is such that the loads applied to the ground are relatively modest. In addition, they are generally distributed uniformly through the external loadbearing walls and any internal loadbearing walls. For this reason, the most popular choice of foundation type is a shallow strip foundation. This is not always the case, however, and as the quality of available building land diminishes, so the possibility of foundation related difficulties becomes more significant. A range of shallow foundation forms are available and the nature of the selected construction form, the likely loads and the bearing capacity of the ground will all be considered when making a selection.

Strip foundations

By far the most common form of foundation in use is the simple mass concrete strip foundation. Used where continuous lengths of wall are to be constructed, the strip foundation consists of a strip of mass concrete of sufficient width to spread the loads imposed on it over an area of the ground which ensures that overstressing does not take place. The distribution of the compressive loading within the concrete of the strip tends to fall within a zone defined by lines extending at 45° from the base of the wall. Hence, to avoid shear failure along these lines, the depth of the foundation must be such that the effective width of the foundation base falls within this zone (Figure 3.8).

Strip foundations are intended for use where the loads from the building are relatively modest, as in the case of house building, and are distributed uniformly (Figure 3.9).

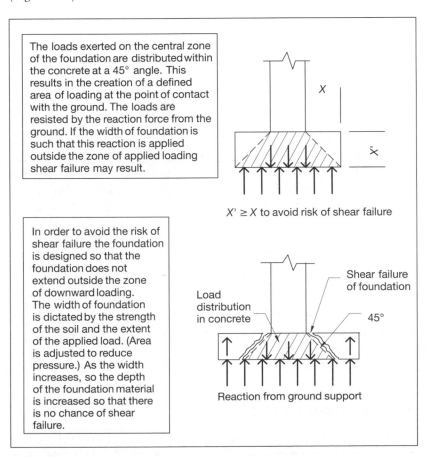

The loads exerted on the central zone of the foundation are distributed within the concrete at a 45° angle. This results in the creation of a defined area of loading at the point of contact with the ground. The loads are resisted by the reaction force from the ground. If the width of foundation is such that this reaction is applied outside the zone of applied loading shear failure may result.

X

$X' \geq X$ to avoid risk of shear failure

In order to avoid the risk of shear failure the foundation is designed so that the foundation does not extend outside the zone of downward loading. The width of foundation is dictated by the strength of the soil and the extent of the applied load. (Area is adjusted to reduce pressure.) As the width increases, so the depth of the foundation material is increased so that there is no chance of shear failure.

Load distribution in concrete

Shear failure of foundation

45°

Reaction from ground support

Figure 3.8 ● Foundation design to avoid shear failure.

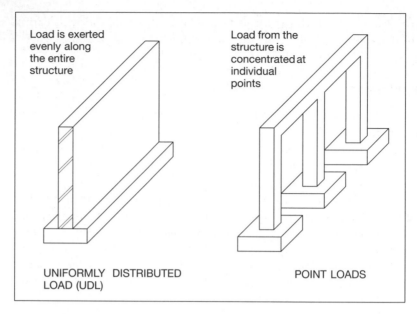

Figure 3.9 ● Uniform and point loads.

Since the external walls of dwellings transfer the structural loads to the foundations they are generally uniform in distribution. In some forms of construction the loads are transferred as localised or point loads (Figure 3.9). In such instances the loads are catered for by the adoption of isolated foundations at each point of load. This is rarely encountered in house building.

The traditional form of most house construction allows the use of shallow strip foundations in most instances (Figures 3.10 and 3.11). The width of the foundation depends on the safe bearing capacity of the soil and the level of loading applied. As discussed elsewhere, the width of the foundation is adjusted to provide a sufficient area of contact to prevent overstressing of the soil. The depth will be related to the depth of appropriate bearing strata, but will generally be in excess of 1 metre so as to avoid the danger of frost-related heave and shrinkage of the soil close to the surface.

 ## Review task

Explain how shear failure can occur in a strip footing foundation and how this dictates certain dimensions of the concrete.

Excavation for shallow foundations

Excavation for the placement of foundations takes place after the building has been 'set out' to indicate the positions of trenches using profile boards and string lines.

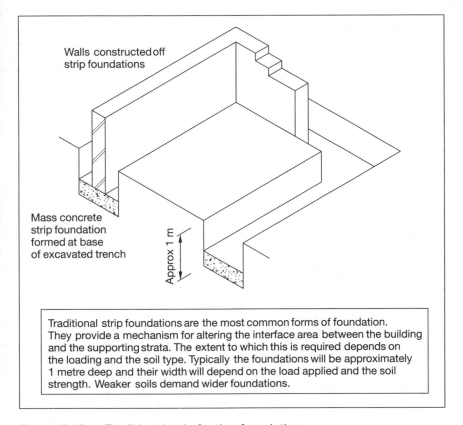

Walls constructed off
strip foundations

Mass concrete
strip foundation
formed at base
of excavated trench

Approx 1 m

Traditional strip foundations are the most common forms of foundation.
They provide a mechanism for altering the interface area between the building
and the supporting strata. The extent to which this is required depends on
the loading and the soil type. Typically the foundations will be approximately
1 metre deep and their width will depend on the load applied and the soil
strength. Weaker soils demand wider foundations.

Figure 3.10 ● Traditional strip footing foundation.

The first stage of the process is the removal of 'oversite'. Following the removal of the oversite, excavation of the foundation trenches will take place to the required depth. On very small sites this may be undertaken by hand; however, the use of compact mechanical diggers makes mechanical excavation practical and economical on even modest sites. For larger sites it is the norm to use mechanised plant for excavation.

The excavation of foundation trenches follows an established sequence of operations, which ensures that they are formed to an appropriate standard and with required levels of safety for the building operatives.

'Oversite' is the term used to refer to the layer of topsoil that contains vegetable matter. This must be removed to ensure that the building is constructed on ground that is in stable condition and will not be subject to change in volume over time, as would be the case as vegetable matter degenerates.

Review task

The sequence of operations involved in excavation for the placement of foundations is important. From the following list of activities select the operations involved in the appropriate order.

- Excavation of trench

- Placement of concrete

- Levelling and ramming trench bottoms

- Setting out

- Excavation of oversite

- Timbering of trench sides

- Trimming of trench sides

Masonry walls often require the formation of piers or projections from the face of the wall. In such instances the foundation should be formed so as to ensure that the projection from the edge of the wall is uniform throughout its extent. This principle is illustrated below.

The excavation of foundation trenches is far less exact than the design drawings of a typical scheme would indicate. Here we see the excavations on a site awaiting the placement of concrete.

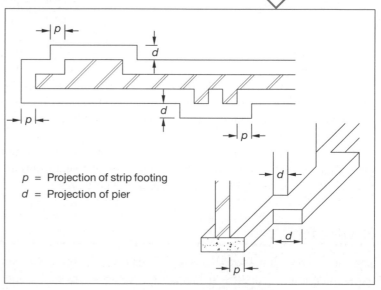

p = Projection of strip footing
d = Projection of pier

Figure 3.11 ● Strip foundations.

As the loading exerted on the foundations increases, or the loadbearing capacity of the ground decreases, so the required foundation width, to avoid overstressing of the ground, increases. In order to resist shear failure in wide foundations, they would be required to be very thick, for the reason previously described; this would normally be uneconomic. Hence, to reduce the required foundation thickness while still resisting failure in shear or bending, steel reinforcement is introduced to the regions subjected to tension and shear. Such a formation is termed a wide strip foundation (Figure 3.12).

One of the practical problems in constructing walls off strip foundations at the depths required is the necessity to provide an excavation which is sufficiently wide to allow operatives to lay bricks in the region below ground level. Hence the

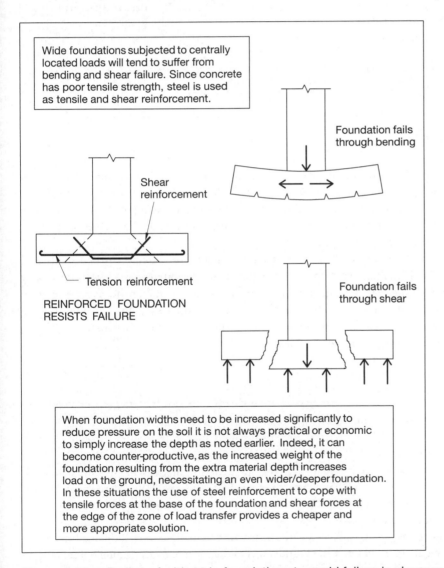

Figure 3.12 ● Design of wide strip foundations to avoid failure in shear and bending.

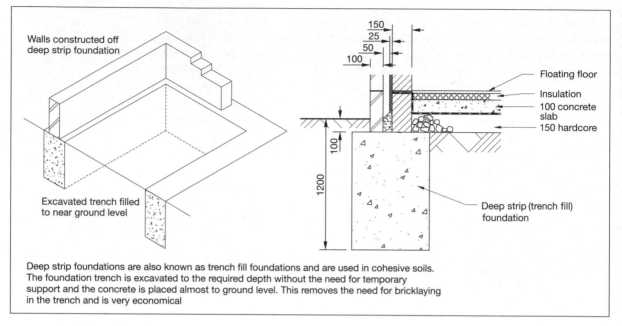

Walls constructed off
deep strip foundation

Excavated trench filled
to near ground level

150
25
50
100

Floating floor
Insulation
100 concrete
slab
150 hardcore

100

1200

Deep strip (trench fill)
foundation

Deep strip foundations are also known as trench fill foundations and are used in cohesive soils.
The foundation trench is excavated to the required depth without the need for temporary
support and the concrete is placed almost to ground level. This removes the need for bricklaying
in the trench and is very economical

Figure 3.13 ● Deep strip foundations.

trench is often excavated to a width which is in excess of that required simply to provide a foundation of sufficient width. When working in cohesive soils, the sides of trenches are able to support themselves when excavated, without the use of earthwork support or foundation formwork. This means that a deep strip foundation (Figure 3.13) can be used.

This method of foundation formation is efficient and effective functionally and in terms of time and cost on-site. The trench is excavated to the width necessary to satisfy loadbearing requirements and to a depth sufficient to avoid the zone affected by moisture variation and frost action. Concrete is then used to fill the excavation to near ground level, thus removing the need for many bricks or blocks to be laid below ground level.

 Review task

Why is a deep strip footing only suited to certain types of soil?

Pad foundations
Pad foundations are rarely used in the construction of houses. They are discussed here only in overview to provide a general awareness of their existence and form, as they may be used from time to time to support elements such as props to car ports, porticos and so on.

In some instances, such as when constructing framed buildings, the loads from the building are exerted upon the foundations in the form of concentrated point loads. In such cases, independent pad foundations are normally used. The principle of pad foundation design is the same as that of strip foundations, i.e. the pad area will be of sufficient size to safely transfer loadings from the column to the ground without exceeding its loadbearing capacity. The pad will generally be square, with the column loading exerted centrally to avoid rotation, and is normally formed from reinforced concrete; although other formations such as steel are possible, they are rare in modern construction. As a result of the concentration of loading applied to pad foundations, it is vital that they are reinforced sufficiently against shear as well as bending.

The nature of the location of the loadbearing columns at the pad foundation can vary greatly in different situations. Figures 3.14 and 3.15 illustrate some of the more common methods.

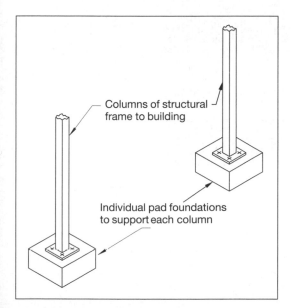

Columns of structural frame to building

Individual pad foundations to support each column

Figure 3.14 ● Pad foundations.

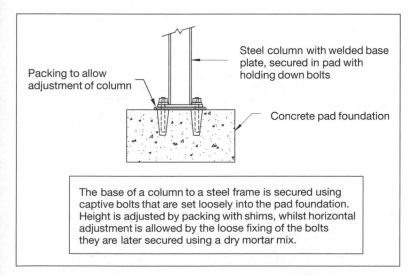

Steel column with welded base plate, secured in pad with holding down bolts

Packing to allow adjustment of column

Concrete pad foundation

The base of a column to a steel frame is secured using captive bolts that are set loosely into the pad foundation. Height is adjusted by packing with shims, whilst horizontal adjustment is allowed by the loose fixing of the bolts they are later secured using a dry mortar mix.

Figure 3.15 ● Standard column fixing at pad foundations.

Raft foundations

Raft foundations (Figure 3.16) are constructed in the form of a continuous slab, extending beneath the whole building, and formed in reinforced concrete. Hence the loadings from the building are spread over a large area and avoid over-stressing the soil. The foundation acts, quite literally, like a raft. Inevitably, however, there tends to be a concentration of loading at the perimeter of the slab,

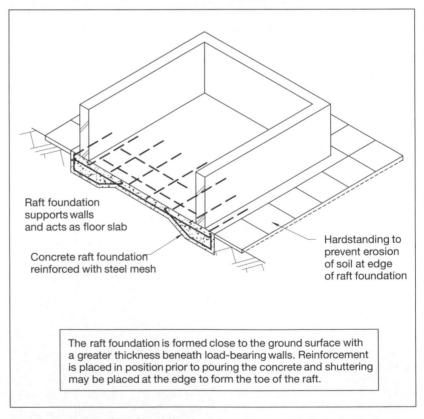

Raft foundation supports walls and acts as floor slab

Concrete raft foundation reinforced with steel mesh

Hardstanding to prevent erosion of soil at edge of raft foundation

The raft foundation is formed close to the ground surface with a greater thickness beneath load-bearing walls. Reinforcement is placed in position prior to pouring the concrete and shuttering may be placed at the edge to form the toe of the raft.

Figure 3.16 ● Raft foundations.

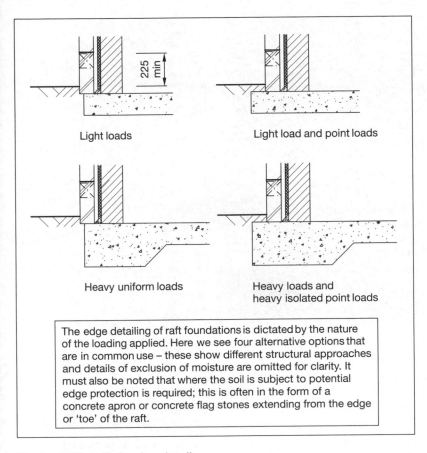

Light loads

Light load and point loads

Heavy uniform loads

Heavy loads and
heavy isolated point loads

The edge detailing of raft foundations is dictated by the nature
of the loading applied. Here we see four alternative options that
are in common use – these show different structural approaches
and details of exclusion of moisture are omitted for clarity. It
must also be noted that where the soil is subject to potential
edge protection is required; this is often in the form of a
concrete apron or concrete flag stones extending from the edge
or 'toe' of the raft.

Figure 3.17 ● Raft edge details.

where external walls are located, and at intermediate points across the main
surface, resulting from loadings from internal walls etc. Hence the raft is thickened at these locations and/or is provided with extra reinforcement. At the
perimeter (Figure 3.17), this thickening is termed the 'toe' and fulfils an important secondary function in preventing erosion of the supporting soil at the raft
edges. If not prevented, undermining of the raft could occur, with serious
consequences.

Foundations of this type are generally utilised in the construction of relatively
lightweight buildings, such as houses, on land with low bearing capacity. One of
the advantages of this form of foundation is that if settlement occurs, the building
moves as a whole unit, differential movement is prevented, hence, the building
retains its integrity.

Reflective summary

With reference to shallow foundation types, remember:

— Strip footing foundations are the simplest and least costly form of foundation for dwellings and may be in a variety of forms – traditional, deep (also called narrow or trenchfill) and stepped.

— Table 12, Section E of Part A of the Building Regulations shows how the width of a strip footing may vary as the load changes or as the soil strength varies.

— Two forms of failure in strip footings are bending and shear failure. Both of these may be prevented by reinforcing or increasing the concrete thickness.

— The deep strip footing may use more concrete than the traditional form but saves time and cost due to the much reduced brickwork below the DPC.

— A raft foundation may at first appear more expensive than, say, a strip footing, but remember that you also gain a ground floor by using this option.

Review task

There are clearly several design solutions for the provision of shallow foundations to dwellings. You should now have developed an appreciation for the criteria upon which they are selected. Using these criteria, select a foundation type from the following list of options for each of the situations listed below.

Options: Surface raft; Strip; Wide strip; Deep strip; Pad

Situation 1
The construction of a two-storey dwelling in an area of solid rock sub-strata

Situation 2
The construction of a two-storey dwelling in an area of firm stiff clay

Situation 3
The construction of a two-storey dwelling in an area of soft clay

Situation 4
The construction of a two-storey dwelling in an area of filled ground

Deep foundations forms

Introduction

After studying this section you should have developed an understanding of the nature and functions of deep foundations to low-rise construction. You should understand the nature and construction form of deep foundations. In addition, you should be able to identify and evaluate the factors that affect their choice.

Overview

The use of deep foundation forms for the construction of dwellings is relatively uncommon. The expense of deep foundation formation is one reason for this. However, the main reasons are functional, since the relatively low loads exerted by dwellings are normally dealt with effectively by shallow forms, such as strip foundations. The increasing need to develop sites with less favourable ground conditions has resulted in an increased use of deeper foundation forms. These are needed to cope with sites where ground quality close to the surface is poor or variable. Hence in some circumstances deeper foundation forms are essential.

Piles

Piles are often described as columns within the ground, since the basis upon which they work is similar to that of a traditional column, in that they transfer loadings from a higher level to a loadbearing medium at a lower level. They can be categorised in two ways (Figure 3.18): by the way in which they are installed, or by the way in which they transfer their loads to the ground (Figure 3.19). Hence the following classifications are used to define pile types.

- Definition by installation method:
  — Displacement piles (driven)
  — Replacement piles (bored)
- Definition by load transfer mechanism:
  — Friction piles
  — End-bearing piles

Displacement piles

Displacement piles are set into the ground by forcing or driving a solid pile or a hollow casing to the required level below ground, thus displacing the surrounding earth. In the case of solid piles, precast piles of required length may be driven into the ground using a driving rig, or alternatively the rig may be used to drive a series of short precast sections, which are connected as the work proceeds. The use of the second of these methods is by far the most efficient, since the length which is required may vary from pile to pile. Thus the use of one-piece

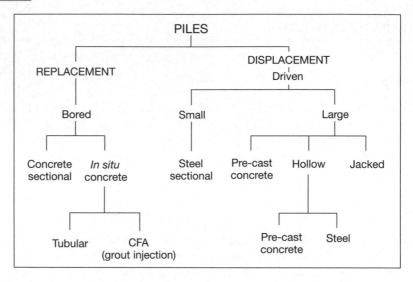

Figure 3.18 ● Range of pile types.

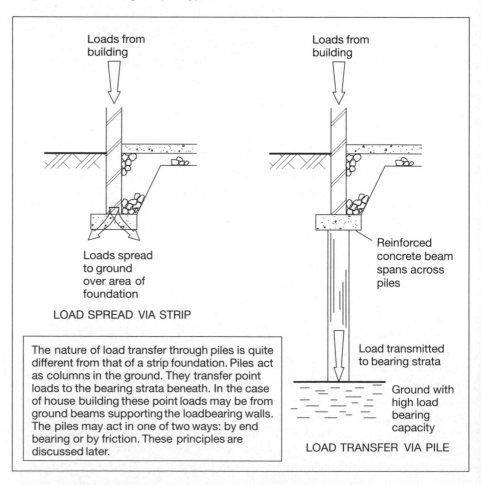

Figure 3.19 ● Load spread from shallow and pile foundations.

precast piles inevitably necessitates adjustment of length on-site. Trimming or extending of one-piece piles is a difficult task on-site.

The difficulties of providing piles of exactly the correct length, together with the danger of damage to the pile resulting from the percussive driving force, have resulted in the adoption of the use of driven shell, or casing, piles. With this method (Figure 3.20), a hollow shell or casing is driven into the ground, using a percussive rig, in a number of short sections; concrete is then poured into the void as the casing is withdrawn, the steel reinforcement having already been

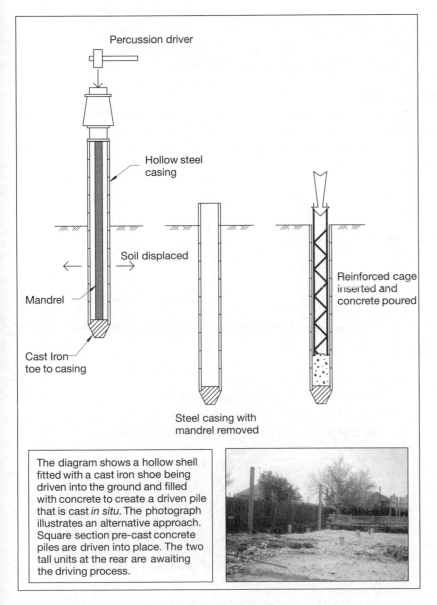

Percussion driver

Hollow steel casing

Soil displaced

Mandrel

Cast Iron toe to casing

Steel casing with mandrel removed

Reinforced cage inserted and concrete poured

The diagram shows a hollow shell fitted with a cast iron shoe being driven into the ground and filled with concrete to create a driven pile that is cast *in situ*. The photograph illustrates an alternative approach. Square section pre-cast concrete piles are driven into place. The two tall units at the rear are awaiting the driving process.

Figure 3.20 ● Installation of displacement piles.

lowered into the hole. By this method, an *in situ* pile is formed in the ground. The vibration of the pile casing as it is withdrawn from the ground, results in the creation of a ridged surface to the pile sides, thus taking the most advantage of any frictional support provided by the ground.

Whether in the form of a solid pile or a hollow casing, the driving of the pile/casing is aided by the use of a driving toe or shoe, often in the form of a pointed cast-iron fitting at the base of the pile to allow easier penetration of the ground. These methods of installation have several disadvantages, in that considerable levels of noise and vibration are generated as a result of the driving operation. Hence they are generally considered unsuitable for congested sites, where adjacent buildings may be structurally affected, or areas where noise nuisance is undesirable. However, they may be used to good effect in consolidation of poor ground, by compressing the earth around the piles.

Replacement piles

Unlike displacement piles, replacement piles are installed by removing a volume of soil and replacing it with a load-supporting pile (Figure 3.21). The holes are bored either by using a hollow weighted grab, which is repeatedly dropped and

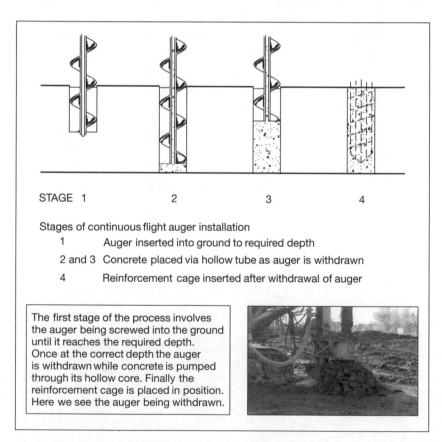

STAGE 1   2   3   4

Stages of continuous flight auger installation
1   Auger inserted into ground to required depth
2 and 3   Concrete placed via hollow tube as auger is withdrawn
4   Reinforcement cage inserted after withdrawal of auger

The first stage of the process involves the auger being screwed into the ground until it reaches the required depth. Once at the correct depth the auger is withdrawn while concrete is pumped through its hollow core. Finally the reinforcement cage is placed in position. Here we see the auger being withdrawn.

Figure 3.21 ● Installation of replacement piles.

raised, removing soil as it does so, or by using a rotary borer or auger. As the excavation progresses, the sides are prevented from collapsing by introducing a shell, or casing, normally made from steel, or by the use of a viscous liquid called bentonite. The bentonite is then displaced by concrete as it is poured into the excavation and is stored for further use. This method is quieter than the displacement method and does not result in damage to surrounding buildings.

The methods of installation of replacement piles described above, however, have largely been superseded by the introduction of continuous flight auger, or grout injection piling (Figure 3.22). This method is highly efficient, with

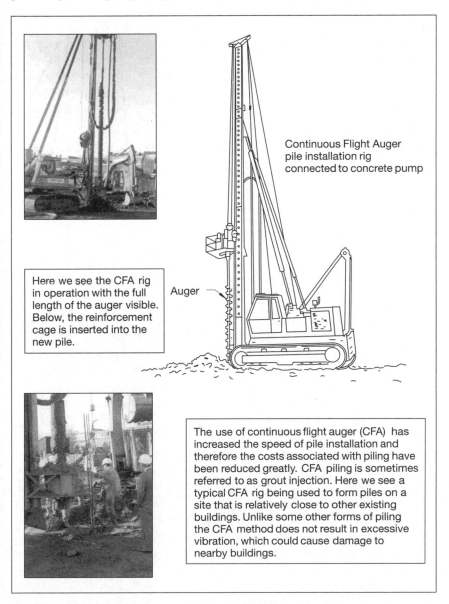

Continuous Flight Auger pile installation rig connected to concrete pump

Here we see the CFA rig in operation with the full length of the auger visible. Below, the reinforcement cage is inserted into the new pile.

Auger

The use of continuous flight auger (CFA) has increased the speed of pile installation and therefore the costs associated with piling have been reduced greatly. CFA piling is sometimes referred to as grout injection. Here we see a typical CFA rig being used to form piles on a site that is relatively close to other existing buildings. Unlike some other forms of piling the CFA method does not result in excessive vibration, which could cause damage to nearby buildings.

Figure 3.22 ● Installation of Continuous Flight Auger (CFA) piles.

exceptionally fast installation possible. A continuous auger of the required length is mounted on a mobile rig and is used to excavate the pile void. The central shaft of the auger is hollow, and is connected to a concrete pumping system, which allows the concrete to be placed as the auger is withdrawn. Hence there is no need to provide temporary support to the sides of the excavation. Once the auger is withdrawn, a steel reinforcement cage is forced into the concrete from above. Thus, the pile is formed quickly and efficiently with little disturbance to surrounding areas.

Friction piles and end-bearing piles

The method by which the pile transfers its load to the ground depends upon the nature of the design of the pile and is dictated to a large extent by the nature of the ground in which it is located. Piles are used as a form of foundation in a variety of situations, each imposing differing demands upon pile design and creating restrictions on the ways in which the piles act. Although there are a great variety of situations which may necessitate the use of piles, the following are some of the most common:

- where insufficient loadbearing capacity is offered by the soil at a shallow depth, but sufficient is available at a greater depth

- where the nature of the soil at a shallow depth is variable and performance is unpredictable, such as in areas of filled land

- where soils at shallow depths are subject to shrinkage or swelling due to seasonal changes

- where buildings or elements are subjected to an uplifting force, and require to be anchored to the ground

It can be seen that in some of these instances one form of pile may be obviously more appropriate than another as a result of the way in which they act. End-bearing piles act by passing through unsuitable strata to bear directly upon soil with adequate bearing capacity, while friction piles are supported by the effects of friction from the ground to the sides of the pile throughout its length (Figure 3.23); hence the formation of ridges to the sides of piles as described earlier. In practice, all piles derive their support from a combination of these factors.

Connections to piles

The processes of installation of piles result in the tops of the piles being far from perfectly level and true; hence a loading platform must be created to take the loads from the building and transmit them safely to the piles. This platform is known as a pile cap, which is formed in reinforced concrete and may transfer loads to a single pile or a group of piles. The caps are normally loaded by the columns of the building and may also take loads from the walls via a ground beam, as shown in Figure 3.24.

Where houses are to be built on ground that is of poor loadbearing capacity or where there are particular problems with shrinkable clay, piles may be

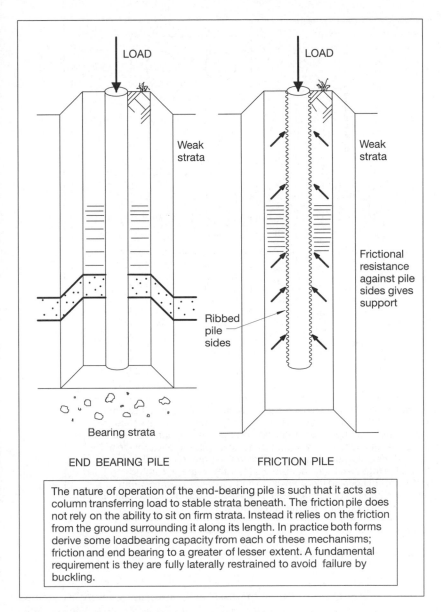

Figure 3.23 ● End-bearing and friction piles.

considered as the best alternative. However, piles are generally associated with the application of point loads such as from the columns of a framed building. In order to allow the transfer of uniformly distributed loads (udl) from the walls of a traditionally built dwelling we must provide a suitable interface between the wall and the piles. This is effected by using a reinforced concrete ground beam. The beam spans the piles to form a continuous support for the construction of the walls. One potential problem in adopting this approach in shrinkable clay soils is

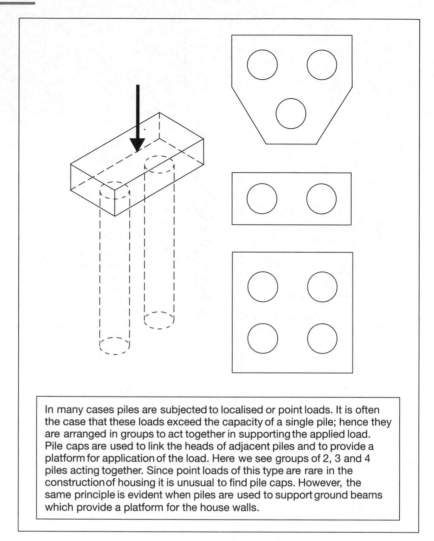

In many cases piles are subjected to localised or point loads. It is often the case that these loads exceed the capacity of a single pile; hence they are arranged in groups to act together in supporting the applied load. Pile caps are used to link the heads of adjacent piles and to provide a platform for application of the load. Here we see groups of 2, 3 and 4 piles acting together. Since point loads of this type are rare in the construction of housing it is unusual to find pile caps. However, the same principle is evident when piles are used to support ground beams which provide a platform for the house walls.

Figure 3.24 ● Pile cap configurations.

that the volume of the ground may increase with moisture content as well as shrinking, depending on the time of year. This would cause heave or uplift on the underside of the ground beam, as this is in contact with the ground at a shallow level. The problem is avoided by the utilisation of a compressible board laid between the ground and the underside of the ground beam.

In the construction of dwellings it is unusual for there to be a need for piles to extend to great depths, since the loads are generally quite low. Hence one of the most common forms of piling used in the short bored pile (Figures 3.25 and 3.26).

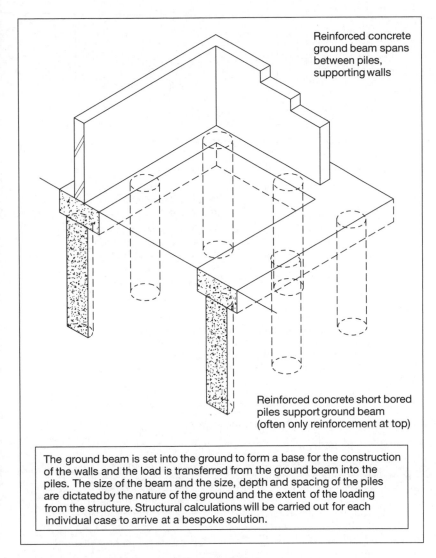

Reinforced concrete ground beam spans between piles, supporting walls

Reinforced concrete short bored piles support ground beam (often only reinforcement at top)

The ground beam is set into the ground to form a base for the construction of the walls and the load is transferred from the ground beam into the piles. The size of the beam and the size, depth and spacing of the piles are dictated by the nature of the ground and the extent of the loading from the structure. Structural calculations will be carried out for each individual case to arrive at a bespoke solution.

Figure 3.25 ● Short bored pile foundations.

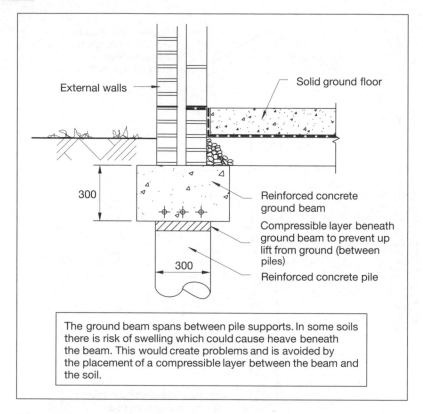

Figure 3.26 ● Reinforced concrete ground beam.

Reflective summary

With reference to deep foundation forms, remember:

— Piles may be classified by the way in which they are placed in the ground: displacement piles displace the earth as they penetrate, while replacement piles fill the hole excavated for them, replacing the soil with pile material.

— Piles may also be classified by the way in which they are designed to transfer load to the ground: end-bearing piles stand in or on a loadbearing stratum, while friction piles tend to be roughly corrugated to release load to the ground down the full length of the pile. The corrugations increase the pile surface area and the grip to the soil.

— Piles may be placed in pairs or in clusters (more than two) when a heavy load is concentrated in a confined area (perhaps a two-storey chimney breast).

— As a loadbearing external walled property cannot be built directly off the piles, we use a reinforced concrete ground beam below the wall to span the heads of the piles distributing the wall load (this beam also stabilises the piles).

Review task

When dealing with domestic scale construction, deep foundation forms tend to be limited to piles. With reference to this form of foundation consider the following questions. *Remember*: there may be more than one correct answer!

1 In which of the following situations may piles be used as a foundation solution?
    (a) where there is firm non-cohesive soil at depths close to the surface of the ground
    (b) where the ground is made of firm clay
    (c) in areas of filled ground
    (d) in areas of peaty ground
    (e) in areas of mining subsidence

2 Grout injection or continuous flight auger (CFA) piles are commonly used. Select the features which you consider to be the advantages of this form of piling.

    speed
    economy
    low disturbance
    ground consolidation
    loadbearing capacity

3 Driven piles also have advantages. Select the features which you consider to be the advantages of this form of piling.

    speed
    economy
    low disturbance
    ground consolidation
    loadbearing capacity

Case study

Formation of piles

Here we see a number of square section precast concrete piles awaiting installation. They are driven into place in a pattern that reflects the layout of the new dwelling. The driven piles extend out of the ground by differing amounts. This is a potential problem with pre-formed piles, and the final length must be adjusted by trimming on-site.

In this case the ground conditions posed problems as there was a layer of made-up ground over the bearing stratum, which was at a depth of around 1.5–2 metres. Since this is an isolated instance on the site, which is otherwise suitable for strip foundations, the cost of bringing a piling rig to site was uneconomic. Hence the innovative solution here is to form piles *in situ* using precast manhole units as permanent formwork.

The sequence of operations involved in the installation of CFA piles is fast and efficient. The centre of the auger is hollow, allowing concrete to be pumped through it as the auger is extracted from the ground. This means that there is no need to support the sides of the pile cavity during the installation, as the process does not create a void in the ground. Following extraction of the auger the reinforcement cage is lowered into the wet concrete to complete the pile.

Comparative study: foundations

Option	Advantages	Disadvantages	When to use
Strip	Cheap Familiar technology No need for specialised plant	Requires formwork in non-cohesive soils Access for bricklaying in trench	Continuous walls on ground with reasonable bearing capacity Used in most cases for construction of dwellings
Deep strip	No need for formwork Reduced bricklaying below ground Fast Cheap No need for specialised plant	Unsuitable for cohesionless soils May be susceptible to movement in shrinkable clay	In cohesive soils where depth of foundation is not excessive and loads are uniform and continuous
Wide strip	Allows increased bearing on low-strength soils Avoids excessive depth of foundation as width increases	Requires reinforcement to resist bending and shear Can become uneconomic compared with raft foundation as width increases	Continuous walls on ground with low bearing capacity.
Piles	Economic when bearing stratum is deep Avoids shrinkable clay zone Allows use of land unsuitable for traditional foundations	Need for special plant Potential for vibration or damage from driven piles More complex structural design required	Used with ground beams to support house walls where loadbearing stratum is deep below ground level Where shrinkable clay layer close to the surface must be avoided Used singly or as clusters to support isolated point loads
Raft	Economic as it combines foundation and floor slab Shallow excavations avoid need for costly plant	Require reinforcement to be designed Can suffer from edge erosion if not protected	Used for relatively light loads on ground with poor or variable loadbearing capacity Popular with timber frame construction Often used on filled or brown field sites

chapter four

Walls below ground

Aims

After studying this chapter you should be able to:

- Understand the nature of the environment in which walls below ground are required to function
- Appreciate the factors that affect the performance of walls below ground level and the materials used for their construction
- Identify and apply criteria for the selection of appropriate design solutions and should be familiar with the form and construction details of the various options

This chapter contains the following sections:

4.1   Functional requirements of walls below ground

4.2   Options for walls below ground

4.3   Entry of services

Hot links

- Building Regulations Approved Document A, Structure
- BS 5997: Guide to British Standard codes of practice for building services
- BS 6515: Specification for polyethylene damp-proof courses for masonry
- BS 8110: Structural use of concrete
- BS 8215: Code of practice for design and installation of damp-proof courses in masonry construction

4.1 Functional requirements of walls below ground

Introduction

After studying this section you should be aware of the main functions of walls below ground. You should be able to identify the key issues affecting the selection of appropriate design solutions. In addition, you should have developed an appreciation of the variable factors linked to the selection of sites for building that may have an effect on the performance of walls below ground.

Overview

The sections of walls below ground level provide an important link between the superstructure of the building and the foundations. The loads from the building must be transferred safely through these walls and the passage of moisture from the ground must be checked to prevent entry to the building. At the same time, the walls are subjected to lateral loadings from the ground surrounding them and, depending on the relative levels of the ground on each side, may be subject to hydrostatic pressure driving moisture through the structure. The issue of resistance to the passage of moisture is dealt with elsewhere in this book. Within this section we shall consider the structural functions of the walls below ground and the implications of selection of various options upon the construction process and the cost of building.

The main functional requirements of these sub-ground walls are structural stability, the exclusion of moisture and durability (Figure 4.1). Since the walls are below ground they are rarely seen; hence appearance is not significant.

Durability of walls below ground

As previously noted, the environment in which some elements of the structure are sited below ground can be hostile to the materials of construction. This imposes some restrictions on the nature of construction of walls below ground level. These walls are subjected to ground moisture for much of the time. The extent of this depends upon the specific nature of the soil and the height of the water table, but in most cases the walls below ground are in a wet environment. Hence materials with low porosity are desirable; these are less likely to suffer deterioration as a result of the freezing of the water close to the surface of the

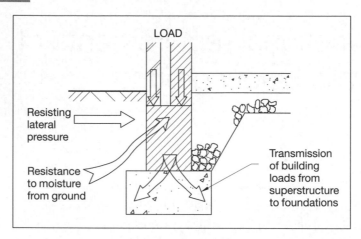

Figure 4.1 ● Functions of walls below ground.

Many building materials, such as brick and concrete blocks, are porous in nature. As a result, they absorb moisture readily when they are placed in situations where water is present. In some cases, masonry below ground level may be almost permanently saturated. Provided the materials are sufficiently durable this should not pose any major problem. However, when freezing occurs, the moisture close to the surface of the material turns to ice, causing expansion and creating minor cracking; on thawing, more moisture is absorbed and the process repeated. Thus an increase in the level of cracking occurs over time, possibly resulting in spalling of the surface of the material

ground in periods of cold weather. Porous materials tend to absorb ground moisture, which expands on freezing causing spalling and friability of the material.

The walls in these areas are also subjected to high pressures, both from the building above ground and the ground itself. The lateral force exerted by the mass of earth which surrounds the walls can have a considerable compressive effect, particularly in the case of cavity walls (Figure 4.2).

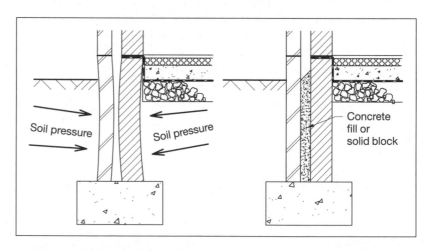

Figure 4.2 ● The effects of soil pressure on walls below ground.

In order to resist the effects of this loading it is common practice to fill the cavity below ground level with weak mix concrete, or to construct the walls up to ground level from solid brick or block, without the cavity. The blocks that are used in this area are very durable, being of high density with low porosity. They are very different from the form of blockwork which is generally used above ground. This type of block is known as 'trenchblock' and is specifically manufactured for use below ground level.

Another factor that must also be considered is the potentially deleterious nature of the soil in which the walls are to be placed. In clay soils there is the potential for the action of soluble sulphates to deteriorate concrete. Thus a full site investigation to identify materials that have the potential to adversely affect the durability of the walls is essential. In the case of sulphate attack in concrete and the cement mortar used to bond the brick or block wall, the effect is to cause expansion, friability and loss of strength. The effects are irreversible and the implications for durability are considerable.

Strength and stability

The requirement for the walls below ground to provide a sound base from which to construct the superstructure of the dwelling is perhaps the main factor affecting the form of these walls. The Building Regulations require that the load transmitted at the base of a foundation does not exceed 70 kN/m run. This restriction, together with an assessment of the safe bearing capacity of the supporting strata, dictates the area of the foundation base that can be varied. The cross-sectional area of the sub-ground walls tends to be fixed by the thickness of the walls of the superstructure. Hence there is less scope for variation in the loading conditions. The levels of pressure exerted on the walls below ground level are relatively high, since the accumulated mass of the entire structure above ground will be directed through these walls. Therefore the strength of the bricks or blocks used must be sufficient to ensure that they are capable of withstanding the loads without risk of failure by crushing. Typically, blocks or bricks with a crushing strength of 5–7 N/mm^2 will be used.

The potentially damaging effects of lateral loading from the surrounding soil are of most concern in areas of shrinkable clay. In these situations the seasonal swelling of the clay results in increased levels of lateral pressure being exerted on the walls. Mechanisms must be introduced to ensure that the effects of this are not severe enough to cause failure of the walls.

Exclusion of moisture

There are several pathways via which groundwater may enter a building (Figure 4.3). It is essential to exclude moisture from the interior of the building to ensure that the conditions internally are appropriate. The nature of the walls below ground level is such that, although they may be wet, they must not allow moisture to pass into the building. This is achieved by the introduction of specific moisture-resisting elements. These are termed damp proof courses (DPCs).

DPCs are placed to prevent ingress of moisture from several sources. Their position is dictated by the need to deal with rising moisture and rain splash. A variety

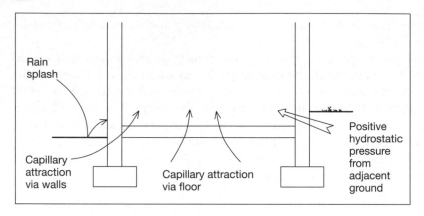

Figure 4.3 ● Modes of water passage into buildings.

of materials have been used historically, including slate and modern pitch polymer materials.

DPCs are positioned in internal and external walls. They must link with DPMs in floors to create a continuous barrier. They are normally placed min. 150 mm above external ground level to avoid rain splash. They also feature 'weep holes' in the brickwork beneath to allow water from the wall cavity to escape to the exterior.

Differing ground levels

In some cases, the construction of buildings on sloping sites is necessary (Figure 4.4). In such circumstances the walls below the damp-proof course level may be required to separate a void beneath the ground floor from the external ground. In these circumstances the wall will need to fulfil functions additional to those discussed previously. The walls extending below ground level, often extending to a considerable depth, are required to resist the lateral loadings that are exerted by the surrounding earth. In this respect they may be considered as retaining walls as well as supporting the walls and superstructure above. They must, therefore, be of robust form and be capable of withstanding the range of forces applied, while remaining durable in the sub-ground environment.

In addition to the requirements for structural stability, the exclusion of ground water will generally be necessary; in some instances, however, water penetration may be acceptable to some extent, where sub-floor drainage is provided, for example. In such cases the long-term build-up of water may be prevented by pumping the water away via a sump. The exclusion of moisture from these sub-ground void areas requires the provision of vertical and horizontal damp-proofing elements around the entire sub-ground structure. This method of moisture exclusion is termed 'tanking'. Impervious materials are used to form the tanking, such as mastic asphalt, bitumen-based materials or any of an extensive

Tanking is a term used to refer to the treatment of walls and floors below ground level to avoid the penetration of moisture from the ground. Impervious membranes are often used positioned against the walls to prevent moisture ingress. The pressure applied by sub-ground water can be considerable, hence, tanking systems must be supported by a robust element, such as a block wall for example.

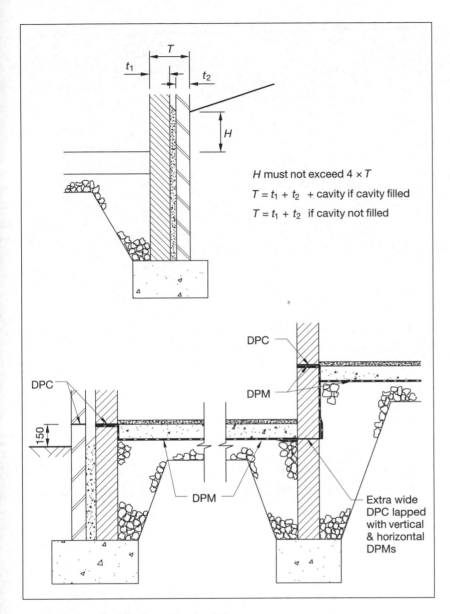

H must not exceed $4 \times T$

$T = t_1 + t_2$ + cavity if cavity filled

$T = t_1 + t_2$ if cavity not filled

Figure 4.4 ● Building on sloping sites.

range of proprietary products, often of an elastomeric nature. It is essential that tanking is continuous, as with damp-proof courses and damp-proof membranes, and it must retain its integrity throughout the area that is to be waterproofed. Great care must be taken, therefore, where elements of the structure, such as beams and columns, together with building services, penetrate the sub-ground floor or walls. This is of particular importance, since the ground water acts against these walls with positive hydrostatic pressure. The damp-proofing elements must be capable of resisting such pressure.

Reflective summary

With reference to walls below ground, remember:

— It is these walls that are used to connect the building with the foundation, so their stability and strength is of great importance.

— These walls need to be strong enough to carry the loads imposed on them, but also need to be able to resist forces that may come laterally (horizontally) from the ground. If these walls are cavity walls, the fine concrete cavity filling is used to create a stronger solid wall up to external ground level. The top of the cavity filling also directs any collecting cavity moisture out through weep holes.

— Ground movement by freeze/thaw effects may also pressurise the wall below ground.

— Walls below ground may potentially conduct ground moisture to the building by capillary action, and therefore we use the DPC to intercept this rising moisture.

— The floor DPM should overlap the wall DPC.

 ## Review task

Outline the factors that can affect the durability of walls below ground.

What do you understand by the term *tanking*?

4.2 Options for walls below ground

Introduction

After studying this section you should be familiar with the main construction alternatives available for the formation of walls below ground level. You should appreciate the forces applied to these sections of walls and the ways in which the construction form attempts to deal with them. In addition, you should understand the implications of soil type and ground level for the choice of design solution. You should also appreciate the cost implications of the selection of the various options and, given specific scenarios, you should be able to make valid judgements regarding selection.

Overview

The requirements for walls below ground level were established in the previous section. Clearly, the main functional needs are the same for all dwellings; however, there are a range of variable factors linked to the nature of the site and the soil characteristics. As with all elements of the construction of dwellings there is likely to be a range of acceptable alternatives in any given situation. Given this acceptable range of options, the basis for selection will relate strongly to cost. Generally, the most cost-effective solution will be chosen. The economy of the chosen option does not rely simply on the materials being cheaper, but also on the simplicity of the design and the level of labour input required. Speedy forms of construction will normally be simpler and cheaper due to the saving in labour costs associated with the reduction in time required.

For the construction of 'traditional' dwellings there are two main options for the construction of walls below ground. These are the filled cavity option and the foundation block option. These could also be utilised, with suitably amended details, for timber frame construction. Also, in some instances there is the option of adopting deep strip or trench-fill foundations. Although this is actually a foundation option and technically not a wall, its adoption largely negates the need for walls below ground level. Hence it is considered here in overview.

Filled cavity construction

The wall below ground level must provide a base for the construction of the superstructure walls. The thickness of the sub-ground wall is therefore dictated by the thickness of those above ground, rather than by specific functional criteria. The lower wall section must not be significantly narrower than the upper section (Figure 4.5).

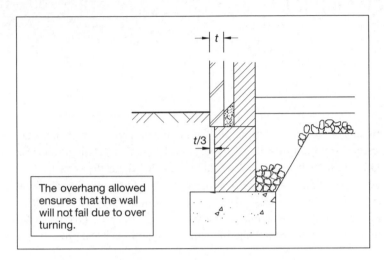

Figure 4.5 ● Building regulation requirements for allowable overhang.

The overhang allowed ensures that the wall will not fail due to over turning.

For this reason the thickness of the wall below ground level is generally designed to be the same as that above ground. Hence, where traditional cavity construction is adopted the wall must be at the very least 250 mm thick. With changes in the thermal requirements for external walls this has increased in recent years. Therefore walls of 300 mm or more are not uncommon. For the reasons outlined earlier it is undesirable to create a cavity below ground level, as the risk of the two leaves of the wall being squeezed together must be avoided. One way to achieve this is to create a solid wall section below ground. The creation of this by building a thick, bonded section would be costly and slow. Hence it is usual to create a cavity wall which then has the cavity filled to ground level with a weak mix of concrete (Figure 4.6). This achieves the desired result and is, at the same time, cost-effective.

Even where the outer leaf of the wall above ground is formed in brick it is common to build the section below ground in dense concrete block. This again is for reasons of economy. Concrete blocks are cheaper and faster to lay than bricks, and since they are hidden below ground there is no aesthetic requirement.

Foundation block construction

A further efficiency gain and resultant cost saving can be made by the utilisation of larger blocks specifically designed for the purpose (Figure 4.7). Foundation blocks are available in a variety of widths to accommodate the commonly used thicknesses of cavity wall. The dimensions of the block allow the full thickness of

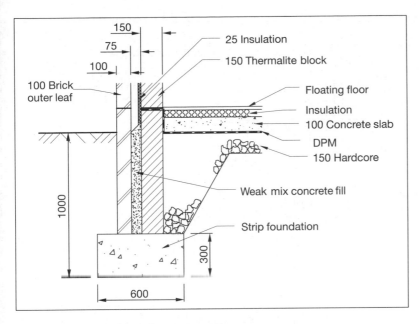

Figure 4.6 ● Filled cavity construction.

Labels in figure:
- 150
- 75
- 100
- 25 Insulation
- 150 Thermalite block
- 100 Brick outer leaf
- Floating floor
- Insulation
- 100 Concrete slab
- DPM
- 150 Hardcore
- Weak mix concrete fill
- Strip foundation
- 1000
- 300
- 600

Case study

Formation of walls below ground

Filled cavity

Trenchblock

Here we see two of the common methods adopted for forming walls below ground. The filled cavity uses two leaves of block or brick below ground, with the cavity filled using weak concrete. In contrast the trenchblock alternative uses a single, wide concrete block. The wall below ground is solid in this case. It is quite unusual for expensive clay bricks to be used below ground; instead, concrete bricks or blocks are used.

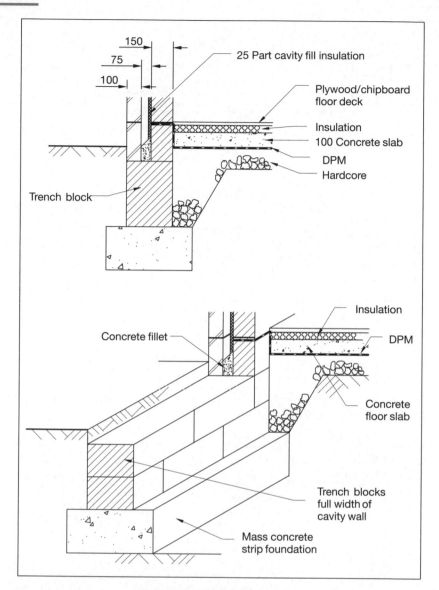

Figure 4.7 ● Foundation block construction.

the cavity wall above to be facilitated in one mass below the ground. Although this results in blocks that are considerably larger than those used above ground, and thus more difficult to manipulate, there is still an efficiency benefit. Rather than building two separate leaves of cavity walling, which then have the cavity filled with concrete, the wall is created in a single operation. In this way there is a considerable saving in time and labour. An added benefit is that the trench excavated for the formation of the foundations and walls below ground can be backfilled very shortly after construction.

Trench-fill foundations

The formation of trench-fill foundations is associated with soils where there is a high level of cohesion between the particles, e.g. clay soils. The reasons for their adoption have already been explored in detail and will not be reiterated here. However, they are worthy of mention since their use combines some of the functions of walls below ground with those of the foundation. The casting of concrete to just below ground level provides a stable base for the construction of the walls above ground and is fast and economical.

Figure 4.8 summarises the options for constructing walls below ground.

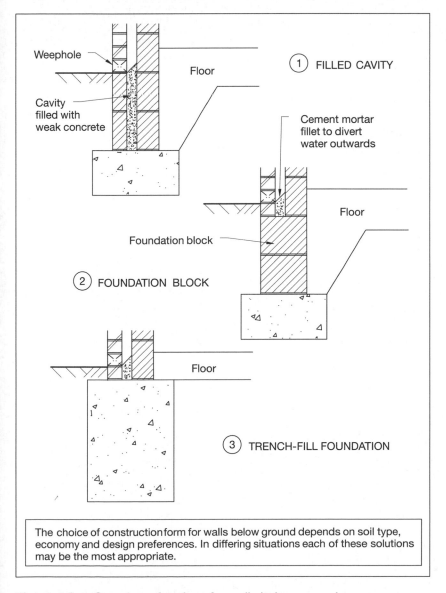

The choice of construction form for walls below ground depends on soil type, economy and design preferences. In differing situations each of these solutions may be the most appropriate.

Figure 4.8 ● Overview of options for walls below ground.

Reflective summary

With respect to options for walls below ground, remember:

— Traditionally with cavity walls we have used two clay brickwork skins below ground level.

— Developing from the traditional cavity wall, blockwork has replaced inner skin.

— The modern option is to use a solid trench block for the bulk of the foundation trench and commence the cavity wall just below ground level (retaining the fine concrete cavity fill finished level with the outside ground).

 Review task

Give *two* reasons for filling the cavity of external walls below ground level when traditional strip footing foundations are used.

What advantages are gained by using foundation blockwork?

Outline the advantages of deep strip compared with traditional strip foundations.

Comparative study: walls below ground

Option	Advantages	Disadvantages	When to use
Filled cavity	Familiar technology Natural continuity of wall construction above and below ground Variable width	Need to lay bricks in trench Several construction activities involved Relatively costly in terms of time	Traditional cavity construction where access to the trench is good and depth to foundation is not excessive
Foundation block	Cheap Single construction activity Reduced laying time in trench	Limited range of widths Need to lay large units in trench	Traditional cavity or solid wall construction where access to trench is good and depth to foundation is not excessive
Trench fill foundation	Cheap No need for temporary support to trench Saves time compared with bricklaying in trench	Unsuitable for cohesionless soils Need to consider services entries below ground Potential for damage in highly shrinkable clays	Traditional cavity or solid wall construction in cohesive soils where trench will support itself without propping and where required depth is not excessive

4.3   Entry of services

Introduction

After studying this section you should be aware of the main services that must be provided to dwellings. You should have developed an appreciation of the manner in which the various service entries must be accommodated. An understanding of the factors that affect the mode and design of these various entries should be developed and you should have a broad awareness of governing regulations. You should also appreciate the implications of passing services through the structure of the dwelling below ground.

Overview

The term 'services entries' is actually rather misleading. This section deals also deals with services that exit the building. The penetration of the external envelope of the dwelling by incoming and outgoing services is unavoidable. It is not the intention to deal with the services specifically here; however, a broad awareness of the services involved is necessary to understand the implications for the design and formation of appropriate entry and exit routes.

The mains services supplied to the building are generally referred to as utilities. In the past these were provided by public sector providers, but more recently they have shifted to a number of private sector utilities companies. Although this is the case, they are still tightly regulated by a series of government regulatory offices. The shift to a larger number of private sector suppliers has provided consumers with the opportunity to purchase utilities from a variety of sources. This does not affect the entry of service supplies to dwellings, since all suppliers will use the same distribution infrastructure for gas, electricity and, in most cases, telecommunications. An exception to this is the provision of cabled telecommunications, for which the infrastructure is still developing and is being provided by cable service providers.

The nature of services supplies to dwellings

Service supplies to dwellings can be categorised in a number of ways. One of the most appropriate ways of grouping them for the purposes of this book is to consider them with reference to the form that their distribution infrastructure takes. The three forms that we are concerned with are large diameter pipes, small diameter pipes and cables. The services involved are set out in Table 4.1.

Table 4.1 ● Forms of service supply.

Form	Description
Large diameter pipes	Drainage waste pipes (up to 100 mm)
Small diameter pipes	Water incoming main supply (25 mm) Gas incoming main supply (25 mm)
Cables	Electricity main supply Telephone connection Cable telecommunications link (may include TV, telephone etc.)

The companies responsible for the distribution of these services are also responsible for providing service connections to the dwelling. This is not necessarily as clear an issue as it might appear, since several companies may compete locally for service supply. In any event there will be a need to coordinate the supply of services during the construction of the building to ensure that essential work is undertaken efficiently without unnecessary duplication. In order to aid coordination of services, advice is provided by the National Joint Utilities Group (NJUG). This group is funded by the utilities providers and provides a focus for their common activities and requirements. In particular, the NJUG makes recommendations relating to common services entries, entry installation and the positions of meters.

In the past it was common for each of the service providers to dig individual trenches for their service supply to the dwelling. This led to numerous trenches being formed and to a prolonged period of installation. The advice of the NJUG is to provide a common trench for the routing of service supplies to the dwelling (Figure 4.9).

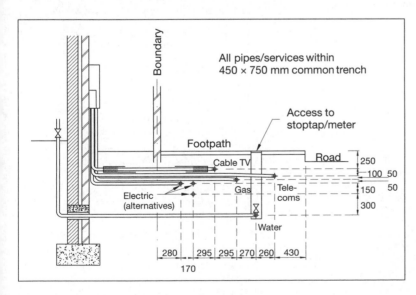

Figure 4.9 ● Combined services trench.

The nature of the service entries to buildings has been improved with the development of flexible materials for ducting and pipework. These allow for more continuous lengths of service pipework and ducting, with fewer joints required to cope with minor changes in direction. Threading of services around potentially troublesome obstacles is also facilitated.

 ## Case study

Services connections

A common service trench with gas (yellow) and water (blue) pipes positioned at a depth to avoid damage from freezing and heavy loads.

Drainage pipework is surrounded by granular fill and is provided with flexible joints to facilitate movement in the ground. Gullies to accept waste outlets are set to the correct level before being bedded in concrete. The depth of the pipework is variable as a result of the required gradient.

Electrical and gas installations enter the dwelling via externally accessible meter boxes. In this case they are set into the wall, but they may also be surface-mounted. These allow access by the service provider in emergencies or for meter reading.

It is worthwhile considering each of the main groups of services in a little more detail.

Large diameter pipes: drainage

The waste and soil pipework for sanitary appliances varies in size from 32 mm to 100 mm in diameter. It is not the intention here to consider the sanitary installation, merely to examine the implications of the need to route the associated pipework through the building fabric. The smaller sizes of waste pipework are restricted to use above ground, and passing them through the external walls is effected by simply cutting a hole of the appropriate size. There is no need for additional support to the surrounding walling.

Of more concern in relation to the walls below ground are the larger sizes of pipework used beneath the ground (Figure 4.10). Underground drainage is

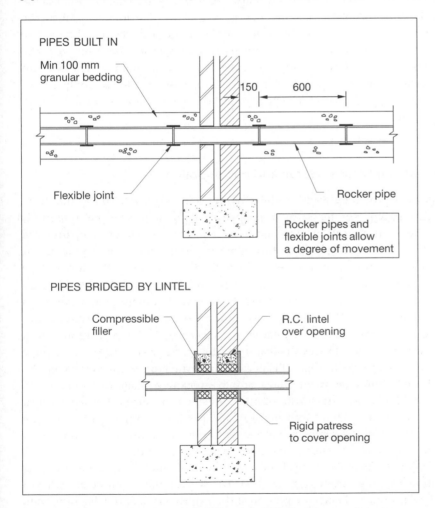

Figure 4.10 ● Pipework passing through walls below ground.

required within the building enclosure to connect to water closets serving the ground floor and as a result of the increased use of internal soil pipes to serve the upper floor sanitary appliances. Where these pipes pass through the external walls below ground there is potential for failure arising from differential movement. There are two major potential causes of such movement. Firstly there is the risk of ground movement resulting from frost-induced heave in the soil surrounding the building. Secondly there is the risk of movement associated with the initial settlement of the new building. All new buildings settle to a small extent due to the minor consolidation of the supporting ground following the construction of the building. This is generally no cause for concern and will not affect the stability of the property. However, where pipes pass through walls that are likely to be affected the movement must be accommodated. If this is not so there is the risk of fracture or deformation of the drainage pipes. The consequence of this would be failure and leakage of the below-ground pipework. In order to avoid this there are two alternative approaches to the installation of the pipework. The first of these relies on the use of flexible joints to allow the pipework, which is built into the wall, to deform within acceptable limits. The second relies on the use of supporting lintels over a larger opening. The size of the opening is such that the slight movement can be accommodated without affecting the pipework. In this case, the pipework is surrounded by compressible material and a rigid pattress is provided to seal the opening and prevent the entry of vermin etc.

Small diameter pipes: water and gas supplies.

Underground services supplies are colour coded to allow easy recognition in the event of exposure during excavation. The National Joint Utilities Group encourages the use of a common services trench in order to minimise disruption and unnecessary excavation during the construction process.

The pipework providing water to the dwelling is in two parts. The section from the main supply to the meter or stop valve at the boundary of the property is termed the communication pipe and is installed by the water company. The section from the boundary to the dwelling is termed the service pipe and is provided by the property developer or the individual consumer. The service pipe will be 25 mm in diameter and will be formed from flexible MDPE pipe. The pipe is blue in colour and is easily recognisable as a water supply pipe. In order to protect the pipe from the effects of frost, and to reduce the effect of compressive loadings from vehicles etc., it is placed in a trench of 750 mm to 1350 mm in depth. In some circumstances shallower depths are allowed, subject to the pipe being insulated against freezing. From the trench the pipe will pass through the walls of the building below ground rising to stop valve inside the property. In order to provide for a degree of differential movement the pipe is housed within a larger diameter sleeve built into the wall and passing through the floor of the dwelling. The sleeve is sealed at both ends to prevent access to vermin and to resist the passage of gas, such as methane, from the ground.

The supply of gas to dwellings is heavily regulated and the rules governing its installation are prescriptive (Figure 4.11). The service pipe is buried at least 375 mm below ground and exits the ground at the external face of the dwelling wall. In older buildings it is common to find the meter for the gas supply located within

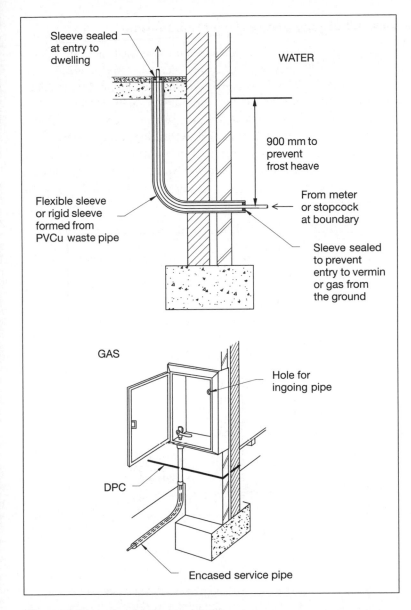

Figure 4.11 ● Service entry details.

the property. In more modern buildings the meter will be located externally and is housed within a protective meter box. This box is accessible to the gas provider for the purpose of meter reading and to allow the supply to be cut off in emergencies. From the meter box the supply pipe will pass into the dwelling through the external wall above ground, and will be provided with a sleeve to prevent leakage of gas into the cavity. The details of this installation are dealt with elsewhere in this book.

Cabled service: electricity and telecommunications

The nature of cabled services is such that they are far more easily accommodated than piped services and their entry to dwellings reflects this. In the case of electricity supplies, as with gas, external meter boxes are now common (Figure 4.12). There is far more freedom in positioning the cables to supply the meter and they can rise within cavities if required. The nature of the telecommunications industry is such that services are changing and expanding rapidly. Hence it is prudent to consider the use of a ducted entry within the common service trench to allow for future expansion. Once at the external wall of the property they are connected to distribution boxes externally, and their entry through the external wall takes place above ground.

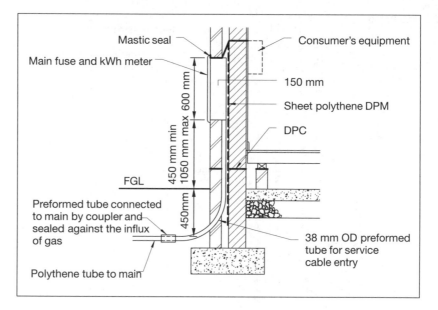

Figure 4.12 ● Electrical service entry boxes.

Reflective summary

With reference to service connections, remember:

— Service connections may involve exiting services (drainage) as well as supply services (e.g. electricity).

— Services of this form tend to be classed as large diameter pipes, small diameter pipes and cables.

— Colour coding of services applies – pale blue for cold water, yellow for gas etc.

— For many of the services a shared trench is now suggested as they are routed from the boundary to the property.

— Where meters are provided these are now generally located to allow reading from outside, eliminating the need to gain access to the interior of the property.

Review task

Name *four* service connections typically made to modern homes.

Name the *three* forms in which these services are classed.

Comparative study: services connections

Form	Option	Colour	Entry treatment	Protection
Cables	Electrical mains	Black	Entry via wall-mounted box containing meter with external access	Typically 450 mm below ground level
	Cabled services	Various, depending on provider of data. Telecommunications etc.	As required by cable service provider	Consider separation of data cabling from power cables to avoid danger of electromagnetic interference
Small diameter pipes	Gas	Yellow	Entry via external meter housed in protective box with external access. Ensure sleeving of pipework through wall cavity	Typically 600 mm minimum below ground level
	Water	Blue	Entry through wall below ground level and ground floor to stop tap internally	Minimum 750 mm below ground level to avoid freezing and damage from loads on ground. Pipework housed on curved sleeve through wall and floor
Large diameter pipes	Drainage	Various, typically terracotta/ brown	Provide facility for differential movement where passing through walls below ground. Use of rocker pipe or lintel required	Laid to falls in granular bedding. Protect from physical damage as required

chapter five

Ground floors

 ## Aims

After studying this unit you should be able to:

- Distinguish between the various options available for the formation of ground floors to dwellings
- Understand the functional requirements of ground floors and the criteria for the selection of alternatives
- Understand the construction detailing associated with each of the potential design solutions and you should appreciate the sequence of operations involved in their formation on site

This chapter contains the following sections:

5.1   Functions of ground floors and selection criteria

5.2   Ground-supported floor options

5.3   Suspended floor options

Hot links

- BRE DAS Suspended Timber Floors: Recommendations for use
- BRE Good Building Guide 25 Radon: Guidance on protective measures for new buildings
- BS 6515: Specification for polyethylene damp-proof courses for masonry
- BS 8102: Code of practice for the protection of structures against water from the ground
- BS 8110: Structural use of concrete

5.1 Functions of ground floors and selection criteria

Introduction

After studying this section you should have developed an understanding of the functional requirements of ground floors to dwellings. You should appreciate the implications of ground conditions and features of the chosen site upon the selection of ground floor options. In addition you should be aware of the implications of foundation and external wall construction forms upon the selection of ground floor design solutions.

Overview

Ground floors to dwellings can take a number of forms, depending, among other things, on the nature of the site, the quality of construction and the required speed of erection of the building. However, all of the available design solutions essentially fulfil the same functional requirements. The detailed functional requirements will be examined in detail later within this unit. Ground floors can be categorised in two basic groups: suspended floors and ground-supported (or solid) floors. In simple terms, the distinction between the two forms is as follows (Figure 5.1):

- Solid floors are formed such that the underside of the floor is in continuous contact with and is supported by the ground.

- Suspended floors are formed such that the structural elements of the floor span between supports, not relying on the ground for support of the floor structure. This may result in the creation of a void beneath the floor and the ground.

Functional requirements of ground floors

The main function of the ground floor is to provide a safe and stable platform for the activities that are carried out within the dwelling. However, in addition to this there are a number of other equally important functions that must be fulfilled by the floor if it is to satisfy user needs and other requirements such as the Building Regulations.

The nature of the construction form of ground floors is dictated by the relative importance of these aspects of performance. In addition, there are a series of

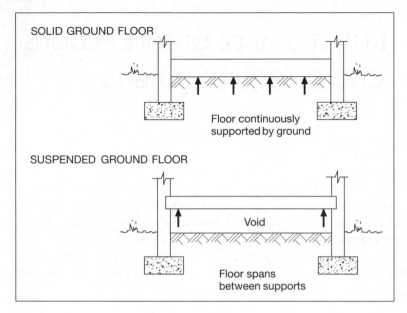

SOLID GROUND FLOOR

Floor continuously
supported by ground

SUSPENDED GROUND FLOOR

Void

Floor spans
between supports

Figure 5.1 ● Ground floor classification.

aspects related to the selected site and the general construction form of the dwelling that will have an impact on the choice of floor; these will be examined in detail later. Let us first consider the generic performance or functional requirements for ground floors of all types. These functional requirements can be summarised as follows.

Structural stability

The ground floor of any dwelling must be designed and constructed in such a way that it is capable of supporting the dead loads and live loads that it is likely to be subjected to. Hence the construction form must be such that the floor is robust enough to resist or transfer these loads without undue deformation or the risk of structural failure (Figure 5.2). In the case of ground-supported floors this relies on the floor structure, which is in continuous contact with the ground, dissipating the loads effectively. In the case of suspended forms the mechanism is one of load transfer to the supporting elements of the structure, normally taking the form of dwarf or sleeper walls at low level.

Thermal insulation

As with all elements of the external fabric of buildings there is a requirement for ground floors to provide a degree of resistance to the passage of heat (Figure 5.3). The degree to which this results in the need for the installation of an insulative

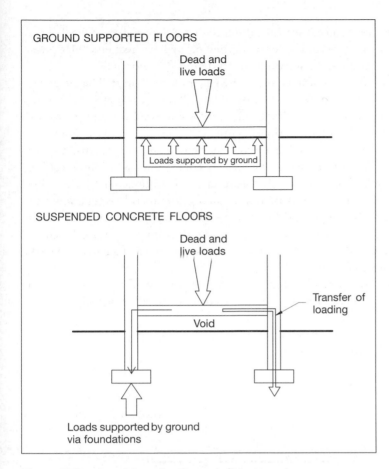

GROUND SUPPORTED FLOORS

Dead and
live loads

Loads supported by ground

SUSPENDED CONCRETE FLOORS

Dead and
live loads

Transfer of
loading

Void

Loads supported by ground
via foundations

Figure 5.2 ● Load transfer through floors.

material varies depending on the floor structure and formation. However, as the required levels of insulation demanded by the building regulations have increased, so the need to provide specific insulative materials as part of the floor composition has increased accordingly. The nature of heat loss through ground floors differs between suspended floor types and ground-supported floor types.

In the case of solid floor types the formation of the floor in contact with the ground results in the creation of a protected zone at the core of the floor area. This effectively provides a degree of insulation to the central area of the floor, which inhibits heat loss. In periods of cold weather it can generally be assumed that the interior of the building will be warmer than the exterior, including the ground which supports the building. The ground beneath the floor will itself absorb a degree of heat from the building. In addition, around the perimeter of the floor there will be heat transfer to the surrounding ground and to the external atmosphere. There will also be heat loss through the edges of the floor at the

Heat loss from buildings occurs when the internal temperature is higher than the external temperature. Steady state heat transfer is the term used to refer to the passage of heat through a building element after the element has itself reached equilibrium. At the start of the process of heat transfer, the element will absorb heat until it reaches a stable temperature. After it reaches a point where it will not absorb any more heat, all heat loss is to the exterior. This is steady state flow.

abutments with the external walls of the building close to ground level. These mechanisms will not occur at the centre of the floor, where heat loss will eventually achieve a 'steady state' and will be much reduced in extent.

For this reason the level of heat loss at the edges of the floor will be far greater than at the central area. Hence in the case of large floor areas it may be economical to insulate the floor to differing levels at different locations. In the past this has taken the form of insulation provision only at the perimeter of the floor, with the central area left uninsulated. However, in the case of floors to dwellings the size of the floors tends to be too small for this approach to be economical. The potential cost saving associated with materials is counteracted by the added complexity of the differing construction detailing. Hence it has generally been the case that ground-supported floors to dwellings have been fully insulated. With proposed increases in the insulation requirements for floors included within the revised Building Regulations the amount of insulative material required will increase further.

In the case of suspended floor constructions the creation of a void beneath the floor results in a more uniform level of heat transfer across the floor. The void will

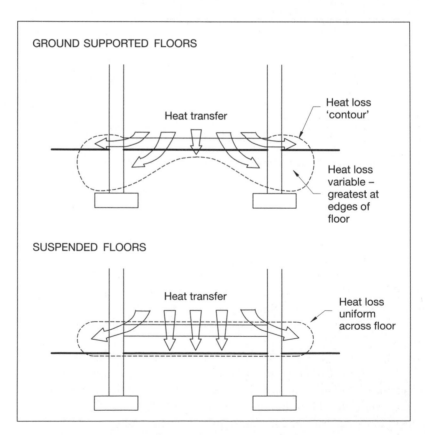

Figure 5.3 ● Heat loss through floors.

be subject to the passage of air, and thus the creation of a steady state central area will not be possible. Hence it is essential to provide a uniform level of insulation across the whole of the floor. As in the case of ground-supported floors, the potential does exist for heat loss to occur at the edges of the floor where it comes into contact with the external walls. This must be taken into account when considering the insulation provision.

Exclusion of ground water

The issue of preventing the passage of moisture to the interior of a dwelling is dealt with in detail elsewhere within this text, but it may be useful to remember that this need is the subject of Part C of the Building Regulations. It is essential to recognise that the potential for ground water to pass through the ground floor of a dwelling is a significant factor. For this reason the construction form of the floor, whether ground-supported or suspended, must include details designed to arrest the passage of moisture.

The normal mechanism of moisture ingress through ground floors is that of capillarity (Figure 5.4). Moisture is drawn into the building element as a result of the capillary action within porous materials such as concrete. This must be resisted by the incorporation of impervious materials or capillary breaks within the floor. In some instances there may be the added problem of moisture being driven into the structure by positive pressure. This is particularly so where the level of the ground is such that the floor structure is below the external ground level. Although such circumstances are now rare, in older properties with cellars, or where the ground level changes considerably, i.e. sloping sites, the situation may still arise. In these cases there is the potential for water to be forced into the building by hydrostatic pressure.

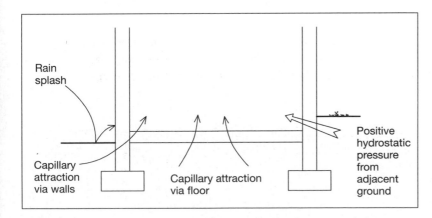

Figure 5.4 ● Moisture entry routes through floors.

Durability

As the nature of the environment within which ground floors must function is rather aggressive the materials that are used must be sufficiently durable to provide a satisfactory lifespan. Thus the selection of appropriate materials is essential for the longevity of the floor.

Provision of appropriate surface finish

Ground floors to dwellings must provide a level and smooth surface finish to allow for the provision of decorative and comfortable floor coverings. Even minor irregularities in the surface of the floor can result in premature wear of finishes. It is also essential that the finish is level and true in terms of safety, since minor undulations and irregularities can result in the creation of trip hazards.

As a result, concrete floors tend either to be finished with a screed (often cement and sand-based) or power floated (see later).

Factors affecting the selection of ground floors

A number of factors affect the selection of ground floor alternatives. These relate to the functional performance of the individual options and also take into account the following:

- the general nature of the construction form

- nature of the site

- anticipated loadings

- required surface finish

- cost

When attempting to evaluate individual design solutions these factors will be considered. It must always be remembered that where two alternatives are able to satisfy the functional requirements equally well, the cheapest option is almost certain to be selected.

Reflective summary

With reference to ground floors, remember:

— We use two classes of ground floor – those which are suspended above a void and those which require continuous support from the soil.

— Certain suspended floors (beam and block) are supported by the walls of the property.

— Cuspended timber floors are supported on sleeper walls and *are not* built off the inner skin of external walls.

— Heat lost from solid ground-supported floors tends to be concentrated around the external wall area, while the pattern of heat lost from suspended floors tends to be more uniform because of the heat flow to the below-floor void.

— Those floors with a void provide a useful space for the installation of heating pipes and electrical cables.

Review task

Rank the following ground floor solutions in order of cost with the cheapest first:

concrete suspended

timber suspended

concrete solid

What influences the cost of each type?

What may be the advantages of having a void below the ground floor?

5.2   Ground-supported floor options

Introduction

After studying this section you should have developed an appreciation of the various alternatives for the formation of ground-supported floors to dwellings. You should appreciate the essential elements of interaction between floors and walls. In addition, you should be familiar with the components of the various floor formations and you should understand their functions and the mechanisms by which they satisfy them.

Overview

As outlined previously, the essential characteristic of ground-supported floors is that they are in continuous contact with the ground beneath and they transfer their loads through this contact area. They are often termed solid floors, since there are no void or hollow areas within the construction. Ground-supported floors may take a number of forms, although all are similar in principle, differing only in detail of design and construction. All of the floor options must fulfil the same performance requirements, and as such the level of flexibility in generic form is limited. However, several alternatives exist as a result of the ability to adopt different positions for individual components of the floor assembly.

Solid floor construction

As previously noted, the term 'solid floor' is often used to describe ground-supported floors; all of the options adopt the same approach to construction with the use of a layered form incorporating several individual elements. The main load-supporting element is the floor slab which will normally take the form of a layer of mass concrete, cast *in situ* to the desired level. In floors which are to take high loadings, or where the loadbearing capacity of the ground is low, the slab may be reinforced with mild steel bars or mesh. In normal circumstances a slab thickness of 100–150 mm would be used.

The surface of the floor must usually be suitable to accept a surface finish or to be trafficked directly; hence the raw surface of a cast slab is often unsuitable. The final finish may be provided in a number of ways, but it is most common to provide a layer of sand and cement screed, approximately 50 mm thick over the slab to provide a wearing surface. An alternative to this is to use a layer of mastic asphalt, which has the advantage of being impermeable, or to grind a level finish direct on the surface of the setting slab using a power float.

As was previously noted, the exclusion of moisture is of paramount importance in areas such as ground floors; hence a damp-proof membrane is installed above or below the slab and linked with the DPC in the walls to form a continuous barrier. The exclusion of moisture is aided also by the provision of a layer of hardcore beneath the floor slab. The hardcore bed consists of a layer of crushed stone, or clean, broken brick at least 150 mm thick. The layer acts to provide a level uniform base onto which the slab can be laid. In addition, however, the voids between pieces of hardcore act to break the capillary path of moisture rising from the earth. If not properly compacted, the hardcore layer may be subject to consolidation following loading of the floor; hence it is laid in thin layers about 100–150 mm thick and is carefully compacted as work proceeds. A thin layer of sand or ash is then laid over the hardcore in order to prevent puncturing of the DPM by the sharp points of the hardcore. This is termed blinding. In instances where the DPM is placed above the slab, the provision of the blinding layer also acts to resist the passage of fine cement particles from the slab to the hardcore, which would weaken the finished floor.

The DPM may be located in various positions when constructing the slab and may even be in the form of an impervious finish such as asphalt, as shown in Figure 5.5.

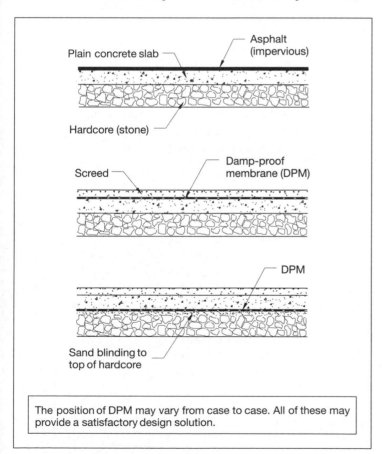

The position of DPM may vary from case to case. All of these may provide a satisfactory design solution.

Figure 5.5 ● Location of the DPM.

When making a floor slab watertight it is essential to have an overlap between the floor DPM and the wall DPC (Figure 5.6).

The provision of insulation in the floor is necessary to reduce heat loss to acceptable levels. Typically, U values of 0.45 W/m^2 K are required for ground floors under the Building Regulations. This is likely to be changed over the coming years to demand a level of 0.22 W/m^2 K by 2005. The inclusion of a layer of high-efficiency insulation material, such as expanded polystyrene is necessary to achieve this level of thermal resistance, this may be placed in a number of alternative positions as illustrated in Figure 5.7.

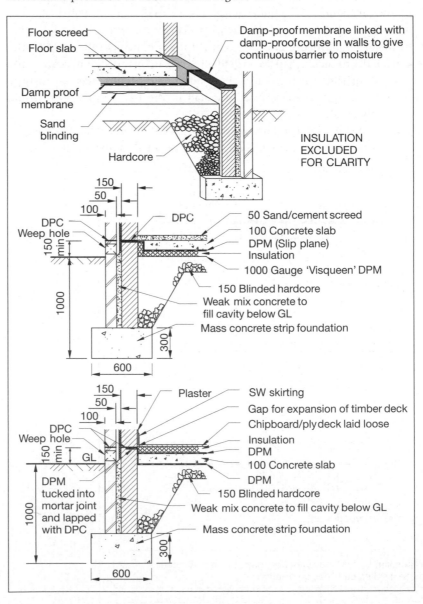

Figure 5.6 ● Meeting between the floor and wall.

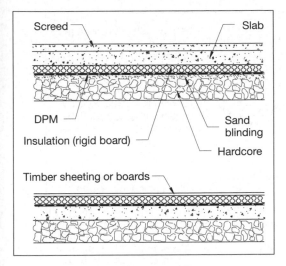

Figure 5.7 ● Insulation of ground floor construction.

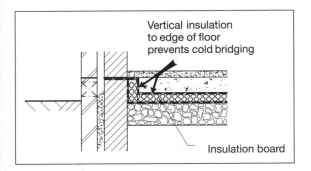

Figure 5.8 ● Preventing cold bridging.

The majority of heat loss occurs at the perimeter of the floor, often by cold bridging at the point of contact between the floor and the external wall. For this reason, insulation is also provided vertically at the junction of the two elements (Figure 5.8).

If a screed is to be used to finish a concrete floor slab rather than power float, there are a number of ways in which the screed itself may be laid. Figure 5.9 shows a number of alternatives; the choice depends on the nature of the building use and the likely loads in addition to the type of finish selected. Where insulation is laid over the slab and beneath the floor screed, a thicker screed is required to resist cracking, as the insulation will give under applied loads.

It is sometimes the case that special provisions need to be made with floors for situations such as disabled access. Here it is important to eliminate any difference in level between the outer paving and the internal floor level to allow a smooth transition from outside to inside. Compatible external and internal levels can be achieved at the entrance door, but creating level surfaces at this position necessitates the incorporation of details to intercept rainwater. Figure 5.10 (see p. 161) indicates potential design options aimed at facilitating level access to buildings without the need for raised thresholds.

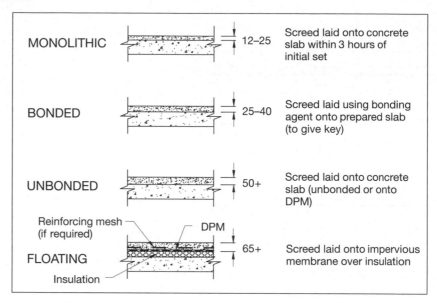

Figure 5.9 ● Screed laying.

Review task

What are the two ways in which we can finish a solid concrete floor slab in preparation for a carpet?

What is sand blinding and where would it be located?

Reflective summary

With reference to ground-supported floors, remember:

— Ground-supported floor slabs may take several forms:
  • plain concrete
  • reinforced concrete
  • insulated or without insulation
  • screeded or power floated
  • damp-proof membrane (DPM) below the concrete
  • DPM below the screed
  • DPM as a surface finish (e.g. asphalt)

— Whatever the form of floor used, the DPM must overlap the wall DPC.

— The excavation level from which we start to build up the floor is known as the Formation Level (FL) – add the floor thickness to the formation level and you reach Finished Floor Level (FFL).

— If we wish to finish the interior floor level with the outside paving to ease access, then special provisions are needed to prevent water entry to the property.

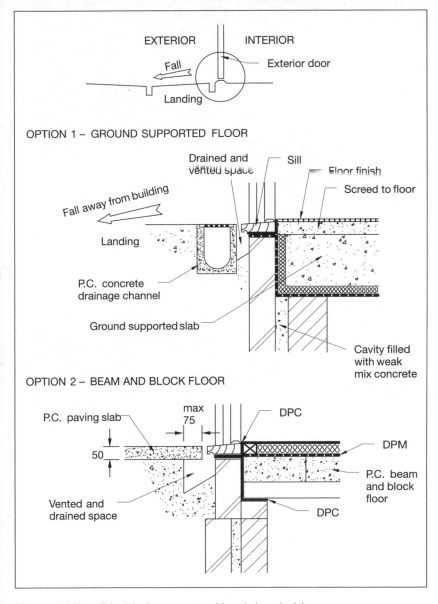

OPTION 1 – GROUND SUPPORTED FLOOR

OPTION 2 – BEAM AND BLOCK FLOOR

Figure 5.10 ● Disabled access and level thresholds.

The Disability Discrimination Act requires that access must be readily achieved by disabled persons. The use of raised door thresholds to exclude rainwater would be obstructive to wheelchair users. Hence level thresholds are now increasing in use.

Case study

Formation of ground-supported floors

One of the most common forms of ground floor construction is the concrete slab. The slab is laid onto a bed of blinded hardcore with an impervious membrane sandwiched between. Here we see the completed slab with the damp-proof membrane dressed up at the edges. It is essential that this membrane is overlapped with the damp-proof course in the walls in order to exclude ground water effectively.

5.3   Suspended floor options

Introduction

After studying this section you should be familiar with the various forms of suspended floor available for use in the construction of dwellings. You should understand the benefits of adopting suspended floor constructions and the reasons underlying the decision to use them in dwellings. You should understand the nature of the timber and concrete alternatives and you should have developed knowledge of the construction details for each.

Overview

In some circumstances the utilisation of ground-supported floors is unsuitable as a result of functional factors. Increasingly the wish to exclude wet trades from the construction process is becoming a factor in the selection process. For this and other reasons the adoption of suspended floors is increasing in popularity. This is particularly the case with suspended concrete forms, although timber variants are becoming less popular, primarily due to cost and issues associated with durability.

   In circumstances where it is necessary to provide a large void beneath the ground floor, the use of a suspended floor system is necessary. In its most traditional form this would have consisted of a series of timber joists, clad with a durable wearing surface such as softwood boarding. This system is still common in the construction of dwellings, but has been replaced in commercial and industrial buildings by more modern systems, capable of carrying great loads and without being subject to decay over time. Such systems are now generally based on the use of precast reinforced concrete units, although the use of simple reinforced concrete slabs, cast *in situ*, is also still an option.

Timber ground floors

Timber ground floors are also referred to as suspended or hollow floors. They represent the traditional form of ground floor and have many advantages to the occupier despite the high cost, which discourages builders from using this floor form. Occupiers would see these floors as aesthetically pleasing, and a modern trend is to have stained or varnished floorboards as the floor finish in preference to carpet. In contrast with concrete floors these are also warmer and provide a degree of flexibility.

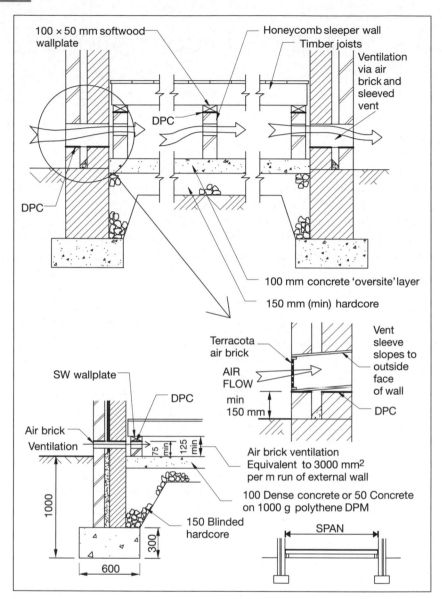

Figure 5.11 ● Timber suspended floor details.

Despite their relatively high cost they have some advantages for the builder too, in that there will always be an air void below the floor, which is an extremely useful route for the installation of water pipes such as central heating pipes and for routing electrical cabling. Both of these services are significantly easier to install in properties with suspended floors.

We have mentioned elsewhere the hygroscopic nature of timber and the consequent need to keep timbers away from any moisture. During the earlier part of last century it was still the practice to install the floor joists of ground floors into the external wall of the property, and whether the external walls were cavity or solid this laid the joists open to moisture absorption. Many of the properties of these times which still exist have had problems with their floors, and many have had their timber suspended floors replaced with a solid concrete alternative due to rot problems.

Irrespective of the age of the property it has always been the practice to ventilate the below floor void to discourage damp conditions which might cause rot. Figure 5.11 shows this practice in a more modern timber hollow floor, where it is now standard procedure to prevent contact between the external wall of the property by standing the floor joists on supportive sleeper walls.

Figure 5.11 shows the desired cross-ventilation supplied through the use of airbricks. It also shows the provision of timber wall plates which take the point loads from each joist and spread them along the supporting sleeper walls. These walls are built honeycombed (with bricks missing) to allow the air below the floor to circulate adequately. One of the reasons that this floor is so relatively expensive compared with other alternatives is that a solid concrete floor is needed to support the sleeper walls. This concrete, as shown, is generally referred to as the oversite concrete layer, and this, as with a concrete floor slab, requires an adequate layer of hardcore for support.

Figure 5.12 shows the same timber floor in a projected section, helping to show the make-up of the sleeper wall and the function of the wall plate in greater detail.

One criticism that might be made of the timber suspended floor is in relation to heat conservation. There is only the floorboarding between the inside of the premises and the air void below the floor. The temperature below the floor is

The relatively high cost of suspended timber floors has resulted in their use being restricted in recent years. They may be used in high-quality dwellings or where there is a deep sub-floor void. However, even in the latter of these situations they have generally been replaced by suspended concrete floors, such as beam and block.

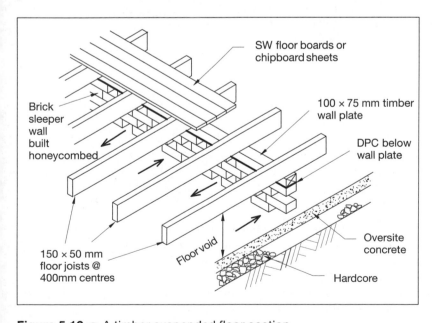

Figure 5.12 ● A timber suspended floor section.

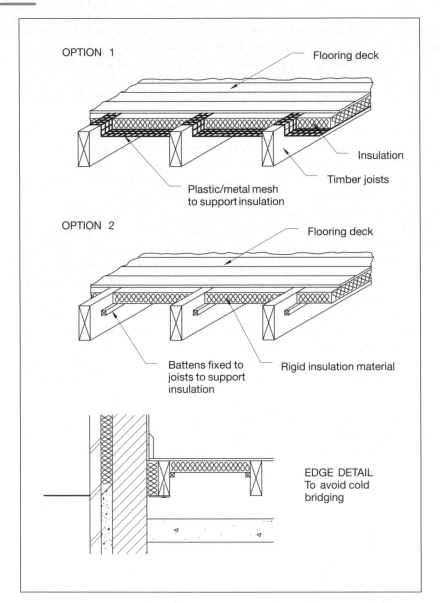

OPTION 1

Flooring deck

Insulation

Timber joists

Plastic/metal mesh
to support insulation

OPTION 2

Flooring deck

Battens fixed to
joists to support
insulation

Rigid insulation material

EDGE DETAIL
To avoid cold
bridging

Figure 5.13 ● Insulation of timber suspended floors.

generally low, and this, with the air circulation needed, helps preserve the timber; but of course this encourages heat loss through the floor. This can be quite easily combatted by the provision of rigid insulation between the joists, as illustrated in Figure 5.13.

The illustration also shows the edge detailing needed if cold bridging at the floor edge is to be avoided.

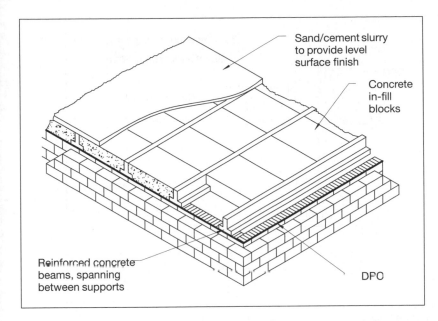

Sand/cement slurry
to provide level
surface finish

Concrete
in-fill
blocks

Reinforced concrete
beams, spanning
between supports

DPC

Figure 5.14 ● Suspended precast concrete (beam and block) flooring systems.

Beam and block floors

The formation of beam and block type floors relies on the provision of a series of profiled reinforced beams, set at relatively close spacings (typically 600 mm), spanning between supporting walls. The beams are often an inverted T shape to allow support to be given to the infill blocks that are dropped in between the beams. A sand/cement screed is then applied over the floor to give a smooth surface finish to receive carpet and other finishes.

This system has the advantage that it comprises a series of small units which can be readily manipulated on-site, without the aid of mechanised plant.

As shown in Figure 5.14, it is acceptable to support this type of floor on the inner skin of a cavity external wall. This is of course because this floor is not in timber but concrete. Where the floor is supported by walls, whether external or internal, a DPC will always be located below the floor units, as illustrated.

Infill blocks are dropped between the reinforced concrete beams and it is easy to finish off the blocks at the end of the beams by cutting blocks to length. At the other floor edge, though, there tends to be a small gap between the beam just inside the external wall and the wall itself. Figure 5.15 shows two ways of supporting the finishing floor screed at this location.

The illustration also shows that, providing topsoil is removed, there may be no need to supply oversite concrete with this type of floor. Additionally, as the floor is not liable to perish due to dampness in the atmosphere of the below-floor void, there is no need to supply ventilating airbricks. This also means that there is less likelihood of heat loss with this floor compared with the timber alternative. It is,

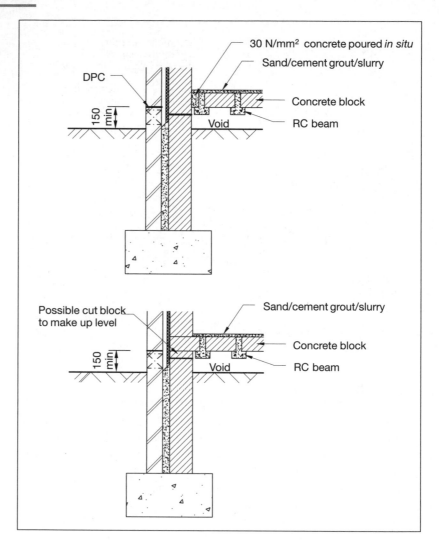

Figure 5.15 ● Edge detailing – beam and block floors.

however, possible to include insulation in the beam and block floor to meet the insulation requirements of the Building Regulations (Figure 5.16).

If support needs to be provided to internal partition walls it is possible to use double beams and wet concrete infill below the partition, as shown in Figure 5.17. This detailing effectively creates a substantially larger reinforced concrete beam below the partition.

Some alternative details are given in Figure 5.18 in a summary of some of the different floor options available with the beam and block floor solution.

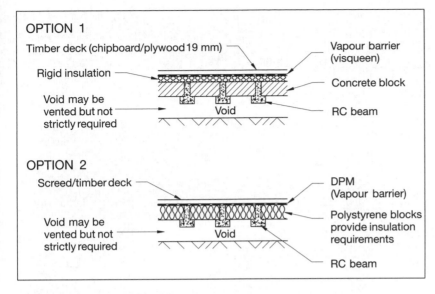

OPTION 1

Timber deck (chipboard/plywood 19 mm)

Rigid insulation

Void may be vented but not strictly required

Void

Vapour barrier (visqueen)

Concrete block

RC beam

OPTION 2

Screed/timber deck

Void may be vented but not strictly required

Void

DPM (Vapour barrier)

Polystyrene blocks provide insulation requirements

RC beam

Figure 5.16 ● Insulating beam and block floors.

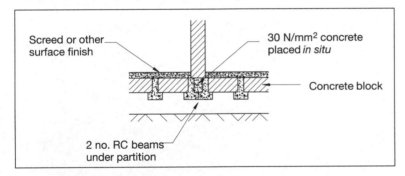

Screed or other surface finish

30 N/mm² concrete placed *in situ*

Concrete block

2 no. RC beams under partition

Figure 5.17 ● Support for internal partitions – beam and block floor.

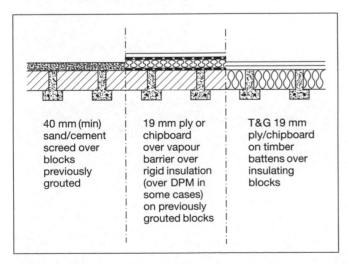

40 mm (min) sand/cement screed over blocks previously grouted

19 mm ply or chipboard over vapour barrier over rigid insulation (over DPM in some cases) on previously grouted blocks

T&G 19 mm ply/chipboard on timber battens over insulating blocks

Figure 5.18 ● Beam and block floors – alternative solutions.

Case study

Formation of suspended concrete ground floors

The use of beam and block floors is now very common in the construction of dwellings. Although timber floors are still used in some cases, they are now rare. In the illustrations we can clearly see the regular layout of reinforced concrete beams with lightweight concrete blocks set between. The size of units is such that they can be easily manipulated. The assembled floor is now ready to receive a sand and cement slurry to give a smooth finish.

Reflective summary

With reference to the use of suspended ground floors, remember:

— These have a void below the floor.

— The void is ventilated if the floor is formed in timber in order to prevent damp conditions and damp absorption by the timbers.

— A bonus of having a floor void is the ease of services installations below the floor.

— A criticism of having a floor void has been the possible heat loss that may occur, but this can be reduced by the incorporation of rigid insulation.

— Ventilation below timber floors is via airbricks built into the external wall, and circulation is assisted by supporting sleeper walls being built honeycombed (with bricks missing).

Review task

How can the insulating qualities of the traditional timber suspended floor be improved?

Give *two* reasons for using sleeper walls.

How is a beam and block floor finished to receive homeowner-applied floor finishes?

What advantages do beam and block floors have over the timber alternative?

Comparative study: ground floors

Option	Advantages	Disadvantages	When to use
Solid concrete	Cheap Familiar technology Easy detailing to insulate and resist moisture Good loadbearing performance	Wet operation slows construction Several operations involved Expensive when dealing with deep voids	Most common form of ground floor Used on relatively level sites with traditional foundation design
Suspended timber	Resilient floor form Can cope with sloping sites and deep floor voids	Potential problems of decay if subject to moisture Expensive Limited loadbearing capacity	Rarely used in modern house building Sometimes adopted for high-quality projects
Beam and block	Cheap Fast Good loadbearing capacity Copes with sloping sites and deep voids	More expensive than solid floor construction on level sites with small voids	Becoming very common in house building Particularly appropriate for sloping sites, sites with poor ground conditions and sites involving deep sub-floor voids

part three

Building superstructure

External walls

Aims

After studying this chapter you should be able to:

- Appreciate the functional performance characteristics required of external walls
- Relate functional performance to the design alternatives for external walls
- Understand the relationship between the changing thermal insulation requirements for walls and the evolution of wall design
- Appreciate the details needed to ensure wall stability
- Understand the role played by the wall in the transfer of loads from other elements, such as upper floors and the roof

This chapter contains the following sections:

6.1 Functions of external walls and selection criteria

6.2 Traditional external wall construction

6.3 Timber frame construction

6.4 Openings in external walls

Hot links

- BS 1243: Specification for metal ties for cavity wall construction
- BS 3921: Specification for clay bricks
- BS 5268: Structural use of timber
- BS 5977: Lintels
- BS 6073: Precast concrete masonry units. Specification for precast concrete masonry units

- BS 8215: Code of practice for design and installation of damp-proof courses in masonry construction
- Building Regulations Approved Document A, Structure
- Building Regulations Approded Document L, Conservation of Fuel and Power

6.1 Functions of external walls and selection criteria

Introduction

After studying this section you should be aware of the functional requirements of external walls and should be able to understand their implications for construction form. In addition, you should appreciate the basis of each of these and the drivers behind the development of increasing levels of performance requirement. You should have developed an appreciation of the overlapping of certain functional requirements and be able to make judgements about their relative importance. Given specific scenarios you should be able to set out a series of criteria for the selection of appropriate external wall solutions.

Overview

The performance requirements of the building fabric have been discussed previously; however, it is appropriate to summarise them here as they relate directly to the construction of external walls. In general they may be considered to include the following:

- strength and stability

- exclusion of moisture/weather protection

- thermal insulation

- durability

- acoustic insulation

- aesthetics

Additionally, the level of buildability is important. 'Buildability' is the term used to provide a measure of the complexity of the building form and construction detailing. This is increasingly important, since it has a direct effect on time, cost and quality in construction.

When considering any one of the potential design solutions for external walls it is important to remember that the end result is a consequence of the need to satisfy these functional requirements.

Strength and stability

The achievement of required levels of structural stability is essential if the building is to withstand the loads that are imposed upon it during its life. Vertical, oblique and lateral loadings must be safely transmitted through the structure to the loadbearing strata. The external walls may or may not take an active role in this transmission depending on the structural form of the building. In some situations the external walls act only as weatherproofing for the building, carrying none of the dead or live loads from the structure. It is possible to consider external walls in categories related to the extent to which they act as loadbearing elements of the building.

Loadbearing walls

In modern domestic construction and in many older buildings most external walls are designed to be loadbearing walls (Figure 6.1), in that they carry their own self weight, together with some element of loading from the rest of the building, such as floor or roof loadings. Masonry is the most common material utilised, with brick

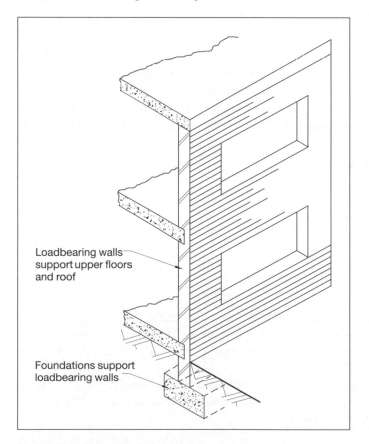

Loadbearing walls support upper floors and roof

Foundations support loadbearing walls

Figure 6.1 ● Loadbearing walls.

or concrete blockwork being almost ubiquitous in this form of construction. The loadings transmitted through the wall are transferred to foundations below ground level. In order to ensure that stability is maintained, certain restrictions are made within the Building Regulations relating to the height and thickness of walls and the number and positions of openings. The provision of lateral restraint is essential to resist the lateral loadings applied to buildings from wind etc. These issues will be explored in detail later within this chapter.

In the construction of low-rise dwellings the use of loadbearing masonry walls is very much the norm. This is often referred to as 'traditional' construction. In recent years timber frame construction has also been adopted by some house builders, although its popularity has suffered due to poor publicity relating to some of the early failings of this form. For most dwellings the traditional loadbearing masonry wall and the timber frame construction are the only realistic options. One important aspect of loadbearing external house walls for the student to grasp is that irrespective of the form of the cavity wall (masonry or timber framed), it is only the inner skin which carries structural load from the upper floor and roof.

Review task

Name *three* performance criteria that we would expect to be provided by an external wall and rank these in importance.

How is your most important criterion satisfied by the design of the wall?

Exclusion of moisture

In the opinion of most building users this may be the main purpose of external wall construction. The ability to exclude wind, rain, snow and excessive heat or glare from the Sun is paramount in the list of user requirements. Yet this must be achieved while still allowing best use to be made of natural light and ventilation. The users must, of course, also be able to enter and leave the building, thus creating the need for numerous openings to be formed in the building enclosure. These openings must be treated carefully to ensure that they do not provide a route for moisture entry to the interior of the building. In modern construction, three differing approaches may be taken to achieving the exclusion of moisture, the choice depending on the nature of the building, its use and location. The three forms are solid porous construction, as used in older brick built properties, impervious cladding and masonry cavity construction, as used in most modern houses (Figure 6.2).

Porous solid construction

External walls formed of porous materials, such as solid masonry walls, have been used with varying levels of effectiveness for many years. Although

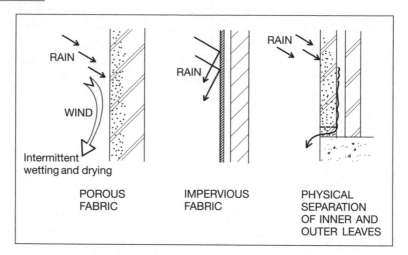

Figure 6.2 ● External walls – moisture-resisting options.

currently out of favour in England, this form of building is still very common in Scotland and other areas where high levels of exposure are experienced. Provided that the wall thickness is sufficient for the specific situation, good levels of weatherproofing are possible. This relies to some extent on the fact that long periods of continuous rainfall are rare; hence the saturated section of the wall is limited to the outer zone, as drying caused by air movement arrests the migration of water prior to it entering the interior of the building. The central zone of the wall may be almost constantly wet, since the drying effect of the air movement is unlikely to dry the full wall thickness before it is once again subjected to rainfall. In order to upgrade the performance of walls of this type an external coating of render which offers a greater level of weather resistance may be used. This, however, may pose problems in the long term, with the possibility of thermal movement causing cracking, allowing water to enter and become trapped behind the protective coat.

Impervious or weather-resistant cladding

An alternative approach to the exclusion of moisture in external walls is to provide an external covering or cladding to the wall, which offers a great level of weather resistance. Materials such as steel and aluminium sheeting or panelling, glass, or plastics may be used to form a continuous impervious covering to the structural wall. This form of construction is common in larger buildings, such as industrial units and multi-storey blocks, with large pane units being lifted into place with the aid of a crane. The necessity to adopt such techniques tends to make these forms unsuitable for small-scale domestic construction, which is still labour-intensive. Weather-resistant claddings may also be used for housing, such as roof tiles on felt and battens. The larger cladding sheets and panels are aesthetically unpleasant for such small-scale buildings and are restricted to larger building types, such as offices.

One potential disadvantage of this form of building is that in the event of a localised failure of the material, the level of water penetration to the interior may be great, since the surrounding material does not absorb any of the water. In a porous construction form moisture is absorbed from any crack or fissure by the material itself, thus limiting the extent of passage to the interior.

Cavity construction

The most common form of external wall in use today for domestic and small-scale construction is the masonry cavity wall. The principle upon which these walls operate is to create a break in the capillary path of the moisture. Water penetration through porous materials relies on capillarity. Once the ability to move by this mechanism is removed, moisture will cease to travel towards the building interior. The outer leaf of the construction is allowed to be saturated to its full thickness; the inner leaf, however, should remain dry. Problems occur in this form of construction where the cavity must be closed for structural purposes and to resist the passage of fire. At these points the inner and outer leaves may make contact and allow the passage of heat and moisture if not treated properly. Hence details must be developed to prevent this, with insulation materials and vertical DPCs incorporated in the structure (Figure 6.3).

The extent to which the passage of moisture will affect the chosen design is, to some extent, variable. The location and orientation of the building will have a considerable impact on the final choice of wall construction. In the UK it is possible to assess the variation in the degree of exposure at different locations by

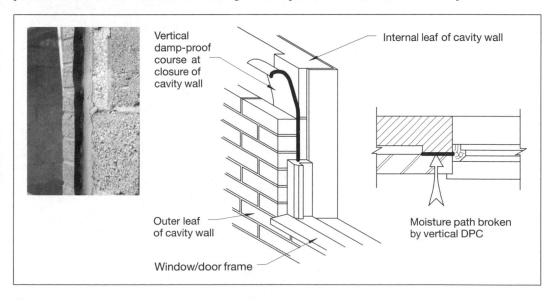

Figure 6.3 ● Exclusion of moisture at the cavity closure.

referring to maps that indicate the driving rain index. Clearly, the greater the level of exposure the greater the need to incorporate design features to prevent moisture penetration.

Review task

Give *two* reasons for the lack of popularity of solid porous wall construction.

Thermal insulation

The increasing requirements for the conservation of fuel and energy, resulting from the wishes of building users and the requirements of the Building Regulations, demand that external walls are constructed to reduce heat loss to acceptable levels. Figure 6.4 shows how the required level of insulation has increased in recent years and how it is anticipated that it will increase further. All new dwellings must be provided with a 'SAP' rating calculated in accordance with the government approved Standard Assessment Procedure (SAP). The rating is given on scale of 1–100 and is based on the calculated annual energy cost for space and water heating. Higher SAP ratings indicate better thermal efficiency, and although there is no requirement to achieve any particular level, buildings with ratings below 60 are considered to require higher levels of insulation. Current Building Regulations demand a maximum U value of 0.45 W/m^2 K for exposed walls of dwellings. It is proposed that this will change to 0.25 W/m^2 K by 2005.

This level of insulation can be achieved in a variety of ways, depending on the nature of the construction used. It has become impractical, however, to attempt to achieve this level without the aid of an insulation material of high efficiency.

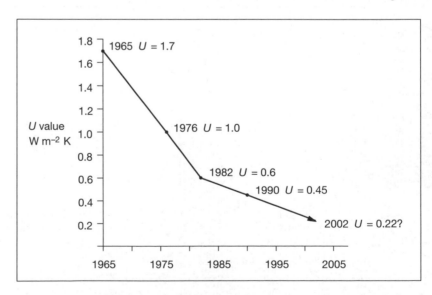

Figure 6.4 ● Insulation changes – cavity walls.

High-efficiency thermal concrete block is available, although the thickness which is required to meet the requirements is too great to be practical (typically 215 mm for solid walls; 175 mm inner leaf for cavity walls). Hence more efficient materials, such as polyisocyanurate are used to raise insulation to acceptable standards. With the anticipated increase in required levels of insulation it is felt that timber frame housing may become the most viable method of construction, as it is ideally suited to the incorporation of insulative materials. It is possible that traditional brick/block cavity walls will become uneconomic and impractical in attempting to meet these standards. One reason for this is the limitation on the width of cavity for structural reasons. This, in turn, limits the extent to which the wall can be insulated.

The positioning of insulation material can have a great effect on the thermal performance of the wall in both solid and cavity forms (Figure 6.5). The external positioning results in the wall fabric absorbing heat from the interior space. This may take some time before reaching steady state. If it is positioned internally, however, the fabric is insulated from the interior space and hence does not absorb heat; this allows the building to respond quickly to heat input. The concept of fast and slow response times or thermally heavy and thermally light construction was dealt with in Chapter 1.

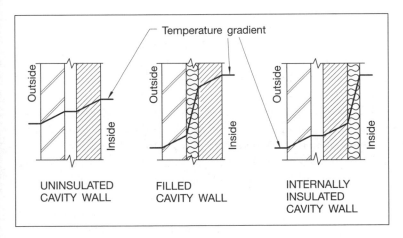

Figure 6.5 ● Temperature profiles in walls with differing insulation positions.

In the case of cavity walls, the need to close cavities around openings presents potential problems in terms of insulation. This is because the bringing together of inner and outer leaves provides a direct route for the passage of heat. This is known as cold bridging or thermal bridging, and has been discussed earlier. Cold bridging must be avoided by the installation of an insulative material at the potential bridge points (Figure 6.6). Alternatively, a thermal break can be incorporated by using an insulative cavity closer.

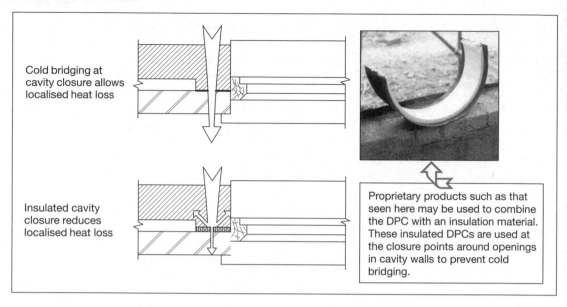

Cold bridging at cavity closure allows localised heat loss

Insulated cavity closure reduces localised heat loss

Proprietary products such as that seen here may be used to combine the DPC with an insulation material. These insulated DPCs are used at the closure points around openings in cavity walls to prevent cold bridging.

Figure 6.6 ● Cold bridging avoided by insulation at closure points.

Durability

The life expectancy of the building and its elements depends largely on the ability of the materials used to withstand the ravages of time and the elements. In the case of external walls they are subjected to a hostile environment, which is often subject to variation between extremes of heat and cold, wet and dry and so on. Also, they must be resistant to physical damage from impact and general wear and tear, while being capable of taking the loads imposed upon them.

In particular, the effects of fire upon durability can be considerable and have consequent effects upon other building elements and other buildings. The external walls of a building are required to contain a fire for a prescribed period of time to inhibit spread to adjacent buildings. In the case of residential buildings this period is 30 minutes, although for industrial and commercial building forms this may increase to up to 4 hours, as in the case of storage buildings. The walls must also retain their integrity and stability until the occupants have had time to escape. The choice of materials dictates the performance of the wall. Performance in the event of fire is prescribed by the Building Regulations in two ways. Firstly it deals with the ability of the fire to spread across the face of the wall. This is termed *surface spread of flame* and is rated from 0 to 4, where 0 is least flammable and 4 is most flammable. Secondly, combustibility is taken into account. This has no units of measurement, but materials are described as being combustible, non-combustible and of limited combustibility.

The choice of components that make up the wall should be undertaken with great care. Masonry walls, due to their inherent qualities, are very durable and generally do not need special protective design features or treatments. However,

Integrity with reference to fire relates to the ability of the material or component to resist the passage of flame.

Stability, by contrast, relates to the ability of the material or component to stand in position and continue to function as intended.

if materials are of poor quality or used in inappropriate combinations premature failure may result.

Acoustic insulation

The need to minimise the level of sound transmission through external walls can arise for a variety of reasons, but in general could be considered necessary when sound levels differ greatly from the inside to the outside of a building. Sound travels in two distinct ways: via a solid material (impact or flanking sound transmission) or via the air (airborne sound transmission). Airborne sound transmission requires a massive or dense construction to reduce it, while physical breaks in the structure may stop impact sound. The creation of physical breaks, however, allows airborne sound to pass; hence there is an inherent problem here. Fortunately, in the case of masonry construction, there is seldom a problem in respect of sound transmission, since it is sufficiently massive.

Selection of external walls

These aspects of the performance of external walls will be taken into account when selecting an appropriate option for the construction of dwellings. In reality, the viable, cost-effective options for low-rise dwellings are restricted to relatively few alternative forms. All will satisfy these requirements to a greater or lesser extent, and the selection is often based on familiarity with a given construction form. The relative lack of popularity of timber frame construction is partly the result of a lack of familiarity on the part of the property developer and on the part of the potential purchaser. As we move towards more sustainable, energy-efficient building forms this is likely to change, and the popularity of the timber frame dwelling may increase.

Reflective summary

With reference to external wall performance remember

— The main performance requirements include strength and stability, exclusion of weather, thermal insulation, durability and acoustic insulation.

— Whether the external wall is of masonry or timber framed construction, it is loadbearing.

— The inner skin of cavity walls carries the load – from the upper floor(s) and the roof.

— Where openings are formed for windows and doors the associated cavity closures may form a cold bridge (easy passage of heat) unless insulation is added.

— When examining the moisture resistance of the wall a cavity provides a natural break to moisture moving laterally (horizontally). The alternatives to this may be a thick porous wall or one which is clad externally with an impervious material.

— As the external wall is a major barrier to heat loss it has been the focus of attention in the last three decades and its construction has changed accordingly.

— The way in which insulation standards are set by the Building Regulations includes the use of U values: the smaller the U value, the better the insulation standard provided.

— The mass of the external wall usually ensures that it is a good insulator.

Review task

Explain what is meant by a building's SAP rating.

Explain what is happening in a cold bridging effect.

6.2 Traditional external wall construction

Introduction

After studying this section you should be familiar with the main forms of traditional external wall construction for low-rise housing. You should be able to understand the reasons for the development of specific design features within each form and to relate these to generic performance requirements. In addition you should be fully aware of the technical details associated with timber frame and traditional masonry walls of both solid and cavity construction. You should appreciate the relative advantages and disadvantages of each form and their differing features. The implications for selection of external wall type upon other elements of the building such as roof, floors and foundations should be understood. You should be able to critically appraise the various forms and, given specific scenarios, you should be able select appropriate external wall solutions.

Overview

The external walls of dwellings provide for a number of specific performance requirements or functional needs. These have been explored in the previous section and will not be reiterated here. However, it must be understood that the common forms of external wall used in dwellings today have evolved specifically to fulfil these needs. The forms of building that are utilised most often fall into two broad groupings: 'traditional' masonry walls and timber frame walls. These can be subdivided further, and the specific features of each type will be examined in detail within this section.

Masonry walls

Masonry walls are formed of bonded stone, bricks or blocks of various materials. Traditionally, the term 'masonry' related to working with stone, but is now taken to include walls based on the assembly of modular units of a variety of materials. Most commonly these include bricks and blocks made from clay or concrete, and less commonly from calcium silicate. The assembly of these units is a highly skilled craft and the degree of accuracy required to ensure structural stability results in very fine levels of tolerance. Even with low-rise dwellings, which tend to have only one or two storeys, it is essential that the verticality of the wall is maintained to avoid failure by buckling.

The assembly of a masonry wall relies on the incorporation of several other elements in addition to the bricks and blocks. These can be categorised as primary elements and secondary elements. By this definition, primary elements are those that are utilised to create the main structure, with secondary elements being those items that are required to finish the structure.

Primary elements used to construct the carcass of the structure might typically include such items as bricks, blocks, damp-proof courses, lintels and wall ties. Secondary elements used in the finishing of the structure might include such elements as air bricks, vents, copings and fittings of various kinds.

As previously noted, masonry wall construction is based on the assembly of a large number of small components in the form of bricks or blocks. These are set and secured in a bonding mixture known as mortar. This method of construction derives from the historic need to assemble the units by hand, without the facility for the use of mechanised plant. Hence the units used are of a size which is easily manipulated. It is worthwhile considering each of the main elements in a little more detail.

Bricks

BS 3921 defines a brick as a 'walling unit not exceeding 337.5 mm in length, 225 mm in width and 112.5 in height' The standard UK size is 215 mm × 102.5 mm × 65 mm. This rather strange size is actually a result of the metric measurement of an imperial size of brick. Metric modular bricks are used elsewhere in Europe, but have been slow in adoption in Britain. Bricks are formed from three common materials, these being clay, concrete and calcium silicate.

Clay bricks

'Fair faced finish' is the term applied to walls that are not intended to receive an application of plaster or render and are to be finished with the brick or block pointed to a good quality.

Clay bricks are manufactured from clay, shale or brickearth, formed to the requisite shape and fired in a kiln. The formation of the brick may take place by hand (although this is costly), by machine pressing or by machine wire cutting, each resulting in a different appearance. The classification of bricks is normally based on variety, quality and type. All of these aspects must be defined when specifying bricks. The various types will potentially differ greatly in their performance characteristics. Thus some bricks are more suitable for certain locations or uses than others.

Three varieties of clay brick are utilised in the construction process. The varieties are known as common bricks, facing bricks and engineering bricks.

Common bricks are suitable for general work, where aesthetics are not too important. Facing bricks are manufactured to give a high quality of surface appearance and to allow fair faced finish to unplastered walls. Engineering bricks are dense bricks with high compressive strength and low water absorption, allowing them to be used below ground or in areas of heavy loading. In older houses examples of all three varieties may be found, with facing bricks to the front elevations, common bricks to the rear elevations and engineering bricks at damp-proof course level. The use of engineering bricks as a damp-proof course is not permitted under modern Building Regulations, but in the Victorian era their use was common.

In addition to the varieties of brick there are three qualities of clay brick that are used. These are internal quality, suitable only for internal walls and partitions; ordinary quality, suitable for external work above ground level in conditions which are not subject to severe exposure; and special quality, suitable for conditions of extreme exposure or below ground.

The final characteristic for defining clay bricks is the type. Solid, perforated and cellular types of brick may be used, where:

- solid bricks include holes through the brick that do not exceed 25% of volume. Frogs do not exceed 20% of the brick volume.

- perforated bricks include holes passing through the brick that exceed 25% of the brick volume.

- cellular bricks include holes that are closed at one end and exceed 25% of the brick volume.

Calcium silicate bricks

Calcium silicate bricks are produced from a sand/flint base mixed with water and lime. They are often provided with colouring pigments to give variety. These bricks give a stark, modern appearance and are used in larger buildings more often than in housing, where a more traditional appearance is generally wanted. Unlike clay bricks they are manufactured by moulding and autoclaving, giving very high degrees of accuracy and consistency in size and shape. Calcium silicate bricks are classified in three main categories. These are:

- 'Specials', which are suitable where great strength is necessary, or where they will be subjected to excessive moisture and/or freezing

- 'Class A', which are suitable for general external work

- 'Class B', which are suitable only for interior use

Concrete bricks

These are produced in the same manner as calcium silicate bricks, but using aggregates and ordinary Portland cement as the component materials. These are often used where high strength is needed without the requirement for the brick to provide an aesthetically pleasing finish.

Although they are now rarely used for house construction, calcium silicate bricks were popular in the 1970s. Their 'modern' appearance was considered fashionable for a short time. This is an example of the influence of people's taste upon the design of houses.

Blocks

BS 6073 defines blocks as walling units larger than the sizes specified for bricks. In housing construction they are generally made from dense or aerated concrete. Although clay blocks are also available they are rarely used in Britain.

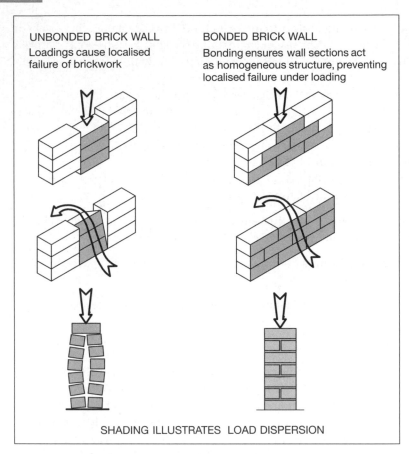

Figure 6.7 ● Loadings applied to wall sections.

Bonding is the overlapping of bricks to ensure that load is dispersed. Several patterns are used, including 'English', 'Flemish' and 'Stretcher' bonds.

The assembly of large numbers of independent units to form a continuous wall section presents difficulties in terms of loadbearing characteristics and structural stability (Figure 6.7). In order to overcome these difficulties they must be assembled in such a way as to achieve the performance of a single homogeneous unit. This is achieved by bonding of the bricks and blocks, together with ensuring that the slenderness ratio of the wall is within acceptable limits, as discussed earlier. The wall sections must be capable of withstanding lateral and vertical loadings. This is aided by the bonding of solid and cavity walls.

The nature of cavity wall construction is such that two slender leaves are formed next to each other, with an air gap between. This results in slender wall sections, which may become unstable. Hence, in order to ensure that they act as one broad unit, they must be tied together using wall ties. The ties must prevent the leaves from acting independently and ensure that the wall remains stable. The slenderness ratio of walls, i.e. the proportion of the thickness of the wall relative to its height, is governed by the Building Regulations.

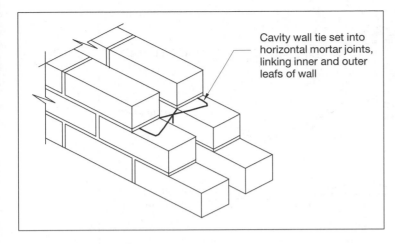

Cavity wall tie set into horizontal mortar joints, linking inner and outer leafs of wall

Figure 6.8 ● Provision of wall ties in cavity walls.

Figure 6.8 shows one of the earlier forms of cavity wall with both skins of brickwork. As bricks are now mainly produced to a standard height of 65 mm the use of brick and brick cavity walls ensures that mortar joints will be at the same level on both skins and that incorporation of wall ties is easily achieved. However, more modern walls use blockwork inner skins, and these are of course significantly bigger (approximately 59 bricks per square metre compared with 10 blocks). A standard brick course is 75 mm high comprising a 65 mm brick and a 10 mm mortar joint. By contrast, a block course is 225 mm high: a 215 mm block with a 10 mm mortar joint. One block course is therefore equivalent to three brick courses. BS 1243 suggests that in ordinary house cavity walls the standard spacing of wall ties is 900 mm horizontally and 450 mm vertically, with ties laid in a diagonal pattern. This means that ties will be built into every second block course or, if you prefer, every sixth brick course.

Clearly bricks and blocks need to be of coordinating size if the mortar joints are to align to allow the building in of the wall ties.

The nature of the environment in which wall ties are used is such that the outer leaf, which is almost permanently wet, provides a corrosive situation for the end of the tie. Wall tie failure is common in older buildings as a consequence; this is in the main due to ineffective anti-corrosion treatment. Modern ties must be formed of corrosion-resistant materials such as galvanised mild steel, stainless steel or, increasingly, plastics (Figure 6.9). The passing of a wall tie across the cavity may give rise to the passage of moisture. This is prevented by the incorporation into the design of the tie of an anti-capillary drip.

Thermal insulation

The evolution of the house external wall in more recent times (since the 1970s particularly) can be linked with the changes in thermal insulation standards required by the Building Regulations (Part L: Conservation of Fuel and Power).

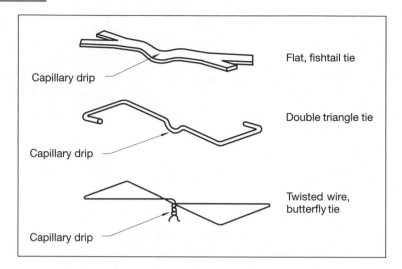

Capillary drip

Flat, fishtail tie

Capillary drip

Double triangle tie

Twisted wire, butterfly tie

Capillary drip

Figure 6.9 ● Forms of wall tie.

The U value is the typical way in which thermal insulation standards are set. The U value is also known as the thermal transmission coefficient and is measured in W/m^2 °C or using the absolute temperature scale W/m^2 K.

Watts are the unit of radiant flux or flow of energy, and the regulations attempt to limit the flow per square metre by setting maximum values for different external elements such as walls and roofs. The Building Regulations 1992 edition requires a maximum U value of 0.45 W/m^2 K for walls and 0.25 W/m^2 K for roofs. This means that roofs have to be better insulated than walls. (Walls can lose almost half a watt per square metre of wall for each degree temperature difference between inside and outside the building, while roofs can only lose one quarter of a watt.)

When the U value of walls was improved some years ago to 0.60 this changed the way in which walls were put together, in that there was a significant pressure placed on the blockwork skin to provide good levels of insulation while remaining strong enough to carry the loads impressed on it. After the U value for walls changed to 0.45 it became very difficult to meet the thermal standards without incorporating insulation into the wall, and today partial cavity fill with rigid insulation boards (batts) is the norm.

Figure 6.10 shows some of the various ways in which insulation may be incorporated into a cavity wall.

If cavity insulation is to be included in the wall it tends to be in the form of rigid boards fitted between the wall ties. Figure 6.11 (see p. 194) shows this process, where complete cavity fill is used (diagram) and where partial cavity fill is used (photograph). Note the circular discs clipped to the tie to hold the partial cavity fill insulation against the inner skin of blockwork.

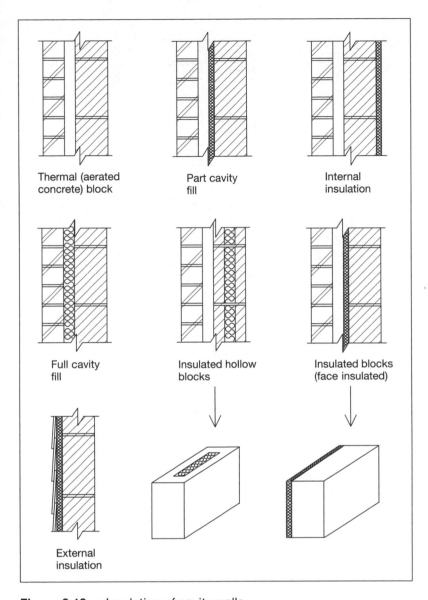

Figure 6.10 ● Insulation of cavity walls.

Movement accommodation

All building materials change their volumes to some extent when affected by changes in temperature and moisture, and masonry is no exception. If unrestrained, the effects of such movement can be considerable; hence movement accommodation joints must be incorporated to allow for such occurrences.

The coefficient of expansion of clay is surprisingly high, and occasionally this will mean the incorporation of movement joints in housing (Figure 6.12). Terraced rows of house units may be typically where the joints are required.

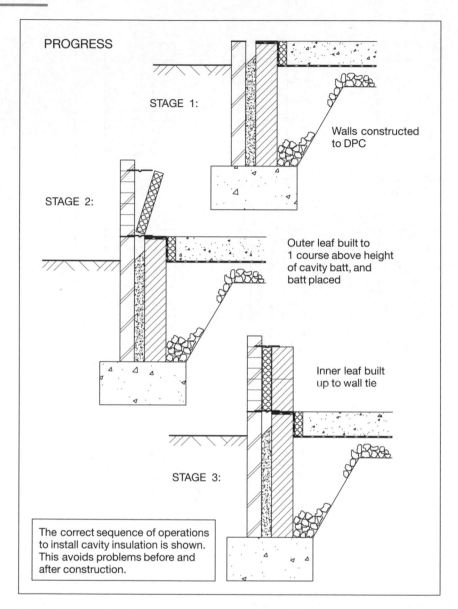

PROGRESS

STAGE 1:

Walls constructed
to DPC

STAGE 2:

Outer leaf built to
1 course above height
of cavity batt, and
batt placed

Inner leaf built
up to wall tie

STAGE 3:

The correct sequence of operations
to install cavity insulation is shown.
This avoids problems before and
after construction.

Figure 6.11 ● Installation of insulation in cavity walls.

A heavy tie may be needed at the movement joint to reinforce this point, where the bond of the bricks is broken. As movement is expected at the joint it is important to allow the wall to move while still taking support from the tie. Figure 6.13 shows some typical details.

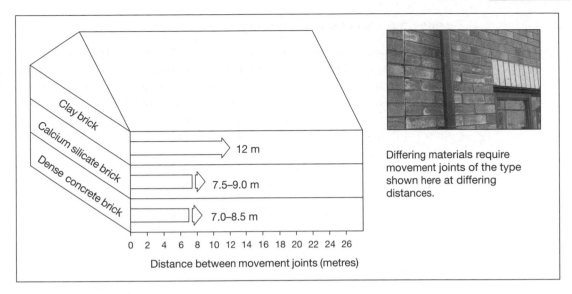

Figure 6.12 ● Movement accommodation joints in brickwork (spacing).

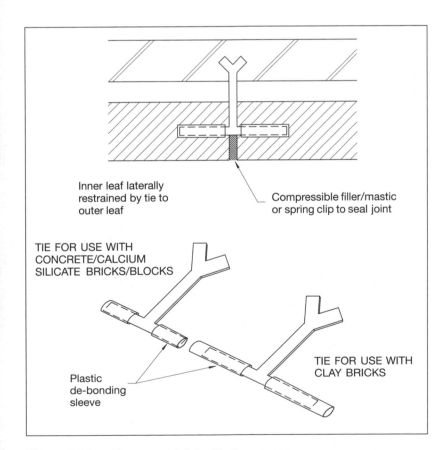

Figure 6.13 ● Movement joint with tie support.

Surface appearance and pointing

The exposed face of the wall is likely to be finished 'fair faced'. The brickwork or blockwork is finished to a high standard and is not intended to receive any form of surface finish or decorative application. In order to achieve this, and to ensure that the surface is weatherproof, the mortar joints are finished by pointing. Several options are available and each will give a different appearance to the wall (Figure 6.14). In addition, they will perform differently in terms of weather resistance. Raked pointing gives a modern appearance, but performs less well than struck pointing in resisting the passage of moisture. Ultimately the selection is a matter of personal preference on the part of the designer.

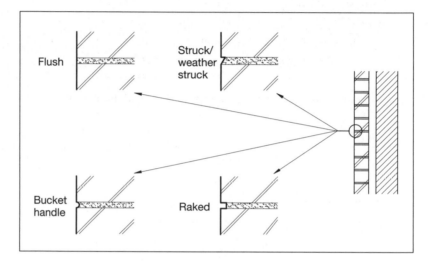

Figure 6.14 ● Options for pointing of brick and block walls.

Case study

Formation of traditional external walls

In order to resist the passage of moisture from the ground it is necessary to install an impervious layer or damp-proof course into the walls at low level. Here we see the black DPC passing over the threshold of a door opening in both inner and outer leaves. Note the weepholes beneath.

Wall ties are built into the wall to link inner and outer leaves. Here the outer leaf has been built first with the ties set as required. At junctions with internal walls it is important to provide means of tying the two together also.

Cavity ties are fitted with restraint clips to hold insulation against the inner leaf. If the insulation falls across the cavity a possible route for water is created.

Where openings are formed it is essential to provide appropriate details to retain the performance of the wall. Here we see the galvanised steel lintel above the opening supporting the inner and outer leaves. The cavity is closed at the reveal by turning a block from the inner leaf to abut the brickwork of the outer. At this point a vertical damp-proof course is installed, clearly visible here.

Reflective summary

With reference to traditional masonry external walls, remember:

— Bonding of the components of the external wall adds considerably to the strength of the wall – bricks in a cavity wall are generally laid in a stretcher bond.

— Bonding helps resist lateral loads (e.g. wind) and helps disperse vertical structural loads as they move down towards the foundation.

— The unusual width of a brick (typically 102.5 mm) has evolved from the Imperial sizes of manufacturer prior to adoption of the metric system in 1971.

— A brick is 65 mm high and a brick course is 75 mm high, including a 10 mm mortar joint.

— Block and brick sizes have to be coordinated in order to allow wall ties to be positioned in coincident mortar joints – 1 block course is 225 mm high (including mortar course) and this corresponds to three brick courses (3×75 mm).

— Wall ties in housing are usually found in every other block course, i.e. every 2×225 mm or 450 mm.

— Mild steel wall ties are still available and are protected with a zinc coating (galvanised), although more expensive alloy materials are often preferred as they are corrosion-resistant (e.g. stainless steel).

Review task

Why is dimensional coordination important when sizing bricks and blocks for use in an external wall?

What is the standard height for a course of bricks and for a course of blocks?

6.3   Timber frame construction

Introduction

After studying this section you should be able to refer to the principles of timber framed construction and how it differs from masonry construction. You should be familiar with the balloon and platform methods of timber frame.

Additionally, an appreciation should be gained of the detailing which is necessary to protect the timbers from damage and which is needed to allow for the dimensional movement expected in the frame due to the hygroscopic nature of timber.

Overview

In most traditional dwellings with masonry external walls the wall is of cavity construction with an outer leaf of brickwork and an inner leaf of concrete block. In timber frame construction the concrete block inner leaf is replaced with a structural timber frame. This frame is the main loadbearing element of the external wall and the outer leaf of brick does not take any of the structural loads from the dwelling. The outer leaf of brickwork provides a weather shield and an aesthetically pleasing appearance. Indeed, the use of a brick outer leaf can be dispensed with, as a variety of other weatherproof claddings could be adopted. Examples of alternatives include timber or plastic weatherboarding, tile hanging and applied render finishes.

In recent years timber frame houses have suffered from a poor public image. This arose as a result of failings associated with early examples. These failings were linked to poor detailing and site practice, resulting in moisture entering the timbers of the frame. In later examples these problems have largely been eradicated and the use of timber frame construction now provides a viable, cost-effective method of construction for dwellings. There are a number of distinct advantages associated with timber frame construction. Firstly the nature of the form is essentially based on prefabrication; panels are formed in a factory environment and assembled as large units on-site. Hence there is the potential for high levels of quality control in manufacture, together with the benefit of economies of scale associated with 'mass' production. In addition, the flexible nature of the construction form lends itself to the manufacture of panels for bespoke designs. Indeed, there has been a great expansion in the level of use of timber frame for self builders.

Secondly, the strength to weight ratio of timber is relatively high. Therefore the dead weight of a timber frame dwelling is significantly less than that of a traditional dwelling of comparable size. As a consequence there will be the potential for savings associated with lighter forms of foundation solution. In addition, the lower level of loading applied to the ground means that strata with lower bearing capacities may be utilised for construction of dwellings. This is a significant issue in terms of the developer's equation, since less suitable sites will be cheaper to buy. It is also relevant to the issue of sustainability of the construction process, as there is increasing pressure to preserve green field sites.

Thirdly, because timber frame construction is largely a dry form of building, there is the benefit of accelerated progress on site. Unlike traditional forms of construction, which require drying out time for the masonry walls and internal finishes, timber frame construction can be almost totally dry. Thus the time-scale of construction can be reduced greatly.

Principles of timber frame construction

The concept of timber frame construction is based on the erection of a loadbearing timber frame supporting the dead and live loads from upper floors, roofs and the timber frame wall itself. This structure is then clad with a weatherproof enclosure. In Britain the enclosure is most commonly formed in brick to mimic the appearance of a traditional dwelling. Two main forms of timber frame exist, termed platform frame and balloon frame. Although the balloon frame form is less common in Britain it is used extensively elsewhere. Both forms are based on the assembly of large prefabricated panels to form the structural external walls of the dwelling. These are then covered with a weatherproof cladding to provide an aesthetically pleasing appearance.

The construction of the individual panels is based on the provision of vertical studs, typically 50 mm × 100 mm, although sometimes larger. The studs are placed at 400 mm or 600 mm centres to coincide with the modular size of plasterboard sheets. The panel studs are fixed between top and bottom timber rails of the same dimensions. These are termed the head rail and the bottom rail. In addition, wherever it is anticipated that heavy fixtures will need to be supported, horizontal timbers, or noggins, will be inserted between the studs. It is therefore important that the positions of items such as wall cupboards and sanitary fittings are considered before assembly of the panels.

In order to provide a durable external face to the panel and to ensure rigidity a sheathing panel of plywood or bitumen-impregnated particle board, typically of 9.5 mm thickness, is nailed to the panel framing at 150 mm centres to ensure that the complete unit is braced against deformation. This is of particular importance in protecting the assembled panel units against the effects of wind loadings. In addition, the sheathing provides a continuous base for the attachment of cladding fixings such as battens for tile hanging or wall ties for external brick cladding.

The external face of the sheathing must be protected against the elements during the construction process. It is possible that the sheathing will be exposed for several weeks prior to the provision of the weatherproof cladding to the

One advantage of timber frame is the fact that much of the work is dry compared with the wet trades of traditional construction. However, the major advantage is generally regarded as the speed of assembly resulting from prefabrication.

An aspect of timber frame construction is the need to carefully design for coordination of the elements and components – economies of scale can result from standardisation.

outside of the building. For this reason a protective covering is applied to the panels; this is termed breather membrane or 'building paper'. The breather membrane fulfils several important functions. Firstly it acts to protect the panels against rain during the exposed period of the construction process. Secondly, it acts to protect the panels against the possibility of wind-driven rain crossing the cavity. Thirdly, it is essential that any moisture that does find its way into the panels during construction or during the life of the property is allowed to escape. In order to facilitate this it is important that the covering is vapour permeable, thus allowing any trapped moisture to escape as vapour to the outside – hence the term 'breather paper'.

The void within the panels must be insulated to achieve the required level of resistance to the passage of heat. This is generally based on the installation of fibre quilt insulation material fitted tightly between the studs. The thickness of the panel dictates the level of insulation that is achievable. It is probable that in the future the panel thickness will increase to provide higher levels of thermal insulation. The installation of this insulation material results in a high level of temperature difference from the inside face to the outside face of the panel. This introduces the risk of interstitial condensation. Clearly this is a serious risk, as the structure is timber, and therefore potentially prone to decay. In order to mini-mise the risk of condensation within the panel it is important that a vapour check is provided at the inner face. This normally takes the form of polythene sheeting, which arrests the passage of moisture generated within the building into the core of the timber frame panel. It must be accepted that this is a vapour check rather than a vapour barrier. The reason for this is that the inner face of the wall will be pierced by fixings and holes to facilitate the installation of light switches, socket outlets and so on. Thus the vapour-resistant polythene is not continuous and will not resist the passage of moisture vapour totally. However, it will reduce it to a minimum.

The inner face of the panel is finished with the application of plasterboard sheeting, which may be dry finished or skimmed with a thin coat of plaster. The ingredients of a typical wall panel are shown in Figure 6.15.

Timber frame alternatives

Balloon frame

In the case of two-storey dwellings the balloon frame consists of wall panels that are the full height of the building (Figure 6.16). Following erection the first floor joists are fixed to ledger timbers that are inserted between the studs of the panel. One disadvantage of this form of frame is the need to provide cavity barriers within the panels to arrest fire spread between floors due to the continuous nature of the void within the panel. This contributes to the lack of popularity of this form. These cavity barriers are often formed from timber sections cut to size and fixed between studs on-site. The need to do this and to provide ledger timbers

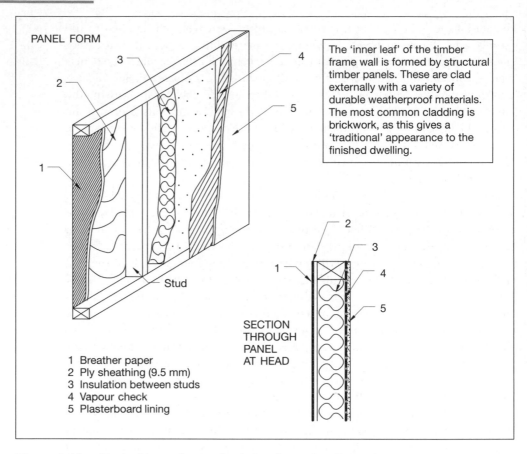

PANEL FORM

The 'inner leaf' of the timber frame wall is formed by structural timber panels. These are clad externally with a variety of durable weatherproof materials. The most common cladding is brickwork, as this gives a 'traditional' appearance to the finished dwelling.

Stud

SECTION
THROUGH
PANEL
AT HEAD

1 Breather paper
2 Ply sheathing (9.5 mm)
3 Insulation between studs
4 Vapour check
5 Plasterboard lining

Figure 6.15 ● Typical ingredients of a timber framed wall panel.

to support the upper floors reduces the benefit of prefabrication and increases the labour input on-site. Hence the construction process is slowed down and the potential for on-site inaccuracies is increased. The main advantage of this frame type is that the external walls are erected independent of the upper floors. Therefore the building envelope can be erected to full height and the roof formed in a very short time. In this way a weatherproof enclosure is created quickly, allowing the work internally to be undertaken in a protected environment.

A feature of the balloon frame is the two-storey high wall panels, which are also shown in Figure 6.17.

Platform frame

The most common type of timber frame construction adopted for dwellings in Britain is the platform frame (Figure 6.18). Unlike the balloon frame this relies on the use of panels that are the height of a single storey. This results in the creation of panels that are very easy to handle during transit and assembly. The ground floor panels are erected first, with individual panels linked together using a

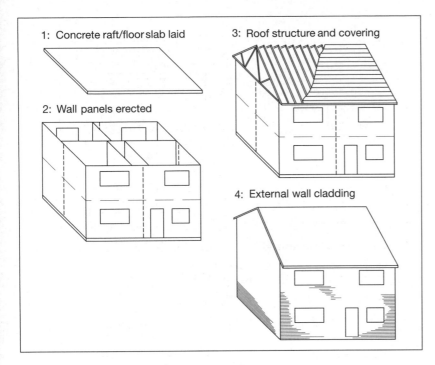

Figure 6.16 ● Balloon frame construction.

1: Concrete raft/floor slab laid

2: Wall panels erected

3: Roof structure and covering

4: External wall cladding

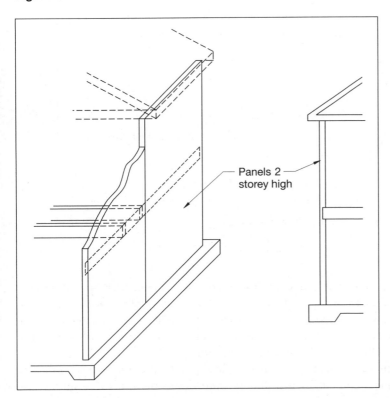

Figure 6.17 ● The two-storey high wall panels of the balloon frame.

Panels 2
storey high

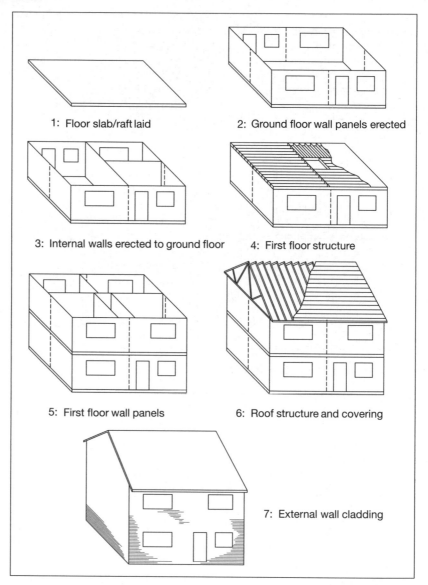

1: Floor slab/raft laid

2: Ground floor wall panels erected

3: Internal walls erected to ground floor

4: First floor structure

5: First floor wall panels

6: Roof structure and covering

7: External wall cladding

Figure 6.18 ● Platform frame construction.

timber head binder. After this the upper floor is formed, including the deck, resting on the head binder. At each end of the floor joists, where they are supported on the frame panel, the floor void is closed off using a header joist. The completed lower section of the building then acts as a platform for the formation of the upper storey, which is formed in the same way.

The platform frame has a number of advantages. Firstly, the panels are easily transported and handled on-site due to their convenient size. Secondly, the

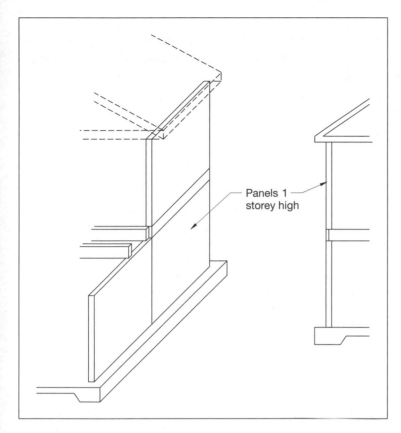

Panels 1
storey high

Figure 6.19 ● The single-storey wall panels of the platform frame.

provision of the upper floor at a relatively early stage allows its use as a working platform for the subsequent operations. Thus the need for temporary working platforms is reduced. However, the formation of the floor at this early stage also results in a disadvantage in that it interrupts the operation of forming the external structural walls. Hence the roof is formed later and the building cannot be made weather-tight as soon, and there is the potential for a longer period of exposure to the elements. Notwithstanding this, platform construction accounts for the bulk of timber frame construction in Britain.

It can be clearly seen that use of the platform frame allows the upper floor to sit directly on top of the lower wall panel (Figure 6.19).

Other variants of the timber frame form exist, although their use is not widespread in Britain and they broadly share the same features as those described here.

Review task

Name *two* features of timber framed construction which are included to prevent moisture entry to the timber.

What distinguishes the balloon frame technique from the platform technique?

Assembly of timber frame buildings

As stated previously, the most common form of timber frame construction in Britain is the platform frame. Although there is some degree of variation in the assembly of the various forms of framing they are essentially similar. Hence we shall consider only the platform frame as an illustration of the broad principles involved. The sequence of operations involved in the assembly of a timber frame dwelling has already been outlined. It is now worthwhile focusing on some of the important assembly details involved. The main areas of importance are the junctions between panels and the connections between wall panels and the foundation/ground floor, the upper floor and the wall/roof junction.

Junctions between panels

In some instances the full length of the external wall may be formed by a single panel. This is unusual, and it is more common for walls to be made up of a number of individual panels linked together (Figure 6.20). The panels are generally butted together and nailed with the addition of a head binder running across the top of the panels to ensure alignment. The head binder also creates a double rail at the top of the ground floor panels, providing a sound base for the formation of the upper floor. At the base of the wall the bottom rail is fixed to a continuous timber cill plate or sole plate. Where panels are joined in continuous lengths the connections are simple in nature. At corners, where adjoining panels are perpendicular, it is necessary to introduce additional studs to facilitate connections. An alternative is to manufacture panels specifically for these positions. This reduces the level of standardisation, and hence the degree of cost-effectiveness. Consequently the addition of extra studs on site is far more common.

Connections to foundations

Timber frame construction is lighter in form than traditional masonry construction. Hence the design of the foundations takes this into account. However, the foundation forms are essentially the same as those available for traditionally constructed houses. In practice there are two commonly used foundation solutions: the strip foundation and the reinforced raft foundation. Where the strip foundation is used it is most common to adopt a ground-supported concrete floor

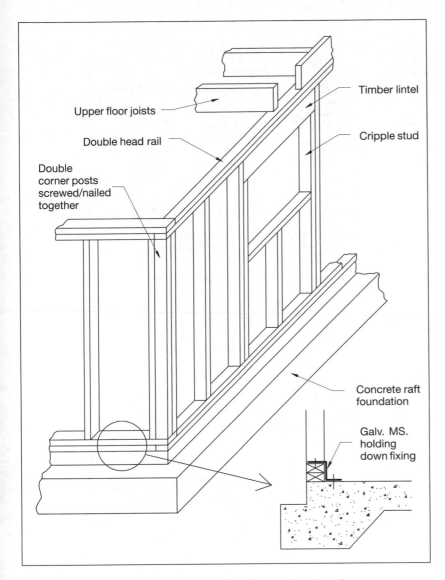

Upper floor joists

Double head rail

Double corner posts screwed/nailed together

Timber lintel

Cripple stud

Concrete raft foundation

Galv. MS. holding down fixing

Figure 6.20 ● Panel junctions in timber frame construction.

slab also. In both of these scenarios the method of connecting the timber wall panels is the same.

A timber cill or sole plate, which has been vacuum impregnated with preservative, is secured to the lower wall section or the raft. This is set onto a length of damp-proof course and is bedded on cement mortar to provide a firm, level base for attaching the wall panels. In the past the sole plate would have been secured to the wall or raft by shot fixing or by drilling holes through the timber and inserting anchor bolts. In both of these cases the untreated core of the timber is exposed and the DPC is pierced. Thus there is the potential for moisture to pass

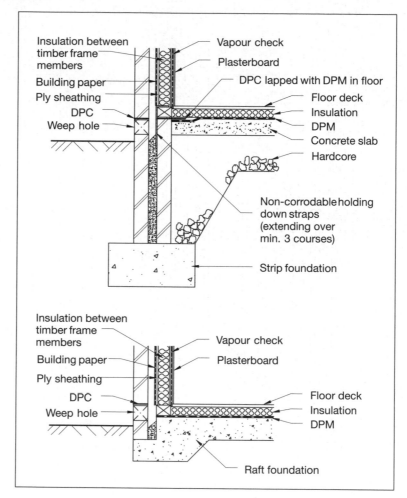

Figure 6.21 ● Connections to foundations.

into the timber, possibly resulting in decay. In addition, where anchor bolts are used it is necessary to either countersink the bolt heads or recess the bottom rail of the wall panel to avoid fouling. More modern techniques adopt the use of a non-ferrous holding-down strap that does not pierce the DPC or pass into the core of the timber. Figure 6.21 illustrates two possible options.

Having secured the sole plate the wall panels are nailed directly to it.

Connections to upper floors

The upper floor construction used in timber frame housing is the same as that used in traditional construction. The mode of connection to the wall panels is rather specific, however. The floor joists bear directly onto the head binder of the

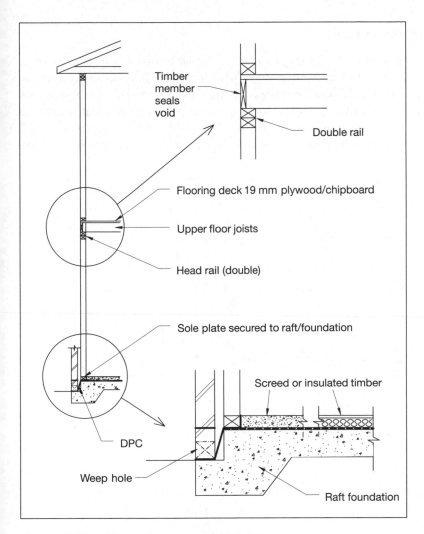

Figure 6.22 ● Timber frame junction details.

lower wall panels. The use of the head binder together with the head rail of the panel results in a robust double section proving the support for the joists (Figure 6.22). It is common, though not essential, for the joists to line up with the studs of the wall panels. The spacing of both studs and joists is generally either 600 mm or 400 mm; this maximises the efficiency of using modular plasterboard sheets for wall and ceiling finishes. After fixing the floor joists a header joist is provided around the edge of the floor to close the floor void and resist the passage of fire. At this stage the floor decking is laid up to the outside edges of the floor/wall assembly. The completed floor provides the platform for the next lift of wall panels, which are connected by nailing through the bottom rail into the floor.

Connections to roofs

The connection at roof level (Figure 6.23) is similar to that at the upper floor. A head binder is provided to connect the head rails of the individual wall panels and to provide a double rail base for supporting the roof. In timber frame construction this is almost certainly a trussed rafter roof structure. The individual trusses are connected to the head binder using galvanised steel saddle connectors. This is effected in exactly the same manner as the connection to the wall plate used in traditional construction.

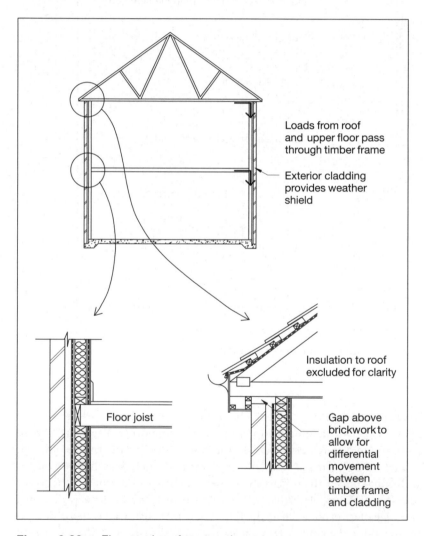

Loads from roof and upper floor pass through timber frame

Exterior cladding provides weather shield

Insulation to roof excluded for clarity

Floor joist

Gap above brickwork to allow for differential movement between timber frame and cladding

Figure 6.23 ● Floor and roof connections.

Claddings to timber frames

A wide variety of exterior cladding options exist for timber frame buildings. When dealing with dwellings there is a tendency to attempt to mimic the more traditional masonry construction form. Hence the most common cladding option tends to be masonry, and in particular brick. Alternatives to this include a range of lightweight claddings such as horizontal or vertical boarding, tile hanging or rendered finishes, although these are far less popular. In all cases it is important that the cladding is spaced away from the timber wall panels to allow for venting and draining of the space. It is also essential to take into account the potential for differential movement between the structural frame panels and the selected cladding. The general principles involved are the same for all claddings, but the specific details may vary considerably.

Masonry cladding

When masonry is used as the exterior cladding to timber frame buildings (Figure 6.24) it acts to a large extent in the same way as the outer leaf of a traditional

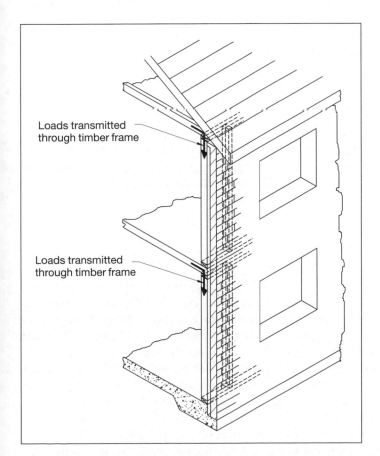

Figure 6.24 ● Masonry cladding to timber frame construction.

cavity wall. It protects the inner frame from the elements and prevents moisture from entering the building by the creation of a capillary break, in the form of a drained cavity. The cavity should be at least 40 mm wide. In timber frame construction the exterior cladding does not take any loads from the building structure other than its own self-weight. The stability of the slender masonry leaf must be maintained by introducing wall ties that restrain the outer leaf by tying it to the timber frame. A common defect in older examples is the positioning of these ties such that they are nailed to the sheathing of the panel rather than to the studs. This does not allow for adequate restraint, and it is now accepted that the ties must be fixed through the sheathing into the studs of the wall panels. An added complexity is introduced as a consequence of the potential for differential movement between the timber frame and the masonry cladding. It is quite possible that the timber structure will be affected by a degree of shrinkage in the period shortly after construction. In addition, the rates at which the different materials will expand and contract when affected by changes in air temperature and humidity levels vary. The ties used to restrain the masonry must allow for this differential movement and must, therefore, have a degree of flexibility. Flexible stainless steel ties are the best solution. These should be fixed to the sheathing to coincide with the positions of studs at centres not greater than 600 mm horizontally and 450 mm vertically. As in the case of traditional cavity walls, they should fall slightly to the outside leaf.

Lightweight claddings

A range of lightweight claddings may be used to provide the weather shield to timber frame buildings. These are generally fixed directly to the frame panels using battens or spacers to create a slim cavity for draining and venting. The cavity should be at least 19 mm wide and should as far as possible be uninterrupted vertically.

Timber frame and fire

In order to control the spread of smoke and flame through the concealed voids and cavities within timber frame buildings it is necessary to install cavity barriers. These are introduced at key locations within the building and must be capable of providing resistance to fire of at least 30 minutes. There are several methods of forming these barriers, but the most common are timber battens or preformed tubes of mineral wool insulation material. In addition to these cavity barriers, fire stops are required where there are a number of dwelling units within a single structural block. Hence in semi-detached and terraced housing fire stops are provided at the junctions of roofs and front and rear elevations with the party walls. The provision of these fire stops ensures that each individual unit forms a separate compartment capable of containing a fire for a period of 60 minutes. The typical location of cavity fire stops is shown in Figure 6.25.

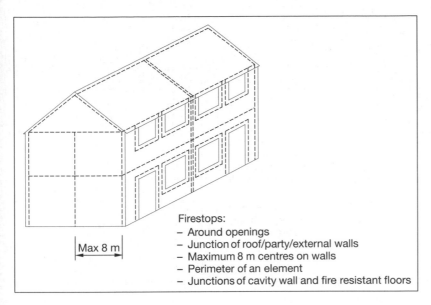

Firestops:
- Around openings
- Junction of roof/party/external walls
- Maximum 8 m centres on walls
- Perimeter of an element
- Junctions of cavity wall and fire resistant floors

Max 8 m

Figure 6.25 ● Fire stops.

In order to achieve this level of fire resistance it is usual for the party wall between dwelling units to be formed as two separate leaves with a gap of 50 mm between. Each side of the wall is then clad with two or three layers of gypsum plasterboard and mineral wool is fixed at the junctions with adjoining elements of structure. Increasing the mass of the party wall in this way also assists in providing an adequate level of resistance to the passage of sound.

Movement accommodation

Previously within this section the issue of differential movement between the timber frame and masonry cladding was noted. This is accommodated by the use of flexible ties as previously described, but it is also important that a series of other features are incorporated into the building to cope with this movement. It is probable that in the early part of the life of the building the timber frame will suffer slight shrinkage. If allowance for this is not made the external leaf will become subject to the application of loads at contact points. The particular areas of concern are the eaves of the roof (Figure 6.26), around window openings and at junctions of different cladding materials. The risk of applied loads to the cladding is controlled by providing gaps to accommodate the potential movement.

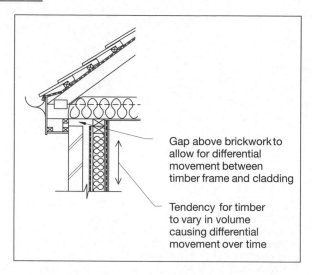

Gap above brickwork to
allow for differential
movement between
timber frame and cladding

Tendency for timber
to vary in volume
causing differential
movement over time

Figure 6.26 ● Accommodation of movement – eaves provision.

Case study

Timber frame house construction

The structural frame of the house is erected and the roof is formed and covered. The timber panels are protected from the elements by breather paper while they await the erection of the external brick cladding.

The timber base rail is fixed to the edge of the raft foundation, ensuring that there is no risk of moisture ingress. The floor screed is then applied up to the base rail. Note the protective breather paper fixed to the external face of the timber frame panels.

The structural frame of the house is formed in pre-manufactured timber panels. Here we see the panel from inside the building awaiting installation of the insulation and fixing of the inner lining. Note that the window is already fixed to the inner panel, surrounded by damp-proof course material. The fixing allows the window frame to project outwards, allowing the external brick cladding to be built around it. Note also the double head rail at the top of the panel that supports the first floor joists.

The internal walls are load-bearing as they support the floors above. Note the deep timber lintel above the door opening

Reflective summary

With reference to timber frame construction, remember:

— The preformed timber frame forms the inner skin of the cavity wall.

— The basic ingredients of the timber framed panel are the plywood sheathing nailed to the softwood studs and rails – the ply gives the panel its rigidity.

— As the frame is in timber, which has the ability to absorb and lose moisture (hygroscopic), we need to allow for structural movements that will occur with moisture content changes. We must also protect the frame from moisture absorption.

— A moisture check membrane (e.g. breather paper) is used to the outside of the completed panel, largely to protect it until the outer finish to the wall is completed.

— A vapour check is used to the inside of the panel (below the plasterboard) to prevent moisture in the air migrating from the inside of the property and into the panel – this is important to prevent possible interstitial condensation within the panel, which could cause rot.

— The balloon frame method involves the use of two-storey wall panels, while the platform frame involves single-storey wall panels.

— Fire stop barriers used in various locations to limit fire movement are an essential ingredient of the design.

— The foot of the timber framed wall needs to be secured to the concrete ground floor slab, but the detailing must ensure that moisture is not allowed to enter the timber – various strap designs are typical.

Review task

Identify *two* features that are incorporated to accommodate frame movement in timber framed house designs.

What level of fire resistance is required by a dwelling? What features are used in timber frame construction to ensure that the fire regulations are satisfied?

6.4   Openings in external walls

Introduction

After studying this section you will appreciate the constructional detailing that may be applied when openings are formed in walls. You will also appreciate that there are a number of criteria to be satisfied when such openings are formed, and these may include structural, insulation, moisture and fire resistance.

Overview

The creation of openings in the external envelope of the building is essential to allow access and egress to the occupants and to allow for the provision of natural light and ventilation or the passage of services. Small openings require no special treatment, the bonding of brick walling being sufficient to allow support of the wall above. Larger openings, however, require the provision of a supporting beam or lintel to the brick/blockwork above; historically this has taken the form of an arch in many situations. Many alternative forms of lintel are available, some more suitable than others for inclusion into cavity walls. Materials commonly used for the manufacture of lintels are steel, treated to prevent corrosion, and reinforced concrete.

The forms of construction that are most commonly adopted in housing are the traditional cavity wall or, increasingly, timber frame. In both of these alternatives the creation of openings must be considered carefully. In addition to the loadbearing capabilities of the lintel, a number of other factors must be noted. Of particular importance are:

- *Structural stability*: The creation of an opening in a major structural element results in the need to cater for the transfer of loads around the opening. The design of the support above such an opening and the nature of the end bearing of such a support must be carefully considered.

- *Thermal insulation*: Since the external wall provides a thermal envelope to the dwelling, the creation of openings can potentially result in excessive loss of heat. The treatment of openings must ensure that such heat loss is kept to a reasonable minimum.

- *Resistance to the passage of fire*: Since most modern houses adopt some form of cavity wall construction or timber frame construction there is potential for the passage of smoke and flame within the cavity. Where openings are formed there is the potential for entry of fire into the cavity. Hence it is necessary to close the cavity around openings or to provide cavity barriers to resist the passage of fire.

● *Passage of moisture*: Where cavities are closed there is the potential for moisture to pass through the permeable masonry of the external wall to the interior of the building. Care must be taken to ensure that details are included to prevent this from occurring.

Openings in external walls: terminology

In order to consider the details involved in the creation of openings in external walls we must first become familiar with the terminology associated with such openings. There are two types of opening that must be identified. Firstly there are the small openings or holes that are formed to facilitate the passage of pipes, ducts and other such elements through the external envelope. These do not normally require special consideration and they are formed as required on-site. Secondly there are the larger openings associated with windows, doors, vents and other larger items that must pass through the external wall.

In the case of the small-scale openings the bonding of brickwork above is generally sufficient to cope with the transfer of loads around the hole. In the case of larger openings this is not the case, and we must therefore take care to ensure that the design and formation of the opening are appropriate. The careful detailing of these openings will ensure that there is no risk of structural failure, passage of moisture or thermal bridging. Specific details will be generated for the head (top), cill (bottom) and jambs (sides) of these openings (Figure 6.27).

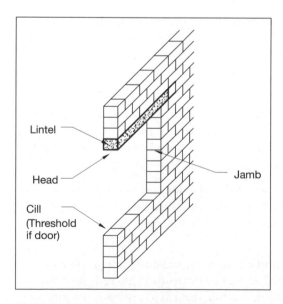

Figure 6.27 ● Opening terminology.

Clearly openings are necessary for access and for allowing in light and fresh air, but it should be recognised that there are limits to opening sizes in order to preserve the structural stability of the wall. Part A of the Building Regulations (Structure) outlines the relationship between opening sizes and the wall panels that remain between the openings. These wall panels are viewed almost as masonry columns between the windows. If the wall between openings were to become too slender, the wall would become unstable and the width of the window opening would need to be reduced.

Because the opening is an area of structural weakness in the wall there is provision for extra wall ties to the vertical sides of the opening, as outlined in BS 1243. Additionally, as stability is needed at the opening it is traditionally the case that the cavity is closed at the window or door using either the internal wall skin (usually blockwork) or the outer skin of facing brickwork. Which skin is used depends on the location of the frame within the reveal of the opening – if the frame sits towards the outside then the inner skin is used to close the cavity. If the frame sat back this could expose the inner block skin in the reveal, and therefore the cavity would be closed with the facing brickwork.

When the cavity is closed we have effectively a solid wall, and this raises two issues – how to prevent moisture entry and how to prevent heat loss.

Figure 6.28 shows the building in of a vertical damp-proof course (DPC) at the cavity closure to isolate the brickwork from the blockwork inner skin. Where timber frames have been used these were often secured in the opening by temporary planks while the bricklayers built up the wall around the frame. In such instances it was easy to hold the vertical DPC in position during bricklaying by nailing this to the timber frame.

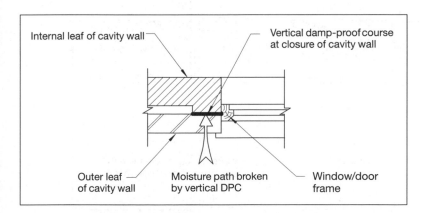

Figure 6.28 ● Vertical DPC at cavity closures.

Having placed the vertical DPC we have now created a barrier to moisture passage, but with still effectively a solid wall the heat loss from inside the property will tend to focus on this spot. This situation, where heat may flow more easily to the outside, is called a *cold bridge*.

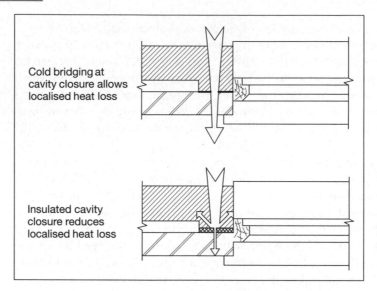

Figure 6.29 ● Cavity closures – preventing a cold bridge.

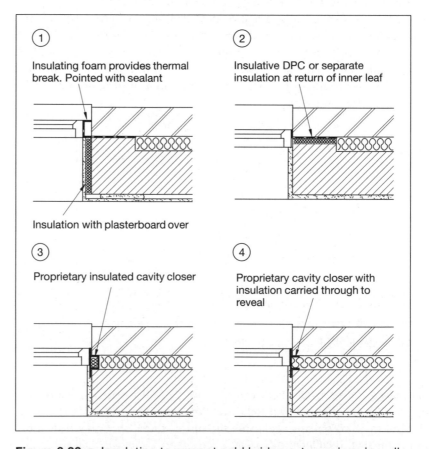

Figure 6.30 ● Insulating to prevent cold bridges at openings in walls.

Pitch polymer DPC material is now available with polystyrene pre-bonded to the back to insulate the vertical DPC. By using this detail the heat loss is substantially reduced. Figure 6.29 illustrates how this is achieved.

There are a number of ways in which the reveal area may be prevented from creating a cold bridge, and four examples are illustrated in Figure 6.30.

Evolution of the lintel form

Prior to the availability of concrete as a material, lintels to external and internal walls were in timber. With the advent of concrete, reinforced concrete and steel, a variety of lintel solutions emerged.

For internal walls and external walls lintels tended to be used of the same width as the masonry of the wall in which they were located (Figure 6.31).

Where cavity external walls were used the lintel detail had to recognise that the outer brick skin is porous and will allow moisture to run down the inner face of the external skin. Knowing that this means that moisture can accumulate on the top of the lintel, and recognising that concrete details are porous, this necessitated the use of a DPC cavity tray.

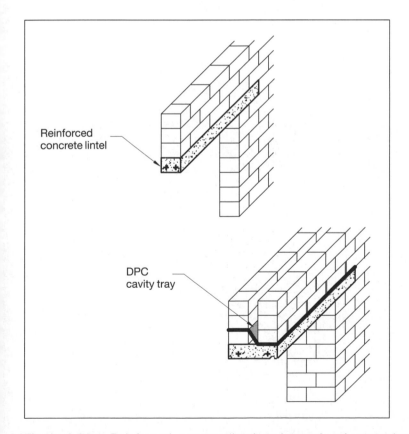

Reinforced
concrete lintel

DPC
cavity tray

Figure 6.31 ● Reinforced concrete lintels to internal and external walls.

Figure 6.31 shows that a cavity tray to encourage moisture to leave the wall externally is built into the inner skin to create the desired slope. Weep holes are generally formed in the external brick skin to allow moisture collected in the cavity to leave the wall. These may be formed by leaving vertical joints between bricks (perpends) free from mortar, or by building proprietary plastic weep holes into these joints. Two or three weep holes per opening are typical.

Following the use of rectangular reinforced external wall lintels the boot lintel was used, which was also able to uphold the inner and outer skins of the wall (Figure 6.32). An alternative to this was to support each wall skin separately, a

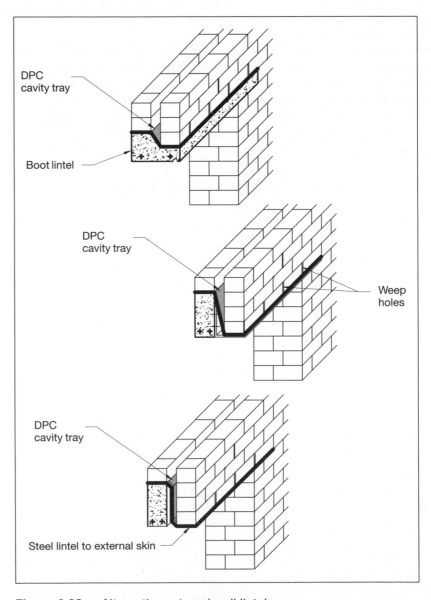

Figure 6.32 ● Alternative external wall lintels.

reinforced lintel used to the inner skin and a steel angle to the outer skin. This also needed a cavity tray, as shown, but this was often a preferred solution if the appearance of a lintel was to be hidden from the outside.

The modern solution tends to favour a steel combined lintel (Figure 6.33), this upholding both the internal and external skins. When these are used there is generally no need for the DPC cavity tray, as the steel tends to be coated against corrosion. However, thought needs to be given to cavity tray ends to hold the water collected on the lintel while it is being encouraged to leave via the weep holes.

The evolution of the lintel has been driven by changes in construction form. In particular, the increasing requirements for thermal insulation and the need to prevent cold bridging have been significant.

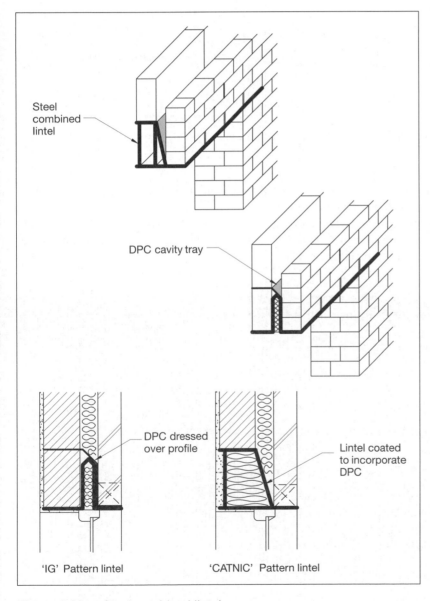

Steel combined lintel

DPC cavity tray

DPC dressed over profile

Lintel coated to incorporate DPC

'IG' Pattern lintel

'CATNIC' Pattern lintel

Figure 6.33 ● Steel combined lintels.

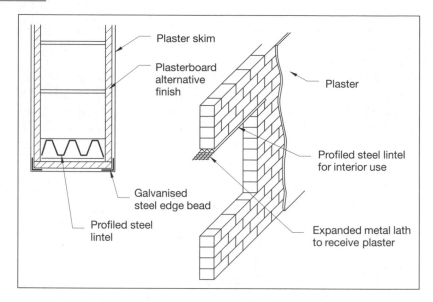

Figure 6.34 Steel lintels for internal walls.

Forms of these lintels are now typically insulated in their body to help reduce heat flow and the possibility of cold bridging.

Where the lintel is needed to an internal wall the favourite solutions are still reinforced concrete and steel. In steel the profile tends to be simple and corrugated for strength (Figure 6.34).

Reflective summary

With reference to openings in walls, remember:

— The four areas of focus when examining wall openings are provision of structural stability, preservation of thermal insulation, prevention of fire spread, and restriction of moisture movement.

— Whatever form of lintel is used it must address the interception of cavity moisture and the need to prevent excessive heat flow.

— Wherever cavities are closed there needs to be a moisture barrier and also sufficient insulation to prevent the *cold bridging* effect of excessive heat flow.

— Although many of our earlier lintels were formed in reinforced concrete, steel is today the preferred material because of its relatively light weight and the ease with which insulation may be incorporated to limit heat flow through the head of the opening.

Comparative study: external walls

Option	Advantages	Disadvantages	When to use
Cavity walls	Familiar technology Good thermal performance Good loadbearing capacity Good moisture exclusion	Slow Based on wet trades Insulating cavity may compromise moisture exclusion Difficult to achieve very high levels of insulation	The most common form of wall in house building Used almost as a default in speculative developments
Solid masonry	Robust Good structural performance	Slow Based on wet trades Difficult to achieve high levels of insulation without excessive thickness May require impervious layer to ensure moisture exclusion	Relatively uncommon in modern house building, but used in areas of high exposure due to robustness
Timber frame	Fast Cheap Can produce weatherproof enclosure quickly Light weight allows cheaper foundations Very good thermal performance Removes wet trade element Reduces labour input on site	Poor image Potential for deterioration if designed and constructed badly	Often used on sites with low bearing pressure due to light weight Use where speed is of the essence or where a variety of external finishes are to be used, such as tile hanging Becoming more popular in speculative developments

Review task

Describe *two* ways in which cold bridging is prevented in the design of cavity wall closures at wall openings.

Define the following wall opening terms with reference to a sketch:

reveal

lintel bearing

cavity tray

chapter seven

Upper floors and stairs

Aims

After studying this section you should be able to:

- Appreciate the functional requirements for upper floors to dwellings
- Outline the various components of upper floors
- Describe the formation of openings in floors to accommodate elements such as stairs
- Appreciate the form and function of stairs

This chapter contains the following sections:

7.1 Timber upper floors to dwellings

7.2 Stairs: design solutions and construction forms

Hot links

- Building Regulations Approved Document A, Structure, Section B
- Building Regulations Approved Document K, Stairs, ramps, and guards
- BS 585: Wood stairs
- BS 5395: Stairs, ladders and walkways. Code of practice for the design, construction and maintenance of straight stairs and winders
- BS 5578: Building construction – stairs

7.1 Timber upper floors to dwellings

Introduction

Although there has been little change in the layout of timber upper floors for decades, the sophistication of the materials has been somewhat refined by the details contained in the Building Regulations. These regulations not only refer to the size and shape of components such as floor joists, but also to the quality of the materials used by reference to grade.

Overview

The primary function of a suspended upper floor must be to provide a sound, level surface, capable of supporting all dead and applied loadings over a given span. In addition, however, factors such as fire resistance, durability, thermal and sound insulation, speed of construction and the provision for services incorporation are important considerations.

Timber floor construction

Timber upper floors are the traditional solution for dwellings and have many of the advantages of timber suspended ground floors. These include providing a void space for the incorporation of services such as central heating pipes and electrical cables. They also have flexibility, warmth and aesthetic appeal.

These floors have few component parts – the joists, a boarded covering, and sometimes herringbone strutting between the joists to prevent warping.

Approved Document A of the Building Regulations (Structure) tabulates the joist sizes which may be used for a certain clear span, and generally there is more than one option which will prove satisfactory. For a particular span you can use either a slightly deeper joist than the alternative thicker joist (a slightly thicker joist will have less depth). The traditional thickness for floor joists is 50 mm, while depths may vary from around 175 mm to perhaps 225 mm. Other thicknesses include 40 mm and 75 mm, which will be examined later.

When the old Imperial system of measurement was in place (feet and inches) there was a very rough guide to the depth of 2" (50 mm) thick joists.

span in feet/2 + 1" = joist depth in inches

e.g. 14/2 + 1" = 8" deep joist (200 mm)

This is clearly only a rough guide, and reference should be made to the Building Regulation table for definitive sizes.

Floor joists rest on the inner skin of the external cavity wall, which in modern property is generally in blockwork (Figure 7.1). This figure also shows the alternative solution of placing the joists into pressed steel joist hangers.

When internal walls are used to support the joists, the joists have the same option of resting on the walls or fitting into joist hangers.

When we lay out the joists for an upper floor it is commonly found that joists run in different directions across different ground floor rooms. This is because the

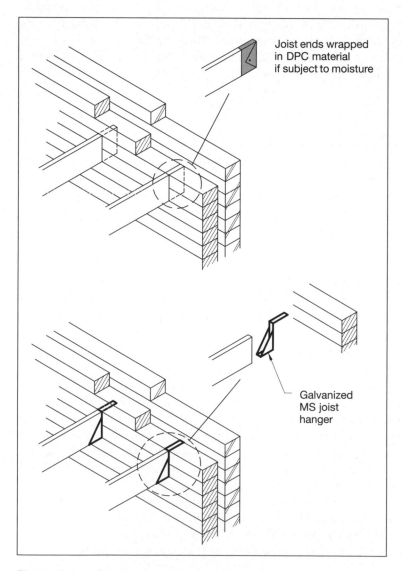

Joist ends wrapped in DPC material if subject to moisture

Galvanized MS joist hanger

Figure 7.1 ● Joist ends support.

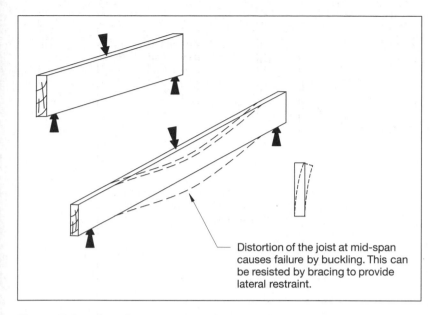

Distortion of the joist at mid-span causes failure by buckling. This can be resisted by bracing to provide lateral restraint.

Figure 7.2 ● Possible distortion of joists under load.

joists tend to run across the shortest room dimension. It should be remembered that when deciding on the joist sizes for a house that the critical dimension is the longest span that is needed for the room design, as this dictates the depth of all the joists if a consistent ceiling level is to be achieved.

As joists tend to be secured at their ends they become vulnerable to movement towards the centre and may have an inclination to buckle, as shown in Figure 7.2.

With the longer spans, particularly, there will be a need to stabilise the joists by either cutting short lengths of joist (noggins) to wedge between the joists (Figure 7.3) or by the provision of herringbone strutting (Figure 7.4). These are both typically located at the centre of the span.

Remember that timber is hygroscopic, which means that it has an ability to absorb and lose atmospheric moisture. As the moisture content of the timber changes, dimensional changes may occur to the joist. These will be marginal along the length of the joist, but sometimes up to 5% across the grain. Moisture increases are associated with dimensional swelling, while decreases in moisture content cause shrinkage and warping.

The herringbone strutting is traditionally in timber but is now available in the form of pressed metal.

Coverings to upper floors include the traditional softwood tongue and grooved floor boarding and flooring grade chipboard. Figure 7.5 shows the tongue and grooved joist of the traditional floor boarding and the kerfed joint, which is a form of tongue and grooved joint associated with sheets of chipboard.

There is a relationship between the spacing of timber floor joists and the thickness of the floor boarding applied (Figure 7.6).

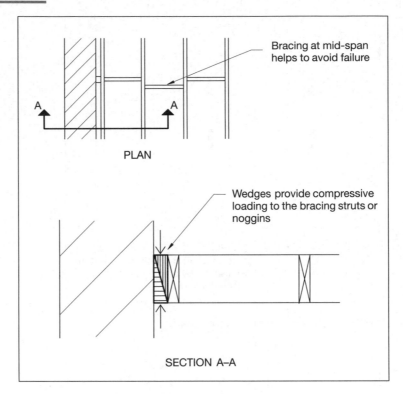

Bracing at mid-span
helps to avoid failure

PLAN

Wedges provide compressive
loading to the bracing struts or
noggins

SECTION A–A

Figure 7.3 ● Joist noggins for stability.

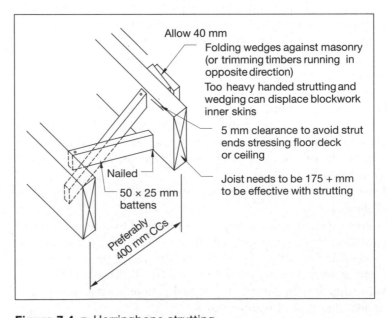

Allow 40 mm

Folding wedges against masonry
(or trimming timbers running in
opposite direction)

Too heavy handed strutting and
wedging can displace blockwork
inner skins

5 mm clearance to avoid strut
ends stressing floor deck
or ceiling

Joist needs to be 175 + mm
to be effective with strutting

Nailed

50 × 25 mm
battens

Preferably
400 mm CCs

Figure 7.4 ● Herringbone strutting.

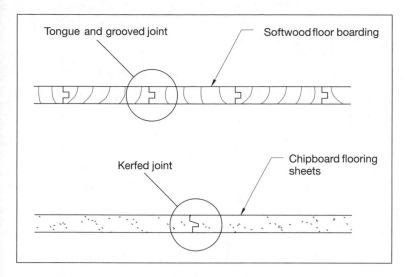

Figure 7.5 ● Joints to floor boards and chipboard sheeting.

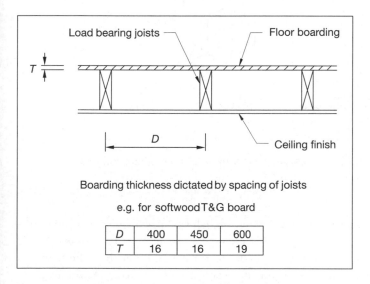

Boarding thickness dictated by spacing of joists

e.g. for softwood T&G board

D	400	450	600
T	16	16	19

Figure 7.6 ● Floorboard thickness for different joist spans.

When placing the joists to create the upper floor, the consistency of level of each individual joist is clearly an issue, as is the consistency of height above the lower floor. Figure 7.7 shows both of these factors under consideration.

Special arrangements have to be made to the floor timbers when creating an opening for the staircase. This opening is generally known as the stairwell.

To form the opening in the floor some of the floor joists have to be reduced in length, and shortened joists are termed *trimmed* joists; see Figure 7.8.

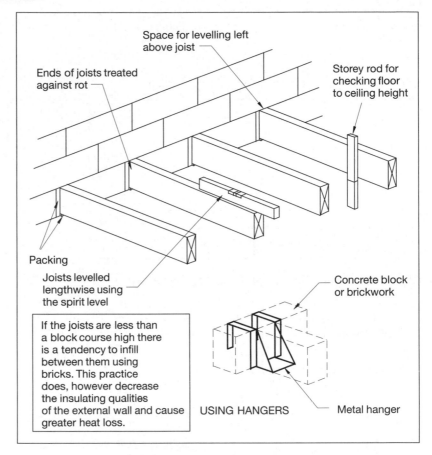

Space for levelling left above joist

Ends of joists treated against rot

Storey rod for checking floor to ceiling height

Packing

Joists levelled lengthwise using the spirit level

If the joists are less than a block course high there is a tendency to infill between them using bricks. This practice does, however decrease the insulating qualities of the external wall and cause greater heat loss.

Concrete block or brickwork

USING HANGERS

Metal hanger

Figure 7.7 ● Locating the joists – consistency of level and position.

As these joists are shortened they cannot reach the supporting wall, and therefore a joist is used to pick up these ends and give them support. This *trimmer joist* is of increased thickness to be able to carry the extra load for each of the trimmed joists that it supports. In turn, the trimmer joist will require attachment at its ends to the floor joists, which occurs at each end of the stairwell opening. These trimming joists also have to be of increased thickness to take the load from the trimmer, which is carrying a number of trimmed joists.

As the opening requires a number of connections between the various joists involved, the use of metal hangers may be most appropriate (Figure 7.9).

In order to hide the sawn (not planed) timbers of the floor construction at the stairwell opening, a lining of planed softwood boarding is used which is of depth equivalent to the floor thickness. This timber board is known as an apron lining and is illustrated later in the section relating to staircases.

One feature of the timber upper floor is the advantage that it offers for the incorporation of pipe and cable services. Where these are to run in parallel with

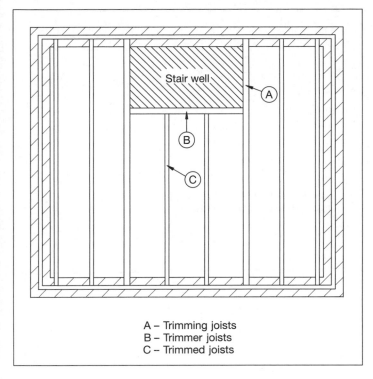

A – Trimming joists
B – Trimmer joists
C – Trimmed joists

Figure 7.8 ● Forming the stairwell opening.

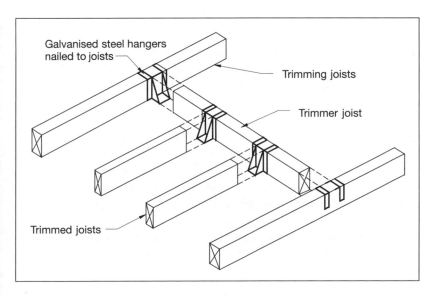

Figure 7.9 ● Joints at the stairwell opening.

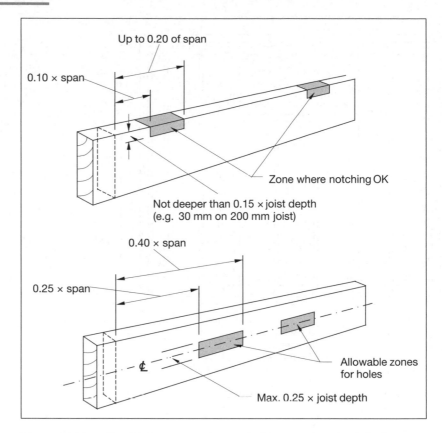

Figure 7.10 ● Restrictions on cuts needed for services installation.

the spanning joists free access is available, but it will be necessary at times to run the services perpendicular to the joist span. The consequent holing or notching of the joists needs to be limited in order to keep within tolerances that are needed to ensure that joist strength is not too adversely affected. Figure 7.10 helps summarise some of the restrictions that apply.

When studying with the various chapters in this text it is sometimes forgotten that the various elements discussed do often have a major structural interrelationship. Timber upper floors do provide significant assistance to the stability of the house walls through the principle of lateral restraint. Steel straps are attached between the house wall and the floor joists to provide the restraint, as illustrated in Figure 7.11.

Figure 7.12 also shows these straps and a general layout of some of the component parts of an upper floor in summary of the text of this section.

Support for partitions

It is often the case that the layout of the first floor rooms in dwellings differs from the layout of the ground floor rooms. In such cases it is not possible to build

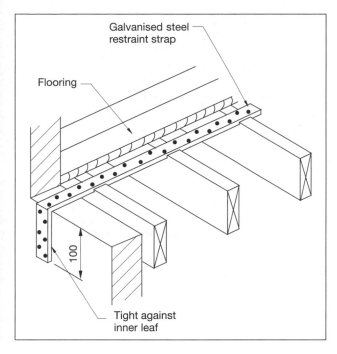

Figure 7.11 ● Lateral restraint straps between wall and upper floor.

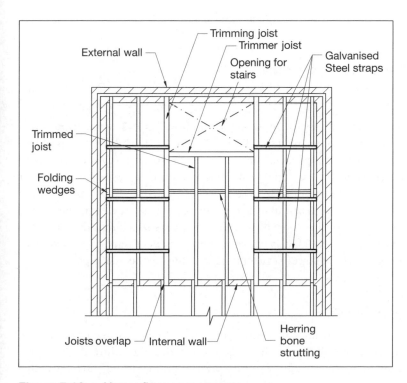

Figure 7.12 ● Upper floor components.

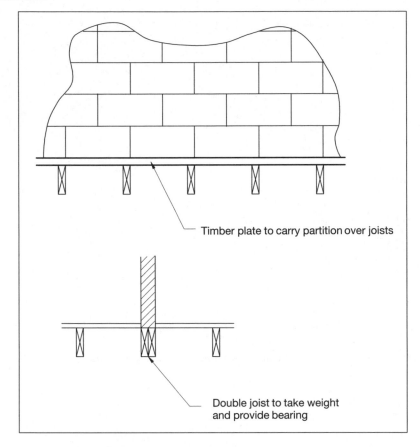

Figure 7.13 ● Support to partitions.

partitions to the upper storey off those at ground floor level. The partitions must be supported off the suspended upper floor (Figure 7.13). This is not a problem provided that the correct approach is taken to the construction of the floor, with particular regard to the layout of the joists. Where a partition runs perpendicular to the floor joists there is no need to take any specific action. This is because the load from the partition is distributed across several joists. However, where the partitions run parallel to the floor joists we must ensure that support is provided directly beneath. Since the load is concentrated, it is necessary to provide two joists bolted together or a larger section joist to cater for the additional load.

Pot and beam floors

The nature of 'pot and beam' or 'beam and block' floors has been touched on previously. To reiterate, these systems comprise a series of reinforced, often pre-stressed, profiled concrete beams, typically at 600 mm centres, between which are laid lightweight concrete blocks. The surface is then provided with a slurry screed coating enabling the application of a decorative finish.

Review task

With the aid of a sketch, describe the formation of a stairwell opening in a timber upper floor and label the name of the *three* special joists that occur at this location.

Reflective summary

With reference to upper floors, remember:

— Timber floor joists are generally spaced at centres to suit the plasterboard ceiling covering, typically 400 mm or 600 mm centres.

— The grade of timber used for the joist and its sectional size for the clear span between supports may be determined by reference to tables in Part A of the Building Regulations.

— To prevent distortion of the joists in position that may arise from changes in timber moisture content, herringbone strutting may be used (timber or metal) to brace the joists at mid-span.

— Opening in timber floors for staircases involves trimming of the opening and the use of trimmed, trimmer and trimming joists.

— The use of concrete-based floor systems such as pot and beam, hollow plank or simple reinforced slabs, is generally restricted to blocks of flats of at least three storey height.

— When precast concrete floor systems are used they require covering with either a cement-based screed or a wet (*in situ*) topping of concrete.

Case study

Formation of suspended timber floors

Floor joists may be built directly into the inner leaf of the external walls. Where they are supported by internal walls they are placed directly onto the wall as shown. It is often necessary to use bricks to adjust the height of the floor, as blocks are too large. This can be clearly seen here.

Joists may also be supported using galvanised steel joist hangers. These are built into the walls as work proceeds. The joists can then be positioned later, thus speeding up the construction process. The metal straps that can be seen running along the sides of the joists are lateral restraint straps. These ensure that the external walls are tied to the upper floor to resist lateral loads.

Here we see the bracing that is provided to the floor at mid-span to resist twisting of the joists. The opening created for the stairs is created by the use of trimmed, trimmer and trimming joists. The connections are made using joist hangers.

7.2 Stairs: design solutions and construction forms

Introduction

After studying this section you should be conversant with the main design limits placed on staircases by the Building Regulations. You should also be familiar with the terminology associated with typical domestic staircase arrangements and component parts. Collectively this should provide you with an insight into the relationship between the limitations of human users and the stair design.

Staircases in timber

Timber is the main material used for the staircase of houses and the variety of types of timber stair emerges largely from the choice of whether or not to use a landing.

Figure 7.14 shows that where no landing is to be used a straight flight of steps may be adopted. Quarter- and half-turn stairs by comparison occur when the use of a landing allows a 90° or 180° change of direction. An older-style arrangement is where tapered winder steps provide a 90° change of direction while still climbing.

The Building Regulations apply various limits on the dimensions of a stair in recognition of the ability of human users and to preserve safety. These restrictions apply to many features of the stair, including design features such as the angle or slope, the steps, guard railing and headroom.

The angle or slope of the stair is termed the *pitch*, and this may not exceed 42° degrees for a private residence. In buildings of other types a 38° maximum pitch applies.

Figure 7.15 shows some of the terminology of the flight of steps.

To each step there is a tread and a rise. The *going* of the step measured between the face of adjacent vertical risers tends to reflect the fact that it is unlikely that a person's foot would be placed right up to a riser. Going appears to be used in the Building Regulations in preference to the tread as a likely consequence of this fact. In the 1991 Building Regulations the step dimensions have to be such that

2 × rise + the going is to lie between 550 mm and 700 mm

Additionally, the vertical rise has to lie within a certain range of dimensions to limit the height a person would need to stretch each time they move forward.

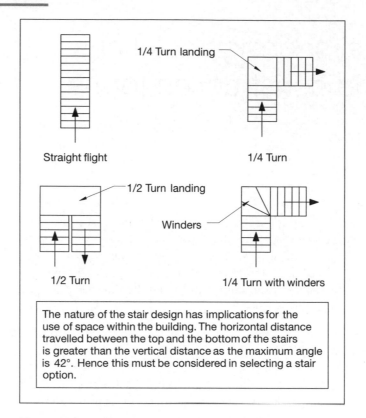

The nature of the stair design has implications for the use of space within the building. The horizontal distance travelled between the top and the bottom of the stairs is greater than the vertical distance as the maximum angle is 42°. Hence this must be considered in selecting a stair option.

Figure 7.14 ● Forms of timber staircase.

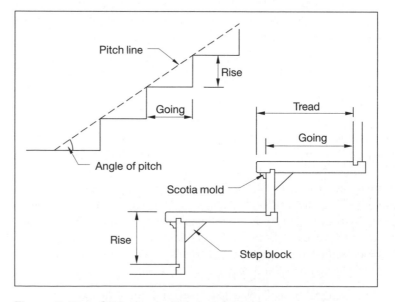

Figure 7.15 ● Some basic stair terminology.

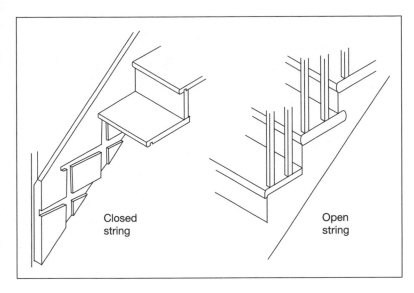

Closed
string

Open
string

Figure 7.16 ● Closed and open strings.

From the underside a timber stair shows that factory assembly is a fairly complicated affair. The treads and risers fit into or onto supporting *strings* at either end of the step. Figure 7.16 shows that where steps fit into these supportive strings the string is machined with housings to take the ends of the tread and riser. Such a detail involves the use of a *closed string*.

By comparison, the string may be sawn to allow the treads and risers to sit on top of the string, in which case this is called an *open* or *cut string*. Additionally, *inner strings* are fitted against a wall, while *outer strings* run between newel posts (see below).

The underside view of the steps in Figure 7.17 shows how tapered fixing wedges are driven into the tapered string housings to wedge each riser and tread firmly in position. This illustration also shows the use of a central supporting timber to the steps, referred to as a carriage.

Figure 7.18 shows a variety of other basic terms which apply to the staircase. The handrails, balusters and newels collectively create the guard railing for the stair. Note the use of an apron lining at the exposed edge of the floor in the stair-well opening. Without the apron lining we would be able to see the sawn timber joists of the upper floor.

For blocks of flats and other non-dwelling situations the staircase has to be constructed in incombustible products and tends therefore to be in either reinforced concrete or steel. These stair forms are the subject of Volume 2 in this series.

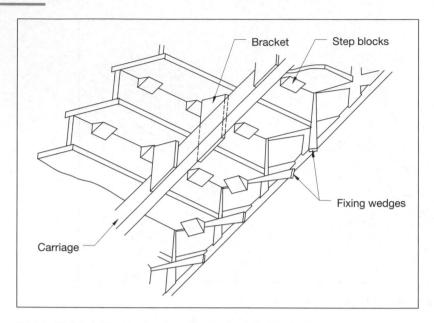

Figure 7.17 ● The underside of a typical flight of steps.

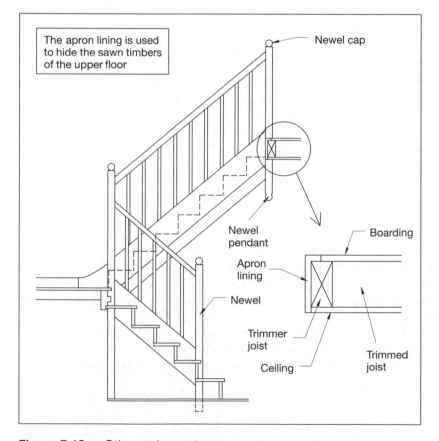

Figure 7.18 ● Other staircase terms.

Reflective summary

With reference to staircases, remember:

— Stair design has evolved to reflect the restrictions imposed by their human users.

— The Building Regulations now limit the angle of pitch, the height of and tread dimensions of the step, the height of the guard railing etc. to ensure practicality and safety.

— Stair designs in dwellings are usually based on the means by which we change direction – quarter- and half-turn landings give quarter- and half-turn classifications of type, and tapered steps (winders) may also take the user through a 90° change of direction.

— The type of string (support to the ends of the step) may give rise to the classes *open* and *closed string* stairs.

— If the rise is open and steps have only a tread we call this an *open rise stair*.

— Stairs for properties in multiple occupation are referred to as *common* and will generally be constructed in incombustible materials such as reinforced concrete.

Review task

What feature of the stair is often used to classify the stair's arrangement?

Name *three* component parts of a staircase which are restricted in dimension by the Building Regulations.

Comparative study: upper floors and stairs

Option	Advantages	Disadvantages	When to use
Timber suspended floor	Familiar technology Flexible in design Good loadbearing capacity Esay accommodation of services Ready access to services	Loadbearing limited by span and ability to obtain large joist sizes	This form is almost always adopted in house building
Concrete beam and block floor	Heavy loads accommodated Good sound insulation Excellent fire resistance	Heavy Services accommodation	This form of floor is really only used where fire resistance between units is important, as in flats

chapter eight

Internal division of space: walls and partitions

 Aims

After studying this section you should be able to:

- Understand the functions and performance requirements of internal walls and partitions
- Appreciate the various design solutions that may be adopted for the internal division of space within dwellings, and you should have knowledge of the construction details associated with each
- Appreciate the criteria upon which selection of the various options is based
- Describe the sequence of operations involved in the formation of internal walls and partitions
- Select a suitable partition solution from a range of alternatives

This chapter contains the following sections:

8.1   Functions of partitions and selection criteria

8.2   Options for internal walls and partitions in dwellings

() Hot links

— BS 5234: Part 1 1992: Partitions (including matching linings). Code of practice for design and installation

— BS 5268: Part 4.2 1990: Structural use of timber. Fire resistance of timber structures. Recommendations for calculating fire resistance of timber stud walls and joisted floor constructions

— BS 8000: Part 8 1994: Workmanship on building sites. Code of practice for plasterboard partitions and dry linings

8.1 Functions of partitions and selection criteria

Introduction

After studying this section you should have developed an understanding of the functions of internal walls and partitions. You should be able to distinguish between loadbearing and non-loadbearing forms and you should understand the functional requirements associated with each. In addition, you should be aware of the sources and nature of loads applied to internal walls and partitions, and you should appreciate their implications relative to selection of materials and construction form.

Overview

The structure and fabric of buildings could be considered within two discrete areas: the main shell of the building and the internal elements contained within it. The shell comprises the main structural elements of the sub- and superstructures, and the internal fabric comprises non-loadbearing elements that act to subdivide spaces. Internal walls and partitions fall into the latter of these groupings. While it is not uncommon for the internal walls and of dwellings to act as loadbearing elements, acting to support upper floors for example, the primary function of partitions that are not loadbearing is to subdivide space within the building. This is the primary function of partitions in all building types, although the nature of partitions in dwellings differs from those used in commercial and industrial building forms. The degree of flexibility required in these non-domestic types of building often necessitates the adoption of partition forms that are easy to relocate. Such forms are termed *demountable partitions*, and a wide variety of sophisticated forms have been developed in recent years.

The remainder of this section deals with the general principles of partition function, selection and form, with particular emphasis placed upon domestic alternatives.

The consideration of partitions could be undertaken with reference to two distinct constructional forms of space-dividing unit: loadbearing and non-loadbearing forms (Figure 8.1).

Loadbearing forms, in addition to dividing space, also carry some loads from the building. In most cases, this load carrying is their primary function, with the division of space being a secondary issue.

Historically the terms 'partition' and 'internal wall' were used to describe differing forms of construction. The internal wall of a building would be considered to be of more robust construction such as masonry, while the partition would be a lighter form such as timber stud. Internal walls would also generally be loadbearing, while partitions would not be expected to take structural loads. In modern construction the terms have become interchangeable and the distinction no longer exists.

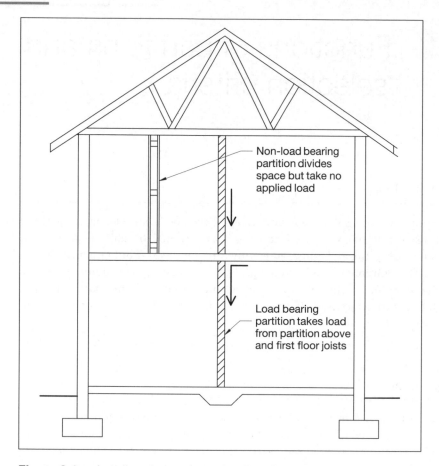

Figure 8.1 ● Loadbearing and non-loadbearing partitions.

The use of non-loadbearing partitions, which carry no structural loading other than their own self-weight, is almost ubiquitous.

As with any building element, partitions are subject to a set of performance requirements that must be achieved to varying degrees in order that the element fulfils its intended function. These will take on differing levels of importance in different situations and building types. In general, however, the performance requirements for partitions may be considered as follows.

Division of space

Partitions are used primarily for the purpose of subdividing spaces within buildings. In dwellings this results in the creation of rooms or spaces that satisfy the users' needs. In non-domestic situations partitions will be used to ensure areas of privacy, to provide visual division or simply to allocate areas of activity to individuals or operational functions. In order to achieve this it is not necessarily the case that partitions will extend to the full height of the room ceiling. Certain forms used in offices and similar situations provide only a partial separation between spaces. Such forms are not strictly partitions.

Durability

Partitions must be able to offer suitable levels of durability to ensure that they perform adequately for the duration of their expected life. In domestic situations the nature of the use of the rooms will impose specific demands upon the partitions. They are likely to be required to withstand loads from a variety of sources. The selection of materials and construction form must be appropriate to ensure that they provide adequate levels of durability for the lifespan of the building.

One of the most significant features of partition construction that affects their level of durability is the ability to withstand the effects of fire. The degree of fire resistance displayed by partitions also has a great effect upon the general level of fire safety achieved by the building. Escape routes must be maintained to allow people to exit a building in the event of fire.

The ability of the partition to resist the passage of fire depends upon the ability of the unit to maintain its insulation, integrity and stability for a requisite period of time (Table 8.1). In the case of partitions or separating walls in and between dwellings it is unusual for the required level of fire resistance to exceed 30 minutes or 60 minutes. However, in other situations greater levels of resistance may be required.

The rate of spread of flame over the surfaces of the partition is another important factor in the control of a fire. Depending upon the use and type of building

Table 8.1 ● Fire resistance of partitions.

	Form	30 minutes	60 minutes
1	Masonry: brick or concrete block	90 mm thickness	90 mm thickness
2	Stud wall with plasterboard cladding	12.5 mm boarding both sides of studs	Two layers 12.5 mm boarding both sides of studs or one layer fire-resistant boarding both sides of studs
3	Solid/layered plasterboard panels	Two layers 19 mm boarding bonded together	19 mm boarding with one layer 12.5 mm boarding bonded to each face

The fire resistance of partitions is defined with reference to three specific criteria. These are defined within BS 476 as:

Stability: the ability to withstand a fire without collapse

Integrity: the ability to resist fire penetration, including smoke

Insulation: the ability to resist excessive heat spread or penetration that could allow fire spread by radiation or conduction

the partitions may be required to meet a classification between 0, when the spread of flame is almost totally inhibited, and 4, when the spread of flame is unchecked. Classifications between 1 and 4 are defined by BS 476. Although Class 0 is not defined within the British Standard, it is referred to within the Building Regulations and is considered to provide a more strict control than Class 1.

Sound insulation

BS 2750 sets out approved methods for the measurement of sound transmission between spaces. Airborne sound such as speech travels as a pressure wave through the air and can be resisted by the placing of a dense partition between rooms. Flanking sound transmission results from direct impact against a building element. It is best dealt with by providing a degree of physical separation between elements.

In some instances the division of space may require that sound insulation between adjacent areas is provided. This is particularly the case in situations where internal walls separate adjacent dwellings. In such situations the Building Regulations set out minimum acceptable standards for airborne and flanking sound transmission. In addition, it is desirable to ensure certain minimum standards of sound insulation between rooms with different uses within a single dwelling, although this is not subject to a specific requirement within the Building Regulations. The prevention of the passage of noise must be considered throughout a range of frequencies. Within dwellings this generally falls within the range 100 Hz–3150 Hz. Measurement of noise levels is sometimes undertaken with reference to dBA; this is a filtered range of frequencies that matches roughly the range of human hearing. Some partition forms may insulate well at a specific frequency while performing poorly across the entire frequency range.

The way in which the partition interacts with the surrounding structural elements is important in achieving effective sound insulation. Any holes in the partition will allow the passage of sound, and there is the possibility of sound passing around the partition if the edge details allow or if the penetration of essential building services is inadequately dealt with.

Sound absorption

In some environments the acoustic qualities of a space are very important. The level of sound that is reflected back into the space is an element that must be considered. In general it is accepted that hard surfaces reflect sound readily, and thus result in a noisier environment. Conversely, soft surfaces or those with a rough or profiled finish do not reflect sound as efficiently, thus resulting in a quieter environment. Hence the nature of the surface finish and the materials from which the unit is made are important factors in this respect.

Strength and structural stability

Partitions within dwellings are not generally loaded heavily, since they do not normally carry the loads from the main building fabric. The partitions to the ground floor area of the dwelling are likely to support the upper floor structure, and in older properties the partitions to the upper floor may provide intermediate support to the ceiling joists. In more modern construction, utilising trussed rafter roof forms, the latter is no longer needed. Whether in a domestic environment or within a commercial or industrial building, partitions are likely to be subjected to various forms and levels of loading and must be capable of resisting them. Forms of loading that must be considered are (Figure 8.2):

- *Axial loading*, such as that resulting from the application of loads from roof or floor members resting on the top of the partition.

- *Lateral loading*, such as that applied by fittings leaning on the partition, or in instances where people are likely to lean against the partition.

- *Impact loading*, resulting from items colliding or impacting with the partition.

- *Applied loadings*, such as those resulting from the positioning of fixtures and fittings on the face of the partition.

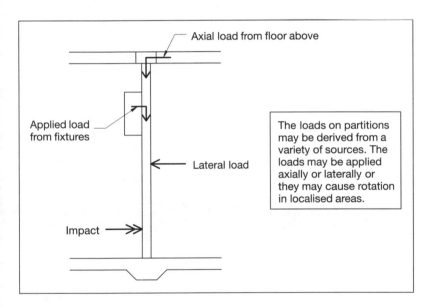

Figure 8.2 ● Loadings on partitions.

Appearance

In terms of the appearance of partitioning, the initial standard of internal finish must be taken into consideration, together with any effects that this choice may have on the provision for maintenance and ease of care during the life of the element. In dwellings it is unlikely that the partition will be required to have any kind of pre-applied decorative finish. It is most usual to provide the partition with a surface coating of gypsum plaster, or to use dry finished boarding with a finishing filler applied to the joints between panels. This allows the application of a variety of decorative treatments by the building user during its lifespan. However, in commercial buildings it is common to require a decorative finish to be applied prior to erection of the partition. Alternative partition forms, including glazed and panelled types, are also adopted because of their aesthetic qualities. In general, the more sophisticated levels of finish are more costly than those of a more basic nature.

Services

Services, in the form of pipes and cables, may be encased within partitions. The type and location of such services may impose restrictions on the use of fixings and the positioning of elements that pass through the partition. Within dwellings it is unusual to allow for access to the embedded services following initial construction; however, in industrial and commercial buildings access for the purposes of repair, maintenance and upgrading must be provided for.

Although the functional requirements for partitions may at first appear to be complex, they are easily achieved in the construction of dwellings by using a range of simple and economical design alternatives. These are explored in the following section.

Reflective summary

With reference to walls and partitions, remember:

— Internal partitions may be divided into loadbearing and non-loadbearing options, but also consider that those materials capable of taking load may be used in a non-loadbearing applications.

— Performance needs may include fire resistance, sound resistance, strength, stability and durability (particularly impact resistance).

 ## Review task

Define stability and integrity as required by BS 476.

How is sound reduction measured and by what scale?

8.2 Options for internal walls and partitions in dwellings

Introduction

After studying this section you should be familiar with the various options available for the construction of partitions within dwellings. You should be able to differentiate between loadbearing forms and non-loadbearing forms and you should be aware of the allowable forms for each. In addition, you should understand the implications of the form and positioning of partitions upon adjacent elements and the required features that must be adopted in floors to support them. You should have a detailed understanding of the construction form and sequence for each of the available alternatives available and, given a variety of scenarios, you should be able to make valid judgements regarding their selection.

Overview

Partitions can be divided into a number of generic types, each with their own characteristics, advantages and disadvantages in terms of the previously noted performance requirements. They are often considered within the generic groupings of loadbearing and non-loadbearing forms. Loadbearing forms are required to withstand or transmit applied loads from intermediate floors, roof structures and other significant elements. In contrast, non-loadbearing forms are expected to carry only their own self-weight. The function of non-loadbearing forms is simply that of space division. Both forms will, however, be expected to deal with loads from fixtures and fittings, such as cupboards and shelving. The extent of these loads is relatively modest in comparison to the more significant loads from floors and roofs; this is reflected in the form of the partitions selected.

Four grades of partition are identified within BS 5234: light duty used in domestic situations, medium duty for offices, heavy duty for public spaces and severe duty for industrial situations. Within dwellings the choice is restricted to relatively few alternatives.

Alternative construction forms

As mentioned previously, the various forms of partition can be categorised in several ways. One way of defining the types is to consider whether they are to be demountable rather than permanent. Another basis of distinction is to consider

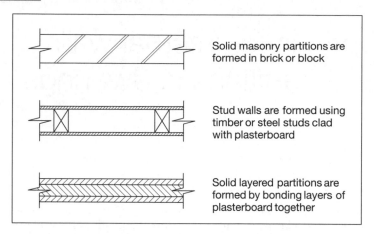

Figure 8.3 ● Partition forms.

whether they are loadbearing or non-loadbearing. In dwellings partitions are almost always permanent, although they may be loadbearing or non-loadbearing. They are considered within this section on the basis of their construction form to aid simplicity. There are many different variations available, but all can be considered within generic groupings relating to the principles of their construction. The main forms commonly found in modern dwellings include solid and hollow alternatives (Figure 8.3).

Solid partitions

The term 'solid' is taken here to mean a partition form that is free from voids in its construction. A variety of materials and design alternatives may be adopted, but the most commonly used in the construction of dwellings are masonry and laminated boards or panels.

Masonry partitions

This form of partitioning is common in all building types and is typically constructed from lightweight concrete blocks or common bricks. Concrete blockwork is by far the most common material of construction, usually 100 mm thick. The use of brick for internal partitions is entirely acceptable in terms of functional performance, but this is not an economic solution. The cost of materials and the increased cost of labour resulting from the use of small brick units rather than larger blocks make this a significantly more expensive solution. In order to maximise the strength and stability of the partition the blocks will be laid in a stretcher bond, as described elsewhere, and will be bonded into external walls and other internal block partitions at abutments. Partitions of this type are

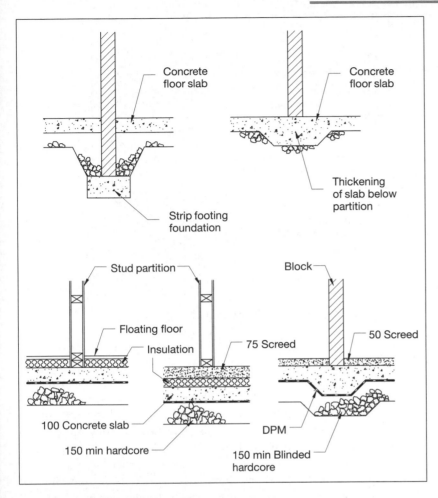

Figure 8.4 ● Foundations to partitions.

inherently robust, but offer limited flexibility in use. They are also much heavier than the hollow alternatives and will be required to be constructed off a thicker section of floor or to have dedicated foundations in order to support their weight (Figure 8.4).

A number of advantages are inherent in the adoption of a solid masonry partition in that it is strong, relatively cheap, easily constructed and flexible in its design and construction form (Figure 8.5). Additionally, the robust construction form allows great scope for the provision of fixtures and fittings following construction without the need to consider any special features or additional support members. In some circumstances the block or brick construction may be left fair faced to provide a robust, utility appearance. This approach is rare in the construction of dwellings, but is common in public buildings and areas that are not required to provide any significant level of aesthetic satisfaction.

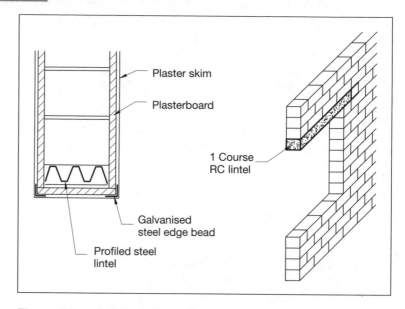

Figure 8.5 ● Solid partitions (lintels to openings).

House construction has developed to adopt 'dry' forms of construction. The use of mortars, plaster and concrete introduces large amounts of water into the construction process. The need to allow for drying time slows the construction process and results in the need to consider the removal of moisture from the building interior following construction.

There are, however, also a series of disadvantages which should be noted in relation to masonry construction. Firstly, the nature of their construction is such that it introduces a 'wet trade' into the construction process. This is an issue in terms of operational sequence and construction duration, as they are slow to erect and require a period of drying out before the application of loadings. They are also relatively inflexible in use following initial construction and are not readily altered or relocated. Another minor issue is that they offer limited capacity for services provision. In domestic situations, services such as electrical cables are secured to the brick or block face and are concealed by the applied surface finish. The surface finish is normally gypsum plaster.

 ## Review task

What two classes may internal partitions be divided into?

What do Class 0–Class 4 refer to with respect to the surfaces of partitions?

Laminated and filled partitions

An alternative form of solid partition is the laminated or filled form. A number of proprietary systems are available such as 'Gyproc' laminated partitioning (Figure 8.6), which is formed by bonding layers of plasterboard to form a solid panel of the requisite thickness. Depending upon the thickness of the assembly, differing levels of fire resistance and acoustic performance are achievable. However, care must be

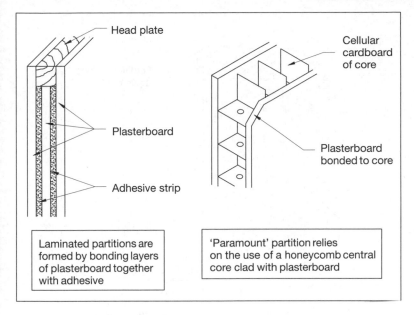

Head plate

Plasterboard

Adhesive strip

Cellular cardboard of core

Plasterboard bonded to core

Laminated partitions are formed by bonding layers of plasterboard together with adhesive

'Paramount' partition relies on the use of a honeycomb central core clad with plasterboard

Figure 8.6 ● Solid partitions.

taken when considering the application of heavy loads such as cupboards. Although not technically a solid form, the cellular filled partition is also included within this grouping. Two layers of plasterboard are bonded to a cellular core to provide a partition system that is readily assembled in panels of required thickness. However, the levels of sound insulation between certain rooms required by the NHBC are difficult to achieve with this system, as the density of the overall construction does not normally provide sufficient mass to inhibit airborne sound transmission. One way of improving this situation is to provide additional layers of plasterboard cladding to either side of the construction. The incorporation of timber fixing blocks is also essential for the securing of heavy fixtures and fittings, since the partition is not in itself strong enough to support such loads without the assistance of some form of load-dissipating element.

Hollow partitions

Stud and sheet partitions

This form of partitioning comprises a series of timber or metal studs clad with a sheet material, normally plasterboard (Figure 8.7). Pre-finished systems are available, however, which do not require post-erection decorating, although these are most normally found in commercial buildings rather than dwellings. In their simplest form, as found in houses, they typically consist of a series of soft-wood vertical members, termed studs, with horizontal cross pieces or noggins

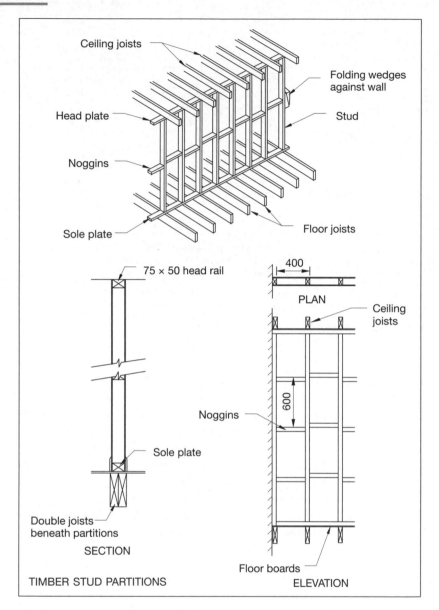

Ceiling joists

Folding wedges against wall

Head plate

Stud

Noggins

Sole plate

Floor joists

75 × 50 head rail

400

PLAN

Ceiling joists

Noggins

600

Sole plate

Double joists beneath partitions

SECTION

Floor boards

ELEVATION

TIMBER STUD PARTITIONS

Figure 8.7 ● Stud and sheet partition.

running between to provide bracing and fixing points for the plasterboards. This assembly forms a basic framework or carcass, which is then clad with plaster-board on each side to form the partition base. Following this, the partition surfaces may be provided with a skim coat of plaster or an application of tape to the plasterboard joints to give a smooth finish for decorating.

The assembly process of a simple timber stud partition includes the input of several building trades. The erection of the timber framing is undertaken by the joiner and is considered as a first fix joinery operation. The installation of electrical cabling and any plumbing distribution pipework to the core of the partition is then undertaken. These are first fix electrical and plumbing operations. The first fix operations are followed by the cladding and skimming of the partition, undertaken by plasterers. The process is then completed with the provision of architraves, skirting boards and electrical and plumbing fittings as part of the second fix operations for these trades. Clearly the phasing of these operations is critical to the smooth operation of the building process. Any delays in the completion of one trade operation will have a knock-on effect on the overall pace of work.

More advanced alternatives consist of galvanised steel studs clad with pre-finished boarding, rather than plasterboard. The advantages of such forms are that they are easy to construct, the components are readily available, they are cheap, and they are flexible in design.

Their disadvantages, however, are that they can be slow to build due to the labour-intensive nature of their fabrication, and also the fact that they are constructed from sections of material which must be cut to size from large sections, so there tends to be a considerable degree of wastage. They are also somewhat inflexible in use, since once erected they do not lend themselves to dismantling and reassembly.

Modern rationalised construction relies on the provision of a wide variety of prefabricated components, such as windows, and manufactured elements such as plasterboard. The assembly of these individual elements is made efficient by adopting a modular approach. An example of this is seen when fixing plasterboard panels. These panels are manufactured to dimensions that are multiples of 600 mm. The placing of studs and joists at 600 mm centres reduces the need to cut panels and therefore minimises wastage.

Reflective summary

With reference to the options available for internal partitions, remember:

— Material options typically include brickwork, blockwork, timber studded, plasterboard, laminates and proprietary preformed plasterboard (e.g. cardboard cored).

— The functional performance of each partition form may vary considerably.

— Costs are related not only to material content but also to speed of assembly.

— it is common to find masonry partitions used on the ground floor and a lightweight partition such as timber studded at first floor level. This particularly suits the attachment of fittings such as kitchen cupboards and allows the partitions to be used to carry the first floor joists.

— When a partition is loadbearing it may have its own foundation, or at least a thickened concrete ground floor slab for support.

Review task

What name applies to partitions whose body is formed largely in layers of plasterboard?

Where would you find noggin pieces and what is their function?

Case study

Formation of partitions

Timber bracing pieces incorprated to support heavy fixtures

The timber framing of the stud partition provides a base for the application of plasterboard cladding. For lightweight fixtures and fittings this provides sufficient strength in itself. Where heavier items are to be fixed, such as WC cisterns, a fixing rail must be provided as shown here. The deep timber section acts as a rigid support for the heavy fixing.

The use of masonry partitions for the ground floor areas of dwellings is common. Their good loadbearing ability and the level of durability are factors affecting choice. Here we see the timber joists of the upper floor supported on a ground floor internal wall. The wall is formed in concrete block with a simple lintel above the opening to a doorway. Note the use of concrete bricks to make up the gap above the lintel.

Comparative study: partitions

Option	Advantages	Disadvantages	When to use
Solid: masonry	Robust with good loadbearing capacity Simple and familiar technology Provides good base for fixtures and fittings Can be left unplastered in some environments Good sound insulation Inherently fire-resistant	Heavy Slow to erect Based on 'wet trade' Inflexible in use/ difficult to alter after construction	Ground floor partitions carrying upper floor loads In areas subject to heavy use or likely to suffer damage Between areas requiring good sound insulation When attempting to create fire compartment
Solid: laminated/ filled	Good fire resistance Simple technology and easy to erect Fast Dry installation	Need to order in advance Components heavy and unwieldy	Often used to accelerate the building process Ground and upper floor locations Used where a dry construction process is desired
Hollow: stud and sheet	Simple and familiar technology Cheap Can be a dry process	Heavy fixtures need support members Inflexible in use/ difficult to alter after construction	Almost ubiquitous in house building for non-loadbearing situations

chapter nine

Roof: structure and coverings

Aims

After completing this chapter you should be able to:

- Describe the functional performance to be provided by roofs
- Appreciate that when dealing with roofs we tend to divide the constructional detailing into roof structure and roof covering
- Describe the different basic methods of forming pitched and flat roof structures
- Describe the different forms of roof covering available for pitched and flat roofs
- Describe the various methods used for the collection of rainwater from roofs
- Understand the problems created by condensation and appreciate the need for good levels of thermal insulation and ventilation

This chapter contains the following sections:

Hot links

- Building Regulations Approved Document A, Structure, Appendix A
- BS 402: Specification for clay plain roofing tiles and fittings
- BS EN 490: Concrete roofing tiles and fittings. Product specifications
- BS 680: Specification for roofing slates
- BS 747: Specification for roofing felts
- BS 5268: Structural use of timber. Code of practice for trussed rafter roofs
- BS 5534: Code of practice for slating and tiling
- BS 6399: Part 3: Loading for buildings. Code of practice for imposed roof loads

9.1   Functions of roofs and selection criteria

Introduction

After studying this section you should be able to understand the functional performance to be provided by the roof element, understand the development of tension and compression forces in the roof, and appreciate its insulating qualities

Overview

The functional performance criteria required of external primary elements to the building are similar and typically include:

- strength
- weather resistance
- durability
- insulation
- aesthetics

Strength

Houses are generally loadbearing external wall structures where the inner skin of the external cavity wall carries the load from the roof and upper floor. It should be remembered that when dealing with roofs the normal procedure is to divide this element into two parts: the *structure* (usually timber) and the *covering* (generally tiles or slates).

Both of these component parts require strength, and we will review each in turn.

The strength of the timber structure of a roof is dependent on the strength of the material – the species of timber, the number of natural features such as knots, and the dimensions (particularly with reference to the unsupported span). Timber is graded by Part A of the Building Regulations, Approved Document A, Section 1B, Table 1, in accordance with BS 4978.

Table 2 of the above document also shows the relationship between the strength required and the pitch of the roof.

The way in which these timbers are then arranged to carry the load over the design span is also clearly an issue when examining strength, and in the sections that follow we will examine the various roof design layouts.

Most construction components are designed to withstand two principal forces: *compression* (*squashing forces*) and *tension* (*stretching forces*). Whether our roof structure is traditional or uses prefabricated trussed rafters, both of these forces will have to be successfully absorbed.

The characteristic strength developed by a roof design needs not only to be able to carry the gravitational loads of the timbers and roof covering the span, but also live loads which may arise from wind action, rain or snow. See BS 6399 and BRE Digest 346.

> In housing most of the loads experienced are either compression or tension loads. Roof structures are no exception.

Weather resistance

Weather resistance has always been the main function of a roof, and over the years many coverings have emerged to achieve this function: thatch, timber shingles, slates and tiles for example.

Recognising that this is a vital function, the Building Regulations Part C, clause C4 reviews the need to prevent the passage of moisture to the inside of the building. There are many features of the roof purposely designed to resist moisture entry, and each of these will be examined when reviewing the constructional details which apply.

A key issue in resistance to weather entry is the slope or pitch of the roof.

Figure 9.1 shows some of the typical roof designs that have evolved over the years. The slope or pitch has particular significance when using slate or tile roof coverings, as the shallower the pitch the greater the likelihood of rain being driven underneath the covering by wind action: see Figure 9.2.

As will be appreciated later, there is a secondary line of defence to such rain entry in the form of sarking felt laid over the roof structure and below the

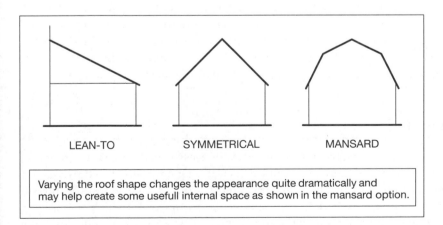

LEAN-TO   SYMMETRICAL   MANSARD

Varying the roof shape changes the appearance quite dramatically and may help create some usefull internal space as shown in the mansard option.

Figure 9.1 ● Roof designs.

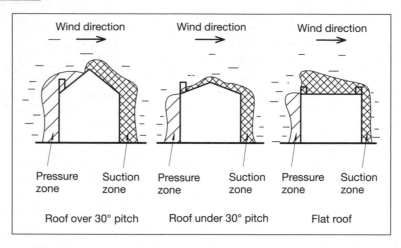

Figure 9.2 ● Wind action and roof shape.

covering. If rain reaches this felt it will be carried down to the rainwater gutter, as the sarking felt terminates at gutter level.

Durability

The ability of the roof covering to be durable has been linked with resistance to rain and to wind action. However, today atmospheric pollution may also be a factor in the equation. Sulphur dioxide in the atmosphere is the source of weak sulphuric acid and *acid rain* – just one of the airborne pollutants to be resisted.

Durability of the timber structure of a roof relates to its strength in many ways and to the sectional size of timbers originally used when forming the roof. The structure will need to resist both gravitational and live loads over the design span between supportive walls. Sometimes the development of rot and insect attack may have a considerable influence on the long-term future of the roof (see BRE Digests 299 and 345 for fungal rot and BRE Digests 351 and 357 for insect attack).

Most domestic timber roof structures are softwood, and this material is generally treated now with preservatives to resist damage over the building life.

Insulation

If we examine the pattern of heat loss from houses we can see that the roof is of major importance in thermal resistance. As warm air naturally rises the tendency is for heat to be lost through the roof, and this fact is reflected in the current Building Regulations Part L and Approved Document L, which impose the greatest need for insulation on the roof element. Currently the U value for a roof is $U = 0.25$ W/m^2 K (one quarter of a watt from each square metre of roof when a

The negative pressure or suction experienced by roofs tends to do far more damage in strong winds than positive pressure. The extent of both pressures is dramatically influence by roof slope (pitch).

one degree temperature difference exists between the inside and outside of the roof). This requirement can be compared with the U value for the wall, which is currently $U = 0.45$ W/m^2 K (allowing almost twice as much heat loss as the roof or half a watt per square metre heat loss for each degree difference in temperature between inside and outside). The 0.25 U value requirement is currently being satisfied by the inclusion of 200 mm of quilt insulation between the ceiling joists of roof structures.

Proposals are in hand to make the insulation standards even more onerous in 2001 and again in 2003.

Insulation, though, does not only mean insulation of heat but also against sound entry. The dBA scale is the means by which we measure sound levels, and the roof can be quite effective in making dB reductions to create an acceptable internal environment. High noise generators, such as aircraft, may still prove problematic, however, if the property is located on a flight path to or from an airport, or if the property is close to a major transport route such as a motorway.

Aesthetics

The shape of a roof is generally dictated by the layout of the house walls which support it and which have a major influence on the final overall appearance of the building. The use of hipped ends, for example, may have a significant effect on the appearance, as shown in Figure 9.3.

The slope or pitch of the roof will also have an impact on aesthetics.

Different visual effects will arise from use of different roof coverings and their colour, texture, shape (Figure 9.4), size and laying pattern.

The more complicated the plan layout of the walls of the building, the more complicated the roof structure solution. Easy solutions will be found where there are two gable walls and a straight run of trussed rafters in between (see Figure 9.11). When the building is other than rectangular in plan, the roof shape moves accordingly and two hipped ends or a hip one end with a gable end at the other, as shown earlier, may be common solutions.

It should be remembered that the more complicated the shape the more costly the roof solution.

Review task

Why is the roof of particular concern with respect to thermal insulation? How does the roof insulation compare to the insulation value required for external walls?

What is one of the biggest influences in the overall aesthetic impact of a roof design?

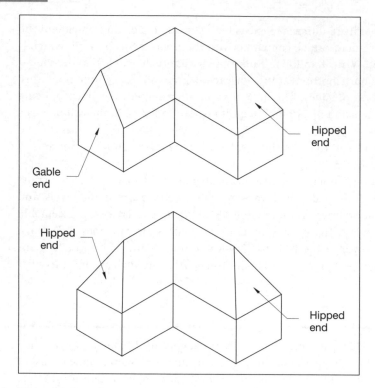

Figure 9.3 ● Changing appearance through shape.

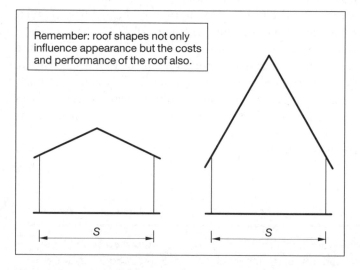

Figure 9.4 ● Roof shapes over the same span.

Reflective summary

With reference to roof selection and function, remember:

— Performance criteria may typically include strength, weather resistance, durability, insulation and aesthetics.

— Roofs tend to be divided into two parts: the structure and the covering.

— The use of features such as hips can significantly influence the overall appearance of a pitched roof.

— As warm air rises, careful thought needs to be given to the insulation qualities of the roof, particularly when we tend to ventilate roof spaces to prevent condensation.

9.2   Pitched roof forms

Introduction

After studying this section you should be able to describe the difference between traditional rafter and purlin roof structures and be aware of roof terminology. You should appreciate the link between the design of a pitched roof and the span between supporting walls. You should also be aware of particular details to ensure roof stability.

Overview

A key ingredient in the design of a roof structure is the span between supporting walls. This is illustrated by consideration of the development of traditional pitched roof designs: designs for constructing the roof out of individual pieces of timber without prefabrication (Figure 9.5).

For small spans between supporting walls, such as in the case of a garage, pairs of sloping rafters are joined at the apex of the roof by the use of a ridge board. This detail, referred to as a couple roof, is inherently weak structurally as the tendency is for the roof to collapse in the centre, pushing out the tops of the walls. There is a very limited span for which this roof form remains stable.

A much more structurally sound detail is created by introducing a horizontal timber between the pairs of rafters, as in the case of a collar roof solution. This collar acts as a tie (a member in tension) preventing the rafters from moving outwards and creating a roof structure which, viewed in elevation, takes an A profile shape.

The other variation is what tends to be applied for domestic housing, namely the closed couple roof. Here horizontal ceiling joists run over the timber wallplate (on top of the inner skin of the cavity wall) and connects to the foot of each pair of rafters. This triangulates the roof structure and provides significant restraint to the outward horizontal spread of the rafter. This ceiling joist (also a tie in tension) provides the means of support for the plasterboard sheets which will later become the ceiling to the room below.

Whether the roof is traditionally constructed or constructed using prefabricated trussed rafters there are a number of terms that generally apply to pitched roofs and these are illustrated in Figure 9.6.

The ceiling joist is the main tie for the roof and is absolutely vital in restricting the natural tendency of the rafters to move outwards, displacing the top of the wall. Without the ceiling joist the deformation experienced would be termed *roof spread*.

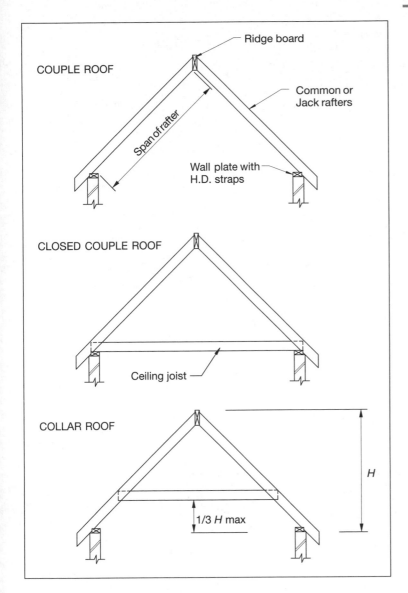

Figure 9.5 ● Variations of pitched roof structure.

Rafter and purlin pitched roofs

Rafter and purlin roofs are the traditional form of pitched roof used in housing. A roof solution, as said earlier, which is constructed from individual pieces of timber without any prefabrication. Figure 9.7 shows the terminology typically associated with this roof form.

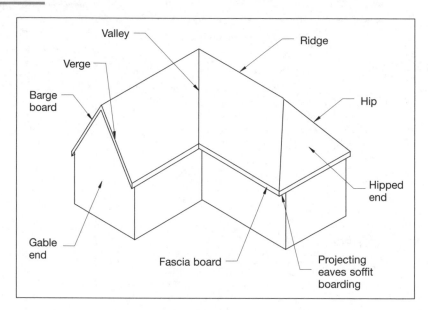

Figure 9.6 ● Pitched roof terminology.

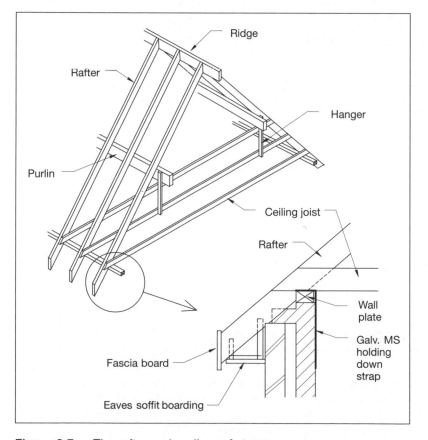

Figure 9.7 ● The rafter and purlin roof structure.

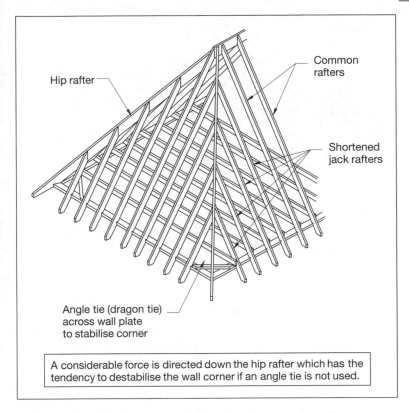

Hip rafter

Common rafters

Shortened jack rafters

Angle tie (dragon tie) across wall plate to stabilise corner

A considerable force is directed down the hip rafter which has the tendency to destabilise the wall corner if an angle tie is not used.

Figure 9.8 ● Common rafters and jack rafters plus hip rafter-supported purlin.

Where rafters are full length and extend from the eaves to the ridge they are termed *common rafters*. In any location where rafters need to be cut to join a hip rafter or a valley rafter these shortened versions are termed *jack rafters* (Figure 9.8).

Clearly the function of the rafter is to carry and support the weight of the roof covering, whether it is in slates or tiles. As the rafter is to transfer its load onto the external wall as well as the purlin, there is a need to spread the heavy point load from each rafter along the wall top in order to keep the wall top stable. The spread is achieved using a timber wall plate, which is usually 100 × 75 mm in section and placed over the inner skin of the cavity wall. The wall plate has another function in that it helps anchor the rafter end by allowing it to be notched over the plate. It also supports the ceiling joists which are attached to the rafters at this level, spreading the loads from the joists along the wall as well.

The gravitational and live loads (e.g. wind) carried by the roof are spread quite efficiently at the point of load transfer to the wall. Further spread of load is achieved by laying the blockwork of the inner skin of the cavity wall in stretcher bond. Figure 9.9 shows how the loads move down through the wall and this of course means that by the time these loads reach the foundation they have considerably reduced in magnitude by the effect of spreading.

Although the traditional rafter and purlin is slow, and therefore expensive to construct, it does provide a useful roof space which may house accommodation space if needed.

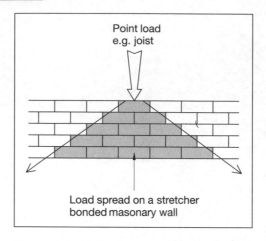

Figure 9.9 ● Load spread through bonding masonry wall.

The heaviest timber in a traditional rafter and purlin roof is the purlin itself. This is a member located below the rafter to carry some of the rafter load (Figure 9.10). If only one purlin line is used the rafter will be supported midway between the wall plate and the ridge. Sometimes two lines of purlins are used which divide the rafter span between the wall plate and the ridge approximately into thirds.

Support for the purlin is achieved at a gable end by building the purlin into the brickwork. Here the purlin was traditionally carried through the external wall and used to support the underside of the roof overhang. Today this support is generally provided by using a gable ladder (see Figure 9.17).

Where we have a hipped end to the roof or where the purlin meets a valley, support for the purlin is provided by the hip rafter or valley rafter used at these points (Figure 9.11). This places considerable responsibility on these special

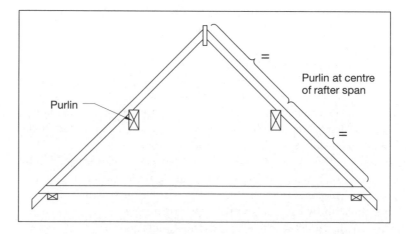

Figure 9.10 ● Purlin location.

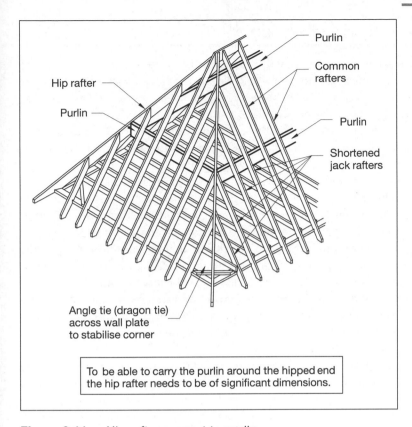

Purlin

Common
rafters

Hip rafter

Purlin

Purlin

Shortened
jack rafters

Angle tie (dragon tie)
across wall plate
to stabilise corner

To be able to carry the purlin around the hipped end
the hip rafter needs to be of significant dimensions.

Figure 9.11 ● Hip rafter support to purlin.

rafters to carry the considerable loads taken by the purlin, and as a result some of the hip and valley rafters are of substantial depth (typically > 300 mm).

One advantage of the rafter and purlin pitched roof solution is that the roofspace can be used for storage or, provided suitable sections of joist are used, for accommodation. The pitch or slope of the roof will dictate how much roofspace is available. In previous years, when slates or plain tiles have been used, the pitch has ranged from around 35–45°, and this has provided a good roofspace. It should also be remembered at this point that there is a link between the pitch or slope of the roof and the nature of roof covering to be employed. Where the pitch is shallow, perhaps for example only 22°, the roof covering needs to be of an interlocking artificial variety to resist penetration of the covering by wind-driven rain (see the next section).

To date the pitched roofs examined have been symmetrically pitched, with rafters each side of a ridge. When the rafter runs up to a wall at the top we form a simple *lean-to* or *pent* detail. The eaves are identical to symmetrical pitch eaves and the same comments apply regarding the size of pitch and the nature of the roof covering (see Figure 9.1).

Trussed rafter pitched roofs

Many of the reports concerned with the efficiency of the construction industry (e.g. Sir John Egan's report for the DETR: *Rethinking Construction: the Report of the Construction Task Force*, July 1998) have recommended prefabrication as a method of improving efficiency by reducing labour intensity on-site. One of the details which has particularly changed due to prefabrication is the timber pitched roof structure. A trussed rafter is the title that is given to the detail which combines rafter and ceiling joist (Figure 9.12).

The trussed rafter eliminates the heavy purlin by replacing it with internal bracing and eliminates the ridge board as a result of factory rather than site assembly. As shown in Figure 9.13, the basic triangle of component parts is provided by the two rafter sections and the horizontal ceiling joist which, as with the traditional rafter and purlin roof, is still a tie member in tension. Once the wall plate is positioned on the top of the wall the prefabricated trussed rafter is lifted into place, usually by two roofers, it is located every 600 mm.

With simple roof designs the basic roof structure can be placed by two operatives in a matter of hours, and is far superior to the rafter and purlin roof in terms of time for completion. Of course, the use of internal bracing to this detail does restrict movement inside the roofspace.

If we examine the function of the internal braces, the two internal timbers which join the rafters at the apex of the detail are always members in tension (ties), as they tend to support the horizontal ceiling joist and stop it sagging. By contrast the shorter members give support to the rafters and stop them sagging by providing a propping function. These members replace the supporting role of the purlin, and as such take compression loads (struts).

The most common profile for the trussed rafter, widely used in housing, is shown in Figure 9.14. Where the internal members of the trussed rafter form a W (two ties and two struts), this is typically known as a *Fink* arrangement. As the

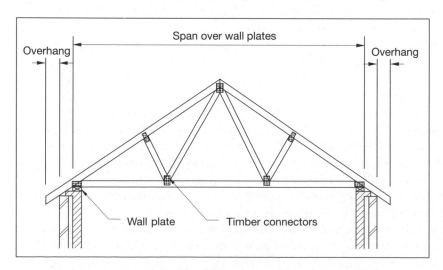

Figure 9.12 ● A simple form of trussed rafter.

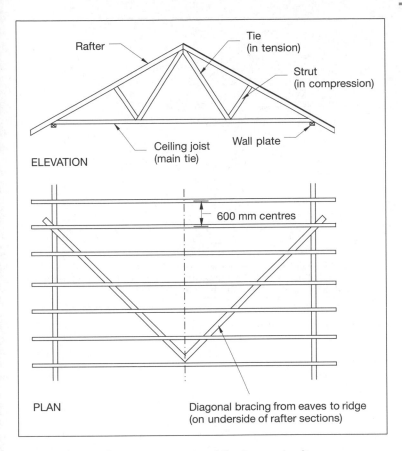

ELEVATION

PLAN

Figure 9.13 ● Component parts of the trussed rafter.

span increases between supporting walls, so does the number of internal members to the trussed rafter.

It should be remembered that in this situation the two internal members that meet at the apex of the detail are always ties in tension supporting the horizontal ceiling joist, while all of the other members are struts in compression supporting the rafter.

Once the basic trussed rafters for the roof have been assembled and spaced at typically 600 mm other timbers will be seen running horizontally between the trussed rafters providing anchorage to space them apart. Alternatively, pre-positioned metal truss clips may be used for location and anchorage purposes.

Another key feature of the system is the timbers used to resist collapse by wind pressures, and this bracing runs diagonally from the wallplate attached to the underside of the rafter and up to the apex of the roof; see Figure 9.16 (see p. 277).

To assist in transportation, the pitch angle of trussed rafters is often quite shallow and this dictates that interlocking tile roof coverings are used as the roof covering. Pitches in the low twenties of degrees may be expected.

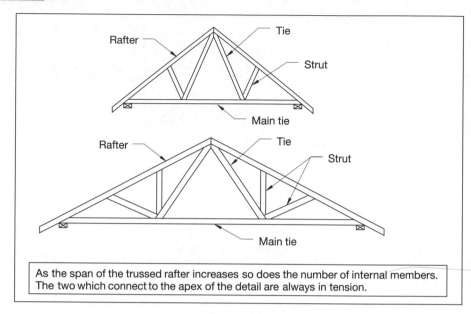

As the span of the trussed rafter increases so does the number of internal members. The two which connect to the apex of the detail are always in tension.

Figure 9.14 ● Trussed rafter variations with span.

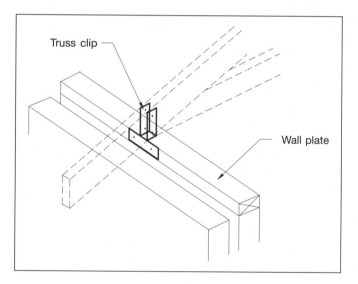

Figure 9.15 ● Truss clip anchorage to the wall plate.

When we reach a gable wall it is generally the case that the roof is to project beyond the wall for appearance benefits. When this is the case, a gable ladder is constructed to cantilever the roof beyond the wall, as shown in Figure 9.17.

If it is the intention to locate the main cold water storage tank within the roofspace, the weight of this needs to be spread over a number of trussed rafters

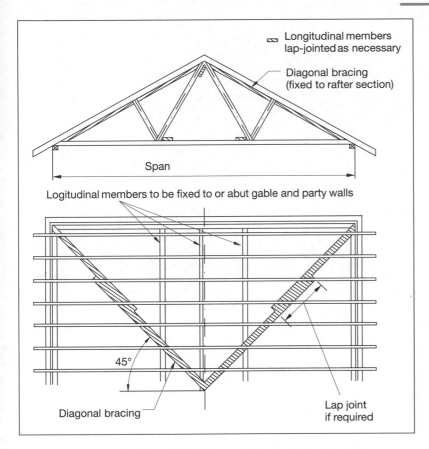

Longitudinal members
lap-jointed as necessary

Diagonal bracing
(fixed to rafter section)

Span

Logitudinal members to be fixed to or abut gable and party walls

45°

Diagonal bracing

Lap joint
if required

Figure 9.16 ● Longitudinal bracing and diagonal wind bracing.

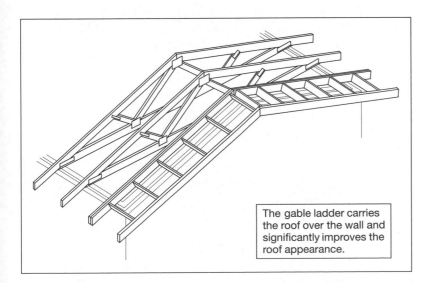

The gable ladder carries
the roof over the wall and
significantly improves the
roof appearance.

Figure 9.17 ● Gable ladder extension of roof over gable wall.

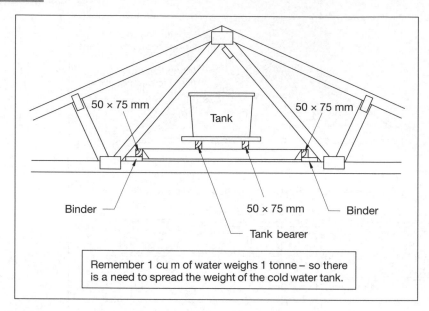

50 × 75 mm

Tank

50 × 75 mm

Binder

50 × 75 mm

Binder

Tank bearer

Remember 1 cu m of water weighs 1 tonne – so there is a need to spread the weight of the cold water tank.

Figure 9.18 ● Support to cold water storage tank.

One drawback of the prefabricated roof structure is that it tends to require careful and special consideration where the roof changes direction. Where roof shapes are simple (straight roof between gables) the prefabricated roof can save significant amounts of money compared with the traditional solution.

by use of a timber platform (Figure 9.18). Remember that 1 litre of water weighs 1 kg.

On simple gable ended roofs the trussed rafter detailing is simple, and of course this means minimal cost. However, where the roof turns direction or is hipped, more complicated and more expensive detailing will be needed.

If the wall to the house is to project into a feature such as a bay and the pitched roof is to continue over this detail then special trussed rafters of varying size or strength may be needed; see Figure 9.19. When hipped ends occur there are two options: use special trussed rafters of variable size or form the detail out of individual rafters rather than use prefabricated components.

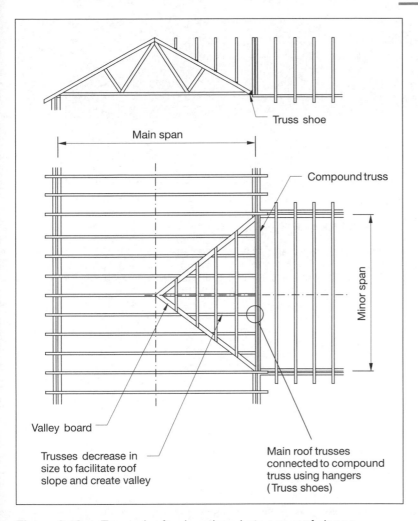

Figure 9.19 ● Trussed rafter junctions between roof slopes.

Reflective summary

With reference to pitched roof forms, remember:

— There tend to be two major forms of pitched roof: traditional rafter and purlin and modern trussed rafter.

— Whichever form of roof is used, a timber wallplate (100 mm × 75 mm) is positioned over the inner skin of the external wall to carry the point loads imposed by the rafter/ceiling joist or trussed rafter and spread these along the wall.

— Rafter and purlin roofs require a ridge board to allow the tops of the rafters to be secured.

— Although the preformed trussed rafter solution is quick to complete and less labour-intensive than the rafter and purlin roof, there is little opportunity to use the roofspace after installation.

— Pitched roof designs include symmetrical, mansard and monopitch (lean-to).

Review task

Where would you find a jack rafter?

Where would a purlin be located?

Name *two* internal component parts of a trussed rafter.

Where would you find diagonal bracing of a roof structure and what is its function?

Case study

Formation of pitched roofs

The trusses are made up of a series of struts and props to transfer loading as needed. They do not rely on intermediate support from partitions etc. Once erected they must be braced longitudinally and diagonally to resist overturning or failure by twisting or buckling.

Bracing is required at the hipped corner of this roof to prevent the spread of the corner due to roof loads. The diagonal tie seen here is referred to as a dragon tie.

Most roofs to modern houses are formed in trussed rafter construction. The trusses are formed by fixing sections of timber together using galvanised steel gang-nail plates, as seen above. The rafters are then secured to the wall plate using saddle fixings at around 600 mm centres.

Roofs are subjected to considerable uplift forces as a result of wind loadings. In order to combat these the wallplate to which the trusses are fixed is secured to the external wall using galvanised holding down straps.

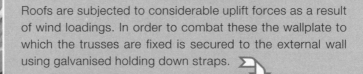

9.3 Pitched roof coverings

Introduction

After studying this section you should be able to appreciate the differences in the laying technique required for different forms of roof covering, and the link that exists between the slope or pitch of the roof and the roof covering.

Overview

There is quite an extensive choice when selecting coverings for pitched roofs, largely a result of the various shapes and colours of the manufaxtured options.

Broadly, the range of options includes slates, plain tiles and interlocking tiles. These will now be discussed in more detail.

Slates

Slate is a natural material excavated from a quarry and cut to thickness and size. This is a naturally hard and durable material, but within the slates quarried there are variations in hardness which causes them to be cut to different thickness and given classifications such as *bests* or *seconds*. Bests are usually thinner.

These are some of the largest forms of this style of covering used on pitched roofs, traditionally identified in Imperial sizes such as 12 × 24 inches (approx. 300 × 600 mm). A length of twice the width is typical.

As they are natural and not artificial materials, each slate has to be holed for nailing to the timber roof battens, and two holes per slate will be located either towards the top (head nailed slates) or towards the centre (centre nailed slates). The latter technique is usually employed for strength, where severe exposure to wind action is expected (Figure 9.20).

The figures also illustrate the need for bonding when laying, and to start off the bond special slate-and-a-half widths are provided at the verge (roof edge at a gable wall) on every other course. The reason for bonding to prevent rain entry is highlighted in Figure 9.21.

Note with respect to the illustrations that the gauge is the centre to centre spacing of the fixing battens and that there is typically a double thickness of slate over the entire roof with a triple thickness at the lap position. Modern slate roofs have a sarking felt underlay which intercepts any rain entry and carries any penetrating rain down to the rainwater gutter for disposal. Prior to the use of sarking felt the slate would be *torched* internally, torching being a mortar-like application to seal the top of each slate course inside the roofspace.

Slate may be in a variety of colours: grey, blue and green being the three basic ones.

Also, the size supplied tends to have a consider-able influence on the overall appearance of the finished roof.

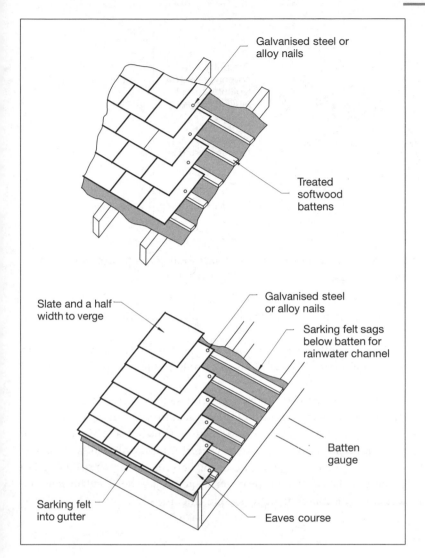

Galvanised steel or alloy nails

Treated softwood battens

Slate and a half width to verge

Galvanised steel or alloy nails

Sarking felt sags below batten for rainwater channel

Batten gauge

Sarking felt into gutter

Eaves course

Figure 9.20 ● Head nailed and centre nailed slates.

Plain tiles

Unlike slates, plain tiles are factory-made units which generally use one of two materials, either clay or concrete. As a manufactured unit this can be moulded to possess features that would be desirable in slates – a camber in the length to resist capillary movement of water between tiles, and two nibs at the top for hooking over the fixing timber battens. Each tile is also pre-holed with two holes in the factory ready for nailing. However, it is often the case that nailing does not occur to every individual tile. In normal exposure situations it is common to nail

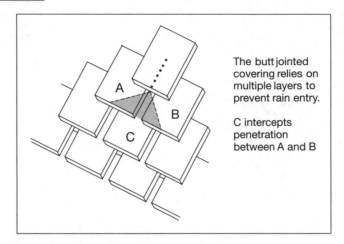

Figure 9.21 ● Preventing rainwater entry with butt jointed roof coverings – multiple layer coverings.

Plain tiles tend to be either body coloured if clay or surfaced coloured if concrete. In the latter case, colours tend to fade with time and the loss of colour has a significant effect on overall appearance.

perhaps only every fourth course as the weight of tile upon tile holds the tiles in position.

Plain tiles are small units measuring typically 265 mm × 165 mm × 12 mm in thickness and as such many are required to complete one square metre of roof covering.

As with slates, these have to be bonded from course to course and a tile-and-a-half width tile will be necessary to start off the bond at the edge of the covering on every other course. Figure 9.22 shows a section through a plain tiled roof covering at the ridge position and this shows terminology shared with slates: gauge (the centre to centre spacing of the fixing battens), head lap (the overlap between tiles) and the fact that over the covering generally there will be at least a double thickness of tile material with a triple thickness where the head lap is measured.

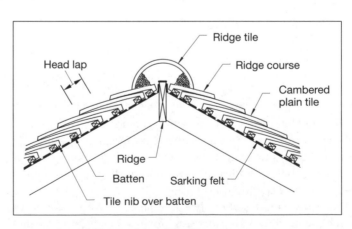

Figure 9.22 ● Plain tiles at ridge level.

At eaves level we can see the supportive roof structure and sarking felt below the roof covering. This felt is the secondary line of defence to water entry and carries any rainwater that penetrates the tiles down to the rainwater gutter. Note that a special short eaves course provided at gutter position again maintains the double thickness of tiles over the full area of the roof and is needed for the reasons illustrated in Figure 9.23. Note also that the roofspace is ventilated through the eaves area, either through ventilation grilles in the eaves soffit boarding or through vent ducts located below the roof covering at eaves level. Cross-ventilation of the roofspace should be achieved as the eaves to each side of the roof are ventilated. The Building Regulations require that this ventilation gap varies with roof pitch. However, provided the gap is a minimum of 25 mm any roof pitch can be used.

At the verge of the roof covering an undercloak is provided (Figure 9.24), traditionally in the form of slates. One of the functions of the undercloak is to tilt the roof edge to hold water on the roof slope.

When a roof changes direction there needs to be continuity of the barrier to protect from rainwater entry, so where a valley is formed we have a number of optional details that may be employed. Traditionally here we would place boarding of about 200 mm width on both rafter slopes at the valley to act as support for a lead lining to the valley (Figure 9.25), stopping the tiling or slating to leave the open lead-lining channel.

Alternatively, we can obtain purpose-made valley tiles in order to be able to continue the tiled covering around the change in slopes or sweep the tiling on a curve around the valley.

Lead, our traditional valley lining, has a limited although fairly long life, and today more modern materials can be obtained for even longer life in the form of plastics. These rolls of valley lining are dished to hold the water and have grips to

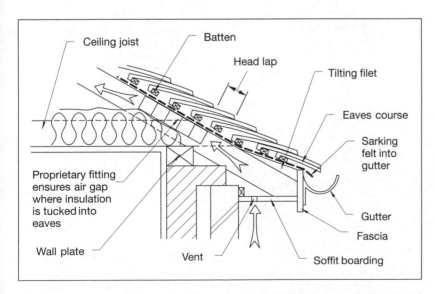

Figure 9.23 ● Ventilation of roofspace through the eaves soffit boarding.

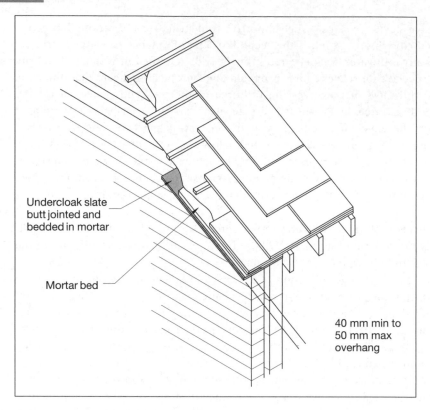

Figure 9.24 ● Undercloak course at the roof verge.

Undercloak slate butt jointed and bedded in mortar

Mortar bed

40 mm min to 50 mm max overhang

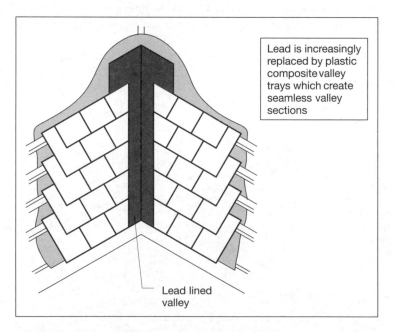

Figure 9.25 ● Lead lining to the valley gutter.

Lead is increasingly replaced by plastic composite valley trays which create seamless valley sections

Lead lined valley

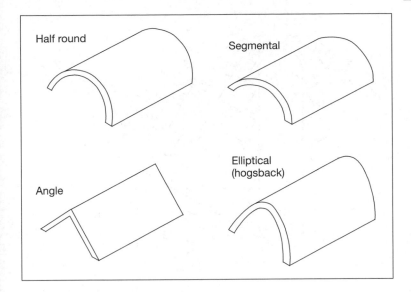

Figure 9.26 ● Ridge/hip tile shapes.

each edge to hold the valley line against the sarking felt, and are simply cut to the required length. Timber valley boards will be used to provide support.

At the ridge of the roof a gap is naturally formed as the roof tiling finishes to each roof slope and this gap is covered with ridge tiles which are usually supplied with the roof tiling as an accessory and in order to have continuity of roof material. The ridge tiling may be in a number of different sectional profiles, as illustrated in Figure 9.26.

When a hip is formed in the roof, ridge tiles are extended from the ridge down the hip and are now termed in accordance with their new function: that is, hip tiles rather than ridge tiles. At the foot of the hip there could be a tendency for the hip tiles to be encouraged to move under gravity should they break their bond with the mortar which is used to bed them in place. To resist this movement a hip iron is screwed to the hip rafter, creating a barrier to possible slip (Figure 9.27).

As an alternative to these planted-on hip tiles, special bonnet tiles (Figure 9.28) may be used to bond into the general tiled roof slope. These are nailed into position and then mortar filled as shown in the detail.

Interlocking tiles

The formation of a plain tiled roof covering involves many hundreds of small units, and consequently the speed of making this covering is slow. A more modern equivalent is the much larger interlocking tile.

The other major advantage of this tile is its resistance to rainwater entry, caused by the fact that, as the name suggests, tiles physically interlock together through a series of projections and corresponding grooves.

Interlocking tiles are often supplied today with fixing clips rather than nails.

Verges may be protected by purpose-made verge tiles or synthetic verge covers.

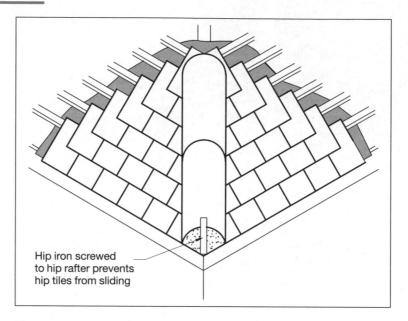

Hip iron screwed
to hip rafter prevents
hip tiles from sliding

Figure 9.27 ● Hip iron to secure the hip tiles.

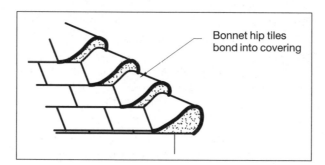

Bonnet hip tiles
bond into covering

Figure 9.28 ● Bonnet hip tiles.

These characteristics of this tile also change the laying pattern. With many of the proprietary forms of interlocking tile there is no need to bond when laying, and as a result this tile may be laid in straight rows up the pitch of the roof. Among other things this means that there is no need for special tile-and-a-half widths at verges and over the general area of roof there is only a single thickness of material except at the headlap, where the bottom of one tile overlaps with the head of another. Figure 9.29 shows sections through this type of tiling close to the ridge and eaves details.

As there is only a simple lap arrangement with this form of tile they are referred to as a *single lap* covering.

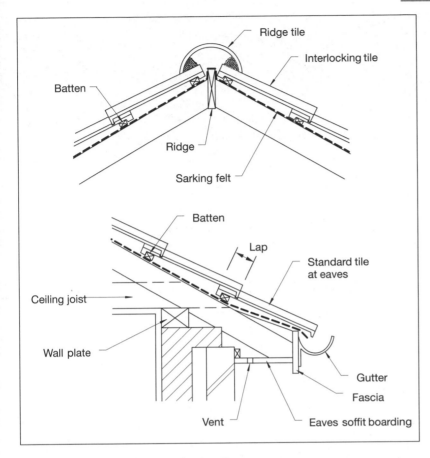

Figure 9.29 ● Interlocking tile details.

Reflective summary

With reference to pitched roof coverings, remember:

— The range of roof coverings may be divided into materials that are natural, such as slates, and those which are artificial, such as plain tiles and interlocking tiles.

— Natural slate needs to be holed and nailed for fixing while artificial tiles tend to have nibs cast on which hook over the roof battens and help secure the tiles.

— Whether natural or artificial coverings are used we will use sarking felt draped over the roof structure as a second line of defence against rain penetration – the sarking felt terminates at the foot of the slope in the rainwater gutter.

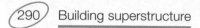

— Treated softwood battens help secure the sarking felt and provide fixing for the covering.

— The nails used tend to be alloy (e.g. copper) or galvanised (zinc-coated) mild steel.

— Natural slates tend to be laid with staggered joints between the courses which ensures that there is always at least a double thickness of material over the roof area to intercept rainwater.

 ## Review task

Describe *two* differences in the laying principles of interlocking tiling and slate roof coverings.

What is the function of sarking felt and where does this material terminate?

When would centre nailed slates be used in preference to head nailed?

Case study

Pitched roof coverings

The completed roof structure is covered with roofing felt or 'sarking felt'. The felt is secured with timber battens that are used as the base for fixing of the tiles or slates. The distance between battens is termed the gauge and is dictated by the size of the tiles, the pitch of the roof and the level of exposure.

In order to avoid the risk of condensation it is important to ensure that the roof void is ventilated. This is achieved here by installing a continuous vent fitting in the soffit of the roof. The grill fitting allows air to pass into the roof void but excludes insects and vermin.

This roof features a hipped corner where two roof slopes meet. The hip is made weather-tight by fixing hip tiles along the junction. The metal hip iron at the base stops them from sliding down the hip.

A feature of this roof is the lead valley at the junction between two roof sections running perpendicular to each other. The valley must remain weather-tight when subjected to the run-off rainwater from the two sections of roof.

Where sections of roof meet with external walls as seen here there is the risk of moisture penetration at the junction. This is avoided by using a lead abutment flashing. The lead is dressed from the wall down and over the roof tiling as an overflashing. If the tiling had been plain rather than interlocking a lead soaker would be needed to each course of tiles in addition to the flashing.

9.4   Flat roof forms

Introduction

After studying this section you should be able to understand the different forms that a flat roof may take. You should also appreciate the importance of details to prevent condensation within the roof.

Overview

'Flat' roof construction is something of a misnomer as this form of roof does require a slope of at least 1 in 80 to clear rainwater. The ways in which this is achieved will be discussed later.

As a construction detail this form of roof is to be avoided if at all possible due to its established poor performance record in respect of maintenance and weather-tightness. As a rough guide you might expect to have at least three to four times the trouble-free period with a pitched roof compared with a flat detail, and today the economical trussed rafter means that the cost of a tiled pitched roof is often comparable.

Problems tend to develop as a result of the deterioration of the covering externally or from condensation of water vapour within the fabric of the roof as warm moist internal air meets cold surfaces in close proximity to the outside temperatures.

In an attempt to improve the performance of the flat roof with respect to internal condensation problems, construction detailing of flat roofs has changed in recent years: ventilation of the *cold deck* solution, which represents the original flat roof form, has been improved.

There are three main forms of flat roof which are distinguishable by the position of the thermal insulation relative to other parts of the detail (particularly the deck). Figure 9.30 illustrates the three main forms of flat roof which are possible, but it should be remembered that in most cases and particularly in housing it is the cold deck detail which is most widely used. The warm deck and inverted roof forms perform better in terms of prevention of condensation and durability. However, their use is most widespread in construction forms other than housing. Therefore they will be discussed in detail in Volume 2 of this series.

Cold deck flat roof

As shown in Figure 9.30, this roof is so called because of the fact that the thermal insulation is located below the deck. This is a good position for intercepting the

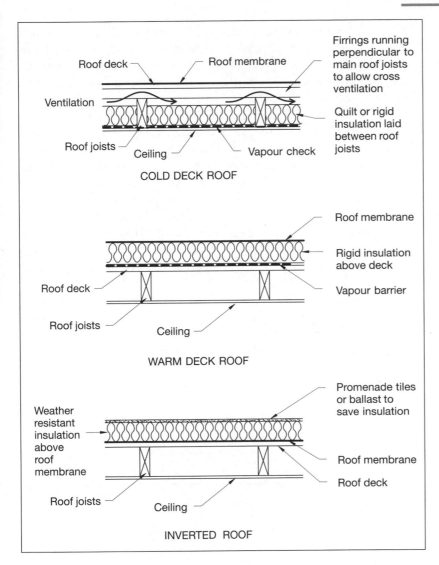

Figure 9.30 ● Variations of flat roof design.

heat which is rising from the building, but it also isolates the timber deck, leaving it cold and providing a surface against which moist warm air may condense. A vapour barrier such as a polythene sheet tends to be used (always on the warm side of the insulation) to prevent moisture-laden air reaching the cold deck, but this barrier is quite difficult to achieve successfully.

Timber, which we usually use for our roof structures, is a hygroscopic material, which means that it can absorb and lose moisture. As it gains moisture it expands, and as it loses moisture it shrinks and often distorts. If condensation causes moisture absorption into the timber we may reach the moisture content level where fungal growth is encouraged, which can have a devastating effect on structural

Cold deck roofs are the most common form of flat roof in housing. This is because flat roofs are very uncommon now in house construction. They are generally used for outbuildings, garages and sheds. Hence the cheapest option will generally be selected.

integrity. Cross-ventilation from side to side of a flat roof by eaves soffit vents is far more difficult to achieve successfully than in pitched roofs, as mentioned earlier. The Building Regulations suggest that the ventilation gap should be the equivalent to a continuous vent 25 mm wide for flat roofs with a span up to 5 m and to 30 mm for spans of 5–10 m.

The main body of the flat roof, as illustrated in Figure 9.31, consists of timber joists generally set at 400 mm centres to suit the dimensions of the plasterboard which will be attached to the underside (soffit) of the joists to form the ceiling finish. The Building Regulations Approved Document A (Structure) should be consulted regarding the grade and section of timber to be used for the clear spans of the design. As with the timber pitched roof, it is normal to place a timber wallplate over the inner skin of the cavity wall to provide the platform to the joists and spread their load along the length of the wall. Where joists run across the building they can be of length to create the desired roof overhang. At right angles to the joist span short lengths of joist called sprockets allow the overhang to be formed to the other two sides of the building.

The slope needed to clear rainwater from the roof (which should be a minimum of 1 in 80 gradient) is achieved by using smaller sections of timber placed on top of the main joists. These may be run either with or across the main joists and may be either tapered (firrings; Figure 9.32) or of diminishing size across the roof to create the fall.

The deck, often plywood, is placed on top of these timbers to create a level surface onto which the roof covering can be placed.

When the plasterboard is attached to the underside of the joists to form the ceiling there is a void between the joists and between the plasterboard and the deck, and it is in this space that the thermal insulation is placed. Most commonly

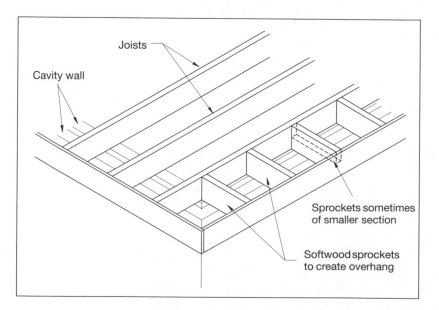

Figure 9.31 ● A joist-based flat roof structure.

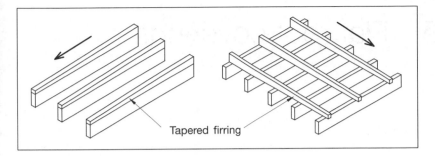

Figure 9.32 ● Timber firrings to provide slope.

this is fibre quilt unrolled onto the plasterboard between the joists. If cross-ventilation through the eaves to prevent condensation is to be achieved, there needs to be sufficient space between the top of the insulation and the underside of the deck.

Other forms of flat roof structure and associated coverings will be covered in Volume 2.

Reflective summary

With reference to flat roof forms, remember:

— Flat roofs are never actually flat, as they require a slope to clear rainwater.

— Tapered timber firring pieces typically create the fall for timber roof structures, while tapered cement-based screeds can provide the fall for reinforced concrete structures.

— Classes of flat roof may arise from the location of the thermal insulating layer. As this is sometimes above or below the deck we create the classes *warm deck*, *cold deck*, and *inverted warm deck*.

— Cold deck flat roofs need ventilation above the insulation to discourage condensation – ventilation through the eaves soffit boarding at either end of the roof joists is the usual way that this is achieved.

Review task

Define: sprockets
          firrings
          wall plate

What, apart from the deck, distinguishes a cold deck flat roof from a warm deck flat roof?

9.5 Flat roof coverings

Introduction

After studying this section you should be able to appreciate the basic ingredients of a built-up felt flat roof covering. You should also be aware of the details needed around the roof perimeter and at junctions with other parts of the building structure.

Built-up felt roofing

Bituminous felt to BS 747 is the original form of covering to flat roofs in housing and other applications. It is usual to have a number of layers in the covering, and two or three layers are typical. Within the British Standard specification there are various grades of felt, and the base, intermediate and top layers all tend to be of different grades.

The usual laying procedure is to overlap the felt as it is placed from the roll and to lay it in bituminous compound as adhesive, applied either cold or hot. As this form of roof covering may be destabilised by the heat from the Sun, a layer of white stone chippings bedded in bitumen has been traditionally applied to reflect the solar heat away from the felt. The weight of the stones also tends to help hold the felt in its laid position. An alternative in more recent years has been to paint the surface of the upper felt layer with reflective silver paint.

Around the perimeter of felt roofs it is best not to position stone chippings, as exposure to weather would inevitably cause displacement, so in these areas it is normal to use a strong felt layer suitable for laying without chippings. This is mineralised felt and easily recognisable from other felts in that it has a fine green layer of aggregate to its surface. When draining rainwater from the surface of the felt with the slopes created in the timber roof structure, only one edge of the roof will have a gutter (Figure 9.33).

The other three roof edges are generally raised in an attempt to keep the water on the roof as it moves to the gutter position. Figure 9.34 shows the timber fillet which is typically used to raise the roof edge and the sprockets needed to carry the roof structure over the external wall.

If a felted flat roof meets an abutting wall the roof covering will be taken up the face of the wall and a flashing tucked into the brick wall will be used to prevent rain entry. To avoid 90° angles in the felt a triangular timber tilting fillet is used to break the angle, as shown in Figure 9.35.

Other forms of flat roof coverings, including some of the more modern alternatives to bituminous felt, are covered in the roofs section of Volume 2 of this text.

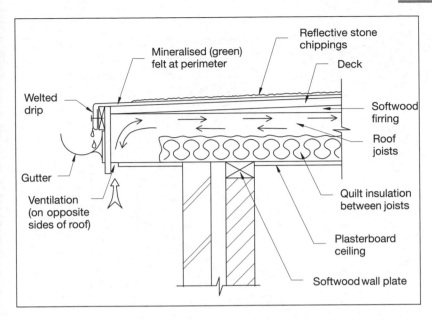

Figure 9.33 ● Flat roof – eaves detail.

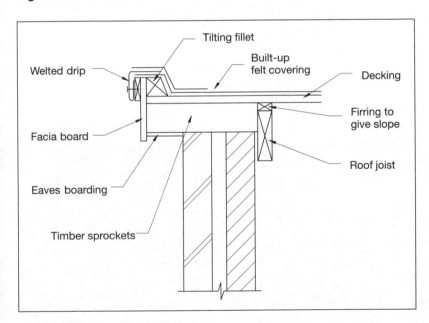

Figure 9.34 ● Verge detail.

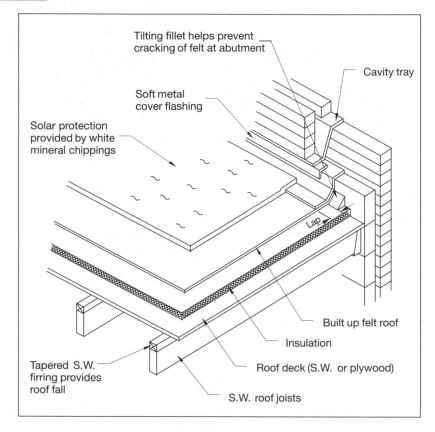

Figure 9.35 ● Junction between flat roof and cavity wall.

Reflective summary

With reference to flat roof coverings, remember:

— In residential work the traditional covering is built-up bituminous felt.

— Coating bituminous felt coverings with either reflective white stone chippings or reflective paint is necessary to discourage solar heat-related melting of the adhesive in which the felt is laid.

— 90° angles should be broken using timber fillets to prevent the felt from cracking at changes in direction.

 Review task

What do we use when roofing felt has to change 90° in direction (for example, where it is dressed up against a wall)?

Sketch a welted drip to a bituminous felt roof covering.

Comparative study: roofs

Pitched roof structure

Option	Advantages	Disadvantages	When to use
Cut roof: formed on site	Flexible in form Can cope with difficult shapes Cheap for small-scale jobs	Expensive for larger jobs Slow to construct Potential for quality problems due to site construction	One-off or small-scale roof construction Complex roof formations or alteration of standard trussed roof shapes
Trussed rafter roof	Cheap for larger jobs Roof designed by manufacturer Loads transferred only to outside walls Factory assembly ensures quality control Long spans possible	Lead-in time required for manufacture Standard components may limit flexibility Transport, storage and assembly of large components Potential loss of roof void space unless using specific trusses	Trussed roofs have become almost standard in modern house building

Pitched roof covering

Option	Advantages	Disadvantages	
Slates	Aesthetically pleasing Available in a range of sizes Easily trimmed on site	Expensive Potential for damage to fixing holes Double lap fixing slows process	The selection of slates or tiles is a subjective decision based on aesthetics, functional requirements and cost constraints. There will inevitably be several potential options in any given case.
Plain tiles	Available in a range of colours and textures Robust	Many tiles required to cover a given area Double lap fixing slows process	
Interlocking tiles	Cheap Single lap fixing ensures speed of fixing Available in a range of colours and textures Robust	Heavy Difficult to detail small areas	

Flat roof structure

Option	Advantages	Disadvantages	When to use
Cold deck roof	Cheap Easy to construct Relatively shallow depth as insulation is contained within structure	Ventilation required to prevent condensation Potential for differential movement between covering and structure	Unusual in house building Often used for outbuildings and garages
Warm deck roof	Does not require ventilation Warm deck resists differential movement of covering	Costly Potential for traffic to damage insulation	A wiser choice than cold deck options, but still unusual in house building.
Inverted roof	Protection of impervious membrane No need to ventilate Insulation is upgradable	Difficult to detect leaks in the event of failure Potential for damage to insulation Requires protective surface covering Costly	A wiser choice than cold deck options, but still unusual in house building

Flat roof covering

Option	Advantages	Disadvantages	When to use
Roofing felt	Cheap Familiar technology	Older forms suffer limited lifespan Multi-layer process subject to quality control problems Solar degradation Problems with differential movement	Flat roofs are rarely used in house building. They would normally only be considered for garages, outbuildings etc.
Elastomeric covering	Often single-layer technology Extended lifespan Able to cope with differential movement	Costly Single-layer covering may suffer from localised damage	
Asphalt	Liquid application is flexible Monolithic application results in absence of joints	Potential to creep at upstands Solar degradation	Usually concrete roof structures

9.6   Roof drainage and roof chimneys

Introduction

After studying this section you should be able to identify the various details that may be employed to collect rainwater from roofs. This will include the use of rainwater gutters, downpipes, hoppers, roof outlets and special details employed with parapet roof solutions.

You should also appreciate the distances that protected fire flue enclosures project beyond the roof of dwellings.

Drainage of pitched roofs

The traditional means of rainwater collection from a pitched roof is the rainwater gutter and downpipe system, collectively known as the property *rainwater goods*.

The gutter has been constructed out of many materials over the years – timber, lead-lined timber, asbestos cement and cast iron – but today plastic predominates. There are many different gutter profiles which can achieve quite different visual effects, but it should be remembered that the prime consideration is in relation to the carrying capacity of the gutter and its ability to handle the run-off from the roof area in question.

Figure 9.36 shows the various gutter profiles, of which the elliptical or deep flow has the biggest capacity.

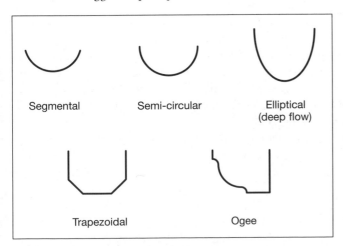

Segmental   Semi-circular   Elliptical (deep flow)

Trapezoidal   Ogee

Figure 9.36 ● Rainwater gutter profiles.

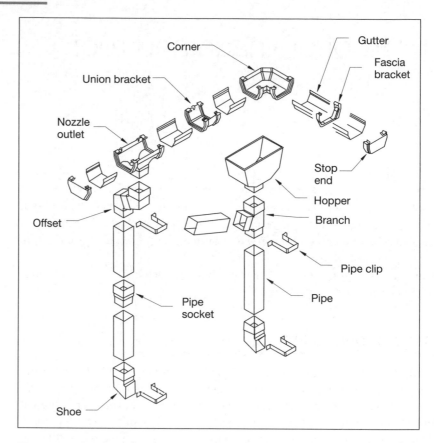

Figure 9.37 ● Rainwater goods terminology.

Where an angular gutter profile is used, such as the trapezoidal type, the downpipe tends also to be edged rather than round. Typical plastic sectional profiles include square, rectangular, and round.

Figure 9.37 shows a trapezoidal gutter with a square downpipe to illustrate some of the terminology that applies to rainwater goods.

In situations where the external wall of the property extends beyond eaves level to form a parapet, a gutter will be formed in the roof structure behind the parapet and connection will be made from this gutter to the rainwater downpipe. Figure 9.38 shows this detail and also summarises the collection options at the roof perimeter and behind parapets.

Rainwater collected in a parapet gutter tends to be moved to the downpipe in one of two ways. It will be taken via a chute formed through the parapet wall and into a box hopper head on the top of the rainwater pipe or it will discharge through a roof outlet accessory into an internally located downpipe.

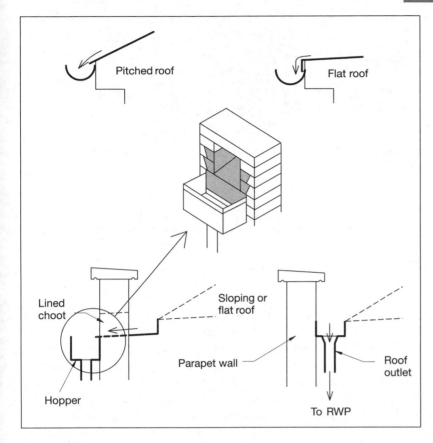

Figure 9.38 ● Rainwater collection options.

Roof chimneys

Many modern houses now contain gas flue block systems for conveying the discharges from a gas fire located in the main lounge through to the open air at roof ridge level. Such flues are embedded in the blockwork of internal partitions as they are of similar thickness to the blocks themselves. A special ridge terminal (similar to a ridge tile) is used at the point of discharge into the air.

These flues are of limited capacity and only capable of dealing with the combustion waste products of gas appliances, which tend to be small capacity discharges. Additionally, the chance of a fire within these flues is very limited, but this is not the case for more traditional open fire flues, which will require roof chimneys to be constructed.

Open fires located in the main lounge have tended to burn coal, coke and logs, generating considerable amounts of combustion waste and needing much larger capacity flues than those required for gas appliances.

BS 1191 covers clay flue liners which are essential to contain the aggressive smoke and condensate that arises from the burning of fossil fuels.

The condensate is so aggressive that it will degrade mortar between bricks and possibly cause smoking within the property where linings are not provided.

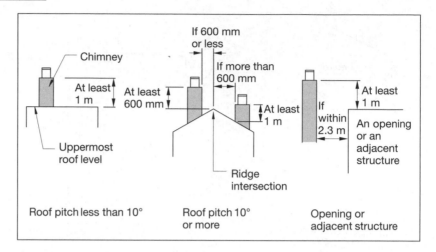

Figure 9.39 ● Incombustible surrounds to open fire flues.

Open fire flues are lined with clay flue liners as they move towards the chimney pot point of discharge. These liners have a number of functions, but tend to contain the smoke of the combustion products. The potential for fire within these flues is quite high, and therefore the tendency is to surround the liners with an incombustible jacket of brickwork. This jacket will extend through the property, through the roof and beyond, as is needed to satisfy the Building Regulations for fire safety. Figure 9.39 gives some dimensions of the enclosing incombustible jacket for different roof situations. Remember that it is the incombustible jacket to which the dimensions relate, not the chimney pot.

Reflective summary

With reference to roof drainage, remember:

— *Rainwater goods* is the collective name given to gutters and downpipes.

— Materials for rainwater goods include cast iron, plastic and aluminium.

— Where parapet walls are provided, rainwater gutters will be formed in the roof structure behind the wall – rainwater outlets may be used to move the water from these gutters.

 ## Review task

What is the collective name for rainwater gutters and downpipes?

Name *two* fittings used on a gutter and *two* used on a downpipe.

Describe where you would use a roof outlet fitting.

9.7 Thermal insulation and condensation prevention

Introduction

After studying this section you should appreciate the features that contribute to condensation effects and be aware of the particular difficulties associated with condensation in roofs. You should also appreciate the difference between surface and interstitial condensation

Overview – the mechanism of condensation

The phenomenon of condensation arises when moisture in the air is released onto surfaces of the building interior that are cold. This release occurs at a critical temperature termed the *dew point*, which depends on the temperature and relative humidity (the amount of moisture in the air). To a point it could be said that the warmer the air the greater its ability to carry moisture, but there is a limit which when reached would allow the air to be described as saturated.

In the UK the relative humidity level is often between 50% and 70%, compared with locations closer to the Equator, where levels of humidity close to 100% saturation are commonplace.

There are two types of condensation that we can experience: *surface condensation*, which we experience on the internal surface of glass to our windows in winter, and *interstitial condensation*, which arises when the critical dew point temperature is reached in the body of the element (within the roof or within the wall).

To explain interstitial condensation it is easiest to use the situation of an external wall in winter. Figure 9.40 traces the temperature drop as we move towards the outside of the wall. For the prevailing relative humidity it could be that the *dew point temperature* occurs part way through the brickwork, and it will be at this point where moisture is released from the air, creating physical moisture and dampness within the wall.

Good levels of thermal insulation in external building elements (principally roof and external walls) will help to keep the interior surfaces of those elements above the dew point temperature, preventing surface condensation from happening and discouraging interstitial condensation in regions of the element which are close to the building interior.

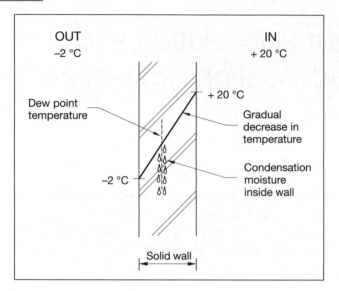

OUT
-2 °C

IN
+ 20 °C

+ 20 °C

Dew point
temperature

Gradual
decrease in
temperature

Condensation
moisture
inside wall

-2 °C

Solid wall

Figure 9.40 ● Interstitial condensation within a wall.

Key factors in condensation control in houses are:

● adequate insulation

● adequate ventilation

● adequate internal temperature

● adequate control of generated water vapour

We will examine each of these in turn.

Insulation and condensation

It is vital to have good levels of thermal insulation in the roof element to prevent heat loss. This will not only reduce the cost of energy but also have a beneficial environmental effect. A key role for thermal insulation to play is in helping to preserve heat internally, thereby maintaining the level of temperature on the inside of external elements such as roofs and walls. If these internal surfaces are allowed to drop to the dew point temperature, surface condensation will occur and dampness will result, causing mould. The *U value* (thermal transmittance coefficient) for the roof prescribed by the Building Regulations is currently 0.25 W/m^2 K, one quarter of a watt of heat energy flowing through each square metre of the roof element for each degree in temperature difference between the inside and outside of the roof. One of the ways of satisfying this requirement is to supply 200 mm of fibre quilt insulation between the ceiling joists of the roof inside the roofspace. In 2002 this *U* value is set to decrease to 0.2 and by 2004 to 0.16. This means substantially thicker insulation will be needed.

Ventilation and condensation

Ventilation and air changes within the property or within an element such as the roof are vital to carry away moisture vapour that is held by the air. If this moist air can be carried to outside the building then the chance of condensation is reduced. We have to recognise that warm air rises and that as a consequence heat loss through the roof is expected to be greater than through the external walls. This is reflected in the better insulation requirements of the Building Regulations for roofs when compared with walls ($U_{roof} = 0.25$, $U_{wall} = 0.45$, 1991 Regulations). When air is warmed it has a greater capacity to carry moisture (up to its saturation limit) and air moving through a ceiling into the roofspace will often contain moisture in significant quantities.

Roof design can be divided into two forms in housing: pitched roofs and flat roofs. For both of these the Building Regulations require ventilation and, ideally, cross-ventilation to carry the moisture away, as discussed earlier in this chapter.

In pitched roofs with the insulation placed typically on ceiling level, the roofspace is relatively cool in winter months while the underside of the roof covering may be very cold. Any airborne moisture finding its way to meet the underside of the roof covering is likely to condense on the inner surface of the covering and form water. By cross-ventilating via opposing eaves, air circulation can be achieved and the possibility of condensation reduced. Instead of ventilating via the eaves we may use vent tiles across the roof area to allow the moisture-laden air to escape. Figure 9.41 summarises some cross-ventilation options for different roof shapes.

Occasionally, the interior of a house may be subjected to applied air pressure by the installation of a fan (often at upper floor ceiling level) to force air into the house interior. If a positive pressure results, air will be encouraged to escape to the outside via whatever route is available (e.g. via spaces around windows and doors). These systems are called *positive pressure ventilation systems* and are generally associated with existing property which is displaying internal condensation problems.

There have been instances when serious condensation problems have been mistaken for roof leaks. In extreme cases water may drip into the interior of the building. This is uncommon in housing; the real concern is related to the risk of interstitial condensation resulting in timber decay in enclosed voids.

Internal temperature and condensation

One of the main issues here is the need to keep the external shell of the building above the dew point temperature. If this can be achieved then condensation will not occur.

We have to consider the form of space heating which is to be used, the nature and adequacy of the heat delivery to the rooms, and the economy of the system employed. Economy may be an issue, as we may have systems which are technically capable of maintaining the desired internal temperatures but are not fully deployed due to the expense of running costs. Many electricity-based space heating systems have fallen into this classification over the years, and these have

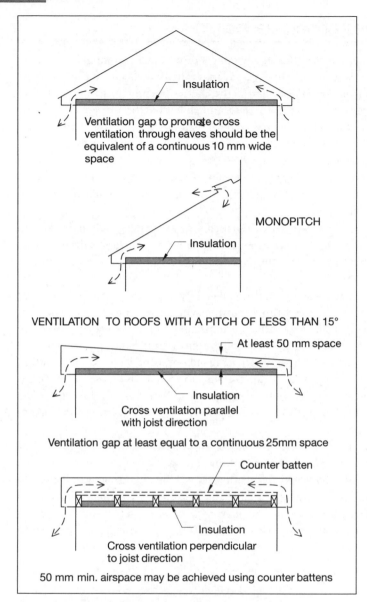

Figure 9.41 ● Ventilation of different roof shapes.

given rise to the expression *fuel poverty* – a situation where the homeowner cannot afford to run the system as a result of high operating costs.

Even in situations where a desirable method of space heating such as gas-fired central heating is employed, if the system is not in operation enough during cold weather or the heating radiators are of insufficient size to heat the rooms then condensation problems may arise.

Control of generated water vapour

Certain activities in the home create extensive amounts of water vapour in the air which may potentially cause condensation. These activities include, for example, clothes drying or bathing. If after using the bath you were to open the bathroom window and close the bathroom door then much of the water vapour would be transferred to the outside. If, however, you were to leave the window closed and leave the bathroom door open, then most of the vapour would move through the house to create great potential for condensation.

Dehumidifiers are a modern solution used for air moisture collection and may be quite effective, but they can also mask rather than cure a problem.

In houses which have inadequate methods of space heating, portable flueless bottle gas heaters are often used to supply localised heat. Unfortunately, it is known that this type of heater generates significant amounts of water vapour, which may add to the condensation problem.

Reflective summary

With reference to thermal insulation and condensation prevention, remember:

— There are two main condensation classes: *surface* and *interstitial* (where the condensation occurs inside the body of the roof).

— The mechanism of condensation relates to temperature and relative humidity.

— The critical dew point temperature at which moisture is given up by air to create condensation depends also on temperature and relative humidity.

— Key factors in condensation control include:
  • adequate insulation
  • adequate ventilation
  • adequate internal temperature
  • adequate control of generated water vapour

— Cross-ventilation of roofspaces is the main effective control for condensation.

Review task

Why is it important to carry the brickwork of the chimney stack beyond the roof covering?

What thickness of quilt insulation would satisfy a 0.25 U value for a domestic roof?

chapter ten

Windows and doors

 ## Aims

After studying this section you should be able to:

- Appreciate the various alternatives available for the provision of windows and doors to dwellings
- Understand their functional requirements and the limitations of the various options
- Understand the ways in which the design of windows and doors is linked to human physical attributes and limitations
- Realise the implications of adopting certain design alternatives in terms of moderation of the internal environment
- Describe the various materials and arrangements used for glazing in windows and doors

This chapter contains the following sections:

10.1 Functional performance of windows

10.2 Window options

10.3 Orientation and glazing

10.4 Door types

 ## Hot links

- Building Regulations Approved Document F, F1: Means of ventilation
- BS 459: Specification for matchboarded wooden door leaves for external use
- BS 644: Wood windows
- BS 4787: Internal and external wood doorsets, door leaves and frames. Specification for dimensional requirements

- BS 4873: Specification for aluminium alloy windows
- BS 5278: Doors. Measurement of dimensions and of defects of square-ness of door leaves
- BS 6375: Performance of windows
- BS 6510: Specification for steel windows, sills, window boards and doors
- BS 7412: Specification for plastics windows made from PVC-U extruded hollow profiles
- CP 153: Glazing
- DD 171: Specifying performance of doors

10.1   Functional performance of windows

Introduction

After studying this section you should be able to describe the ventilation and insulation requirements and limitations of windows, together with other desirable characteristics such as security.

Overview

Although the Building Regulations stipulate the areas of opening glazing to be provided to habitable rooms, there is of course no guarantee that the householder will ever open the windows.

The provision of windows is essential to allow light entry and ventilation to the interior of the building, but a window also has many other desirable performance characteristics.

For compliance with the Building Regulations Part F for habitable rooms and sanitary accommodation, the natural ventilation provision is an openable area of window which is equivalent to 1/20th of the floor area of the room served. Additionally, part of the openable window has to be at least 1.75 m above floor level. This last point recognises that warm air rises and that it is likely therefore that stagnant air will accumulate towards the top of the room.

Habitable rooms should also have a minimum of 4000 mm^2 of background ventilation. To put this into perspective, a 150 mm diameter pipe has an cross-sectional area of 17 000 mm^2. Trickle ventilation is often a feature of aluminium and PVC window frame designs and this may considerably help compliance with the background ventilation requirements.

Where natural ventilation through openable windows is not achievable, mechanical ventilation via a fan and a pipe duct may be the solution. This should provide the room with fresh air.

When we examine light entry to the building, a feature of the window framing that applies is shaping to maximise light entry. If we were to take timber as a material to illustrate this point the tendency is to taper the frame components rather than leave them square edged (Figure 10.1).

As can be seen, the square-edged frame would allow significantly less light into the building.

Windows are also the subject of focus for the Building Regulations, Part L (Conservation of fuel and power) in respect of heat loss, and this is primarily due to the materials used for the glazing rather than the frame material itself. If we examine the heat insulation to be provided by external elements such as the walls and roof, the insulation required is often reflected by the U value needs of

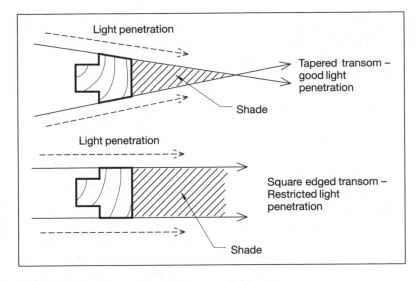

Figure 10.1 ● Frame restrictions on light entry.

the regulations. Walls of houses are currently to have a maximum U value of 0.45 W/m^2 K and roofs a value of 0.25. The value for walls is proposed for reductions (better insulation) from 0.45 to 0.35, 0.3 and 0.25 by 2005, and the roof from 0.25 to 0.20 and 0.16 by 2004.

If we contrast the U value currently to be provided by these external elements with that of glazing, we can see that the glass allows a lot of heat to escape. The U value for single glazing, for example, is approximately 5.7 W/m^2 K. This means that glass loses around twelve times the amount of heat that is allowed to flow through the wall. Because of this, as would be expected, the Regulations limit the amount of single glazing in an external wall to 15% of the total floor area of the building. This will be examined at the end of this chapter in the glazing section.

Resistance to weather penetration may relate to both rainwater and air entry. Timber again is a good material to illustrate some of the problems faced in these two areas, as timber is less dimensionally stable than, say, PVC sections. Timber is hygroscopic: it has the ability to absorb and lose moisture from the air and from physical contact. As the moisture content in timber changes, the dimensions of the component may change, and this is most noticeable across the grain of the wood. Such changes will of course increase or decrease the gap between the openable component and the framing in which it sits, and of course this has to be considered when looking at penetration of rainwater and air entry under wind action.

Timber opening windows incorporate throats and check throats into the framing to intercept water, and these will also play a part in resistance to air entry (see Figure 10.4, later).

With more modern materials, such as PVC (which by chance are also fairly stable dimensionally), the way to deal with these two issues is by inclusion of

Glass is a source of rapid heat loss, and this is the reason for the Building Regulation limits on areas of single glazing.

Approximately twelve times the amount of heat flows through single glazing compared to a modern house wall.

Some difficulty existed with earlier PVC windows in terms of the stabilising ingredients included in the mix to prevent yellowing under the effects of ultra-violet radiation from the Sun.

weather sealing between the moveable components. In this way both rainwater and air are stopped at the face of the unit, and even partial penetration is prevented.

Unfortunately, such advances in performance may also create problems. A frequent example is the occurrence of condensation.

When ill-fitting timber windows are removed and tight-fitting PVC windows are installed the natural background ventilation of the room in question can change dramatically. Although the ill-fitting windows created draughty conditions and undesirable heat loss, they can provide a useful source of air change within the room. Once this is removed the more stagnant air conditions that may arise can be a significant contributor to condensation and mould growth. Examination of maintenance of air change rates when about to fit PVC windows is often a consideration of local authority housing improvement schemes.

We could say that one of the desired features of a window in terms of functional performance is durability, and to an extent this characteristic alone has been an influence in the way in which the market for different window types has developed. After the Second World War the predominant window material used was timber, and of the timber varieties softwood was the most widely used material. In the last twenty years or so of the last century, hardwood (principally Brazilian mahogany) became fashionable for its appearance and its durability. It was at about this time that energy conservation became a national issue following the fuel crisis of the 1970s, and double rather than single glazing was in demand. These hardwood units required considerably less maintenance than their softwood counterparts and oiling or staining appeared to be far more popular than painting. Matters moved on in the same direction as double glazed units in PVC started to emerge with the advantage of no exterior application for preservation, just washing.

Security has been an issue with windows for many years. The alternative to putty (linseed oil plus chalk) for glazing is to hold the panes of glass in position with beads. Beads may be nailed (bradded), screwed or clipped into position (PVC).

For security purposes those windows which use beads as a pane-fixing option tend to locate the beads internally now rather than externally, as was the original practice.

Opening windows are often restricted in size or in the extent to which they open in a reflection of the need for security. Locking is now a common feature rather than the use of casement stays with pegs and casement fasteners.

Reflective summary

With reference to the function and performance of windows, remember:

— Although the primary function of a window may be considered to be light, ventilation and vision, the heat-resisting capabilities are increasingly important.

— The glass used and the glazing technique used (e.g. double glazing) are influential in heat retention as is the general area of glass to be supplied.

— The Building Regulations limit the area of single glazing to be provided in an external wall.

— Security aspects of windows are also increasingly important.

Review task

Compare the likely U value of single glazing with that of a modern external wall and suggest the likely relative performance.

For habitable rooms, what fraction of the floor area is to be the equivalent openable area of window?

10.2   Window options

Introduction

After studying this section you should understand how the limitations on window size have evolved from the capabilities of the user. You should also appreciate the differences in the sectional shape of the frame caused by the use of different window materials.

Overview

The main distinction between different types of window has emerged from the different ways a window can be arranged to open (Figure 10.2). Additionally, there tends also to be a division of types caused by the supporting mechanism for the opening component. If an opening window is supported on hinges we tend to call those openers *casements*. By contrast, if the window opens using some other form of support (e.g. pivot), then we tend to call these windows *sashes*.

The amount of window that opens outwards has to be limited for at least two reasons: human reach and possible wind action on the component as opened, which could make it very difficult to handle if large. As a general rule, this limits the amount opening outwards to around 600 mm. Note the varying amount of opening for ventilation that we have when opening a side-hung casement against

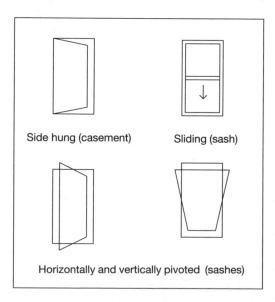

Side hung (casement)   Sliding (sash)

Horizontally and vertically pivoted (sashes)

Figure 10.2 ● Opening window design options.

a vertically pivoted window. In the latter case, half of the window opens inwards as the other half opens outwards, creating perhaps 1200 mm of ventilation opening.

As designs and the technology of supportive ironmongery have advanced we now have a range of tilt and turn windows which can be moved to allow internal cleaning of the exterior face.

Timber windows

BS 644 is the standard applied presently for timber windows. These are commonly arranged into a number of fixed and opening lights.

As shown in Figure 10.3, the opening lights may be identified using dotted lines, the apex of which points to the edge where the hinges are located.

Examination of the framing of a standard timber section shows, as mentioned earlier, the tapered sections of timber machined for the window in order to maximise the light entering the room from the unit. In Figure 10.4 the top hung casement is shown in section as a *vent* light. This type of sectional profile of the supportive perimeter frame and opening components is also often referred to as 'double rebated' as rebates occur on the main frame and on the casements themselves.

The traditional house window emerging around the mid-19th century and still popular today is the vertical sliding sash window. This vertical movement arrangement is unusually effective for a material which is known to expand and contract as it loses and gains moisture. Friction is one force which holds the window in position when opened, and this, together with the weight of the glazed sash, needs to be overcome by the user of the window. With this in mind the original designers of the window included cast iron balancing weights

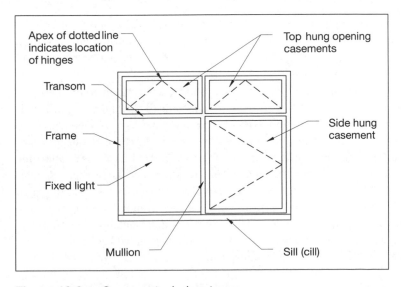

Figure 10.3 ● Casement window terms.

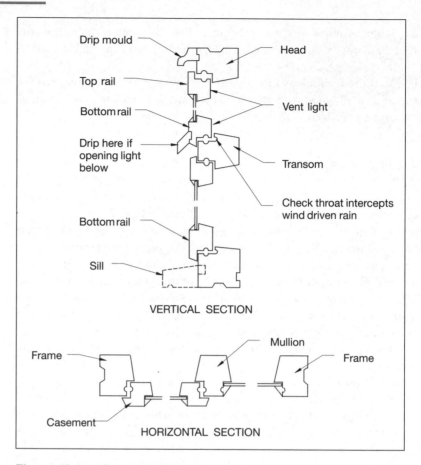

Figure 10.4 ● Casement terminology.

attached to the sliding sash via a cord and pulley. The pulley and weight are located in the box side frame which was a feature of this window type. The rope cord passed over the top of the pulley and out of the box frame, attaching to the side of the rebated sash as shown in Figure 10.5.

Figure 10.5 shows the traditional vertical sliding sash window in sectional elevation and in plan section towards the left-hand side of the diagram. Although this window with its cast iron counterbalance weights works very well, the rope sash chords used between the sliding sashes and the weights tend to deteriorate over time, and broken sash cords are common. To replace the cord is a laborious task, as we have to dismantle the box frame to allow access to the cast iron balance weight. Mindful of this, the modern equivalent sliding sash uses balance springs rather than weights and a more conventional frame rather than a box frame. The balance spring casing is attached to the side frame and the end of the spring to the underside of the sash. When the window is closed the spring is at its maximum extension, ready to help counteract the weight of the sash when in motion.

Although the sliding sash window proved to be a considerable success as a design, broken sash cords in the traditional window are often encountered in old examples of this window style.

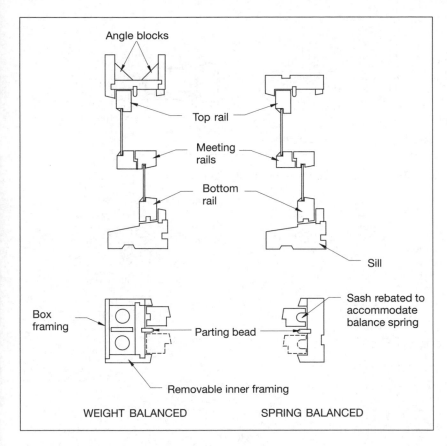

Figure 10.5 ● Vertical sliding sash options.

Other window materials

There are a range of alternatives to timber (which includes of course both soft-wood and hardwood). These include:

● steel

● aluminium

● PVC

Steel windows use predominantly N or Z sectional profiles as shown in Figure 10.6, where a pivoting sash closes on its frame.

By contrast, aluminium window sections tend to be box sections for strength, and although the extruded section seems complex, it is still basically a box.

PVC also tends to be box-like in section, containing steel to improve its strength capabilities and give the performance that is necessary for security.

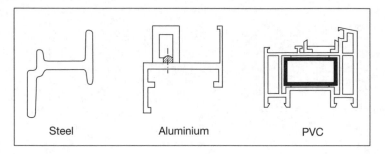

Steel	Aluminium	PVC

Figure 10.6 ● Frame sections – different materials.

Reflective summary

With reference to window options, remember:

— Opening windows supported on hinges are termed casements, and those on other supports such as pivots or cords are termed sashes.

— The opening width of window is limited to human reach and to our ability to operate the opener safely in wind.

— We tend to taper timber window frames to allow maximum light penetration.

— Alternative materials to softwood and hardwood are steel, aluminium and PVC.

 ## Review task

Why is the frame used for a window often tapered towards the inside of the property?

Apart from timber, name *three* other materials used for windows.

What distinguishes a casement from a sash?

10.3 Orientation and glazing

Introduction

After studying this section you should appreciate the importance of orientation to the performance of windows. You should also be aware of the evolution that has occurred in glass production, the range of glasses that are available, and the methods of fixing the glass to the window component.

Overview – orientation

The orientation of a building is the way that it faces relative to the path of the Sun. As the Sun rises in the east and sets in the west, passing south as it moves, any elevation facing north will not receive any sunlight directly onto its walls. This can have a considerable influence on the amount of solar heat entering a building via the windows, depending on where the windows are located and their size.

If the main front elevation of a house faced North there would be a tendency to place the bulk of the windows in the north and south elevations, with far less glass in the east and west elevations. Although no sunlight will be incident on the north-facing windows, considerable amounts would penetrate the windows facing south and rooms would often be purposefully located facing south to gain the benefit of this sunlight.

In the study of energy conservation we must recognise useful heat gain as well as heat loss, and this has been an issue in previous years for buildings other than houses. Today, modern energy-absorbing design is starting to take advantage of sunlight entry even in housing to minimise the need for artificial heat energy, with the associated benefits for the environment.

Glass forms

Before the advent of the float glass production process, which was patented by Pilkington of St Helens, all glass was produced by the rolling process. As this did not produce a pane with parallel sides the glass had various degrees of image distortion and a range of qualities emerged, such as SQ (selected quality) and SSQ (special selected quality). In certain locations, such as shop and store windows visual distortion was not tolerated, and the only way parallel-sided glass could be assured was by grinding and polishing flat. *Polished plate* glass was obtained in this way. Today, only the patterned glass is produced by rolling.

The float process uses a molten bath of tin on which the molten ingredients of glass float, hence the name. The result is glass which is perfectly parallel on its opposing sides and of a thickness which is determined by the speed of drawing through the firing chamber across the molten tin. Thicknesses with the float process can be as little as 2 mm (agricultural) and as large as 25 mm (cladding).

Glass tends to be labelled *transparent* (you can easily see though it), *translucent* (allows light through but distorts the visual image – e.g. patterned glass for use in bathroom windows and the like), and *opaque* (you cannot see through this due to the colour pigment added to the mix).In addition to theses classes we also have special glasses for solar control and for energy conservation.

The solar control range largely generates three classes of glass: *surface modified*, *body tinted*, and *laminated*. With surface modified glasses a reflective deposit is placed close to the surface of the pane to decrease the amount of solar light and solar heat allowed into the building. With body tinted glasses (usually green or smoke grey), a metal pigment is introduced to the glass mix and these tend to work on the pigment, absorbing solar heat, holding it, and then re-radiating it outwards. Good levels of light control may also be effected using this type of glass. The laminated glasses can provide the greatest degree of control on the amount of solar light and solar heat entering the building. As the name suggests, these panes are produced from two pieces of glass fused together with a metal-based deposit placed between the laminates. Colours are varied by the nature of the metal used and are typically gold and bronze. Such glass can prevent large percentages of light and heat from penetrating the building (> 80%), primarily to prevent excessive glare or heat gain, and have particular application in areas of the world with much hotter climates than the UK.

Energy conservation glass is also surface modified to reflect internal heat back into the building. Pilkington's energy glass is known as K glass, or Kappafloat.

We mentioned earlier that the U value insulation standard to satisfy the Building Regulations for the external wall of a modern house wall is to be 0.45 W/m^2 K (year 2000). By comparison, about twelve times more heat will flow through single glazing, which has a U value of around 5.7 W/m^2 K. If we double glaze with ordinary glass the U value can be improved to around 2.0. Double glazed units which have an energy control glass as the inner pane should achieve less than 2.0 grading, which represents a significant improvement to heat loss when compared with single glazing.

The influential factors in heat insulation will be the thickness of glass, the arrangement of glass (single or double glazing), and the characteristics of the glass (e.g. with or without reflecting additives).

In glass supply there is an inseparable link between the size of a glass pane and its thickness. As a result, when you order large panes of glass they will be of thickness predetermined by the manufacturer.

The strength characteristics of the glass may also be changed by processes subsequent to the initial formation of the pane. For example, further controlled heat treatments will make the pane more resistant to impact shocks, and such *toughened glass* would now be a standard feature of glass when used in large panes in the home for patio doors and the like.

The thermal resistance to heat loss of glazing may be dramatically improved not only by using double glazing, but also by use of special glass.

Glazing techniques

The quality standard for glazing windows and doors is Code of Practice (CP) 153. The traditional way to glaze timber windows was with a putty seal to the frame. Figure 10.7 illustrates the putty glazing process.

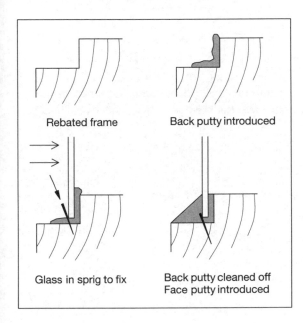

Rebated frame

Back putty introduced

Glass in sprig to fix

Back putty cleaned off
Face putty introduced

Figure 10.7 ● Traditional glazing with putty.

Putty tends to age with exposure to the elements and eventually becomes brittle and shrinks. Once rainwater can penetrate the putty down to the timber frame, rot may commence, so replacement and regular inspection are essential.

As an alternative to putty we may hold glass in position with timber beads of a variety of profiles, for example quadrant, scotia, moulded and tapered (Figure 10.8).

With external components such as windows the normal position for beads holding glass panels in position is on the inside of the component. This provides the best security. Of course, there will still be a need to make the pane of glass

Putty is a mix of chalk and linseed oil. Its use has largely been superseded by glazing compounds. These have the advantage that they do not suffer from the lack of durability that affects putty. Many are referred to as 'non-setting', because they retain resilience *in situ*.

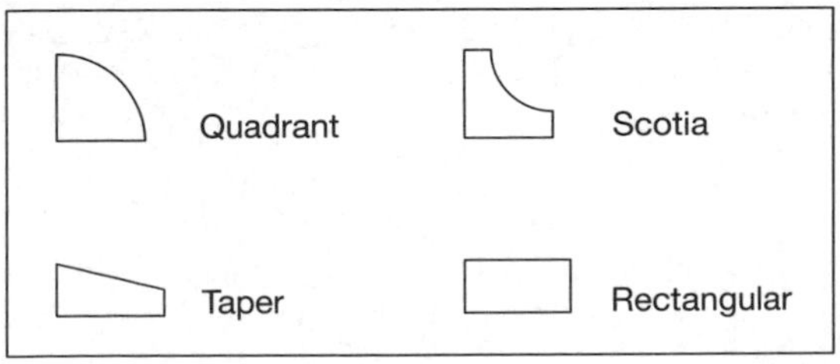

Quadrant

Scotia

Taper

Rectangular

Figure 10.8 ● Bead profiles for securing glass.

resistant to moisture entry with sealant which currently may take the form of non-setting compounds or preformed strips. The latter tend to be U profile in shape and are simply pushed onto the perimeter of the pane before positioning.

Beads may be fixed by nailing or screwing (for timber) or by clipping when using PVC.

Reflective summary

With respect to glazing and orientation, remember:

— Orientation relates to the path taken by the Sun and the way the building faces in relation to this path.

— Transparent glass is now largely produced by the float process, while patterned glass is produced by rolling.

— Special glass is available for solar control, energy conservation, safety and security applications.

— Traditional glazing uses putty, whereas more modern solutions may use non-setting compounds or dry glazing techniques.

— Beads of various profile shapes may be used to securely locate the glass when glazing.

 ## Review task

Define 'Orientation'.

Compare the U value characteristics of single and double glazing.

Define 'translucent' as applied to glass.

Case study

Windows

The windows seen here are of two different types. The window to the left is a soft-wood unit, whereas that to the right is manufactured from PVCu. They are both fixed using galvanised steel brackets screwed to the external wall reveal. Note, in the case of the PVCu unit, that the cavity is closed using a proprietary insulated closer.

10.4   Door types

Introduction

After studying this section you should be able to describe the functional performance generally required of doors. You should be able to identify the range of doors typically available for domestic use and you should appreciate the difference between frames and linings.

Overview

There are a number of different types of door suitable for use in houses, and the range may be extended by considering the various materials and finishes also available.

You should appreciate typical door sizes, and the importance of the hygroscopic nature of timber in door design.

Some of the functions that doors need to fulfil are purely functional (for example, allow access), while others are non-functional (for example aesthetics or appearance). Additionally, sometimes doors are divided into two classes before considering function, namely external doors and internal doors. Performance for an exterior door may involve more criteria than for its internal counterpart.

External doors need to:

- provide security

- be acceptable in appearance

- preserve the internal heat of the building

- maintain levels of sound insulation

- have durability in respect of the weather

- be of sufficient width to allow the entry of household items such as furniture as well as pedestrians

Particularly in light of the need to be secure and to resist deterioration by weather, external doors tend to be more robust, heavier and thicker than internal doors. Typical widths include 762 mm, 838 mm and 914 mm, while height tends to be consistent at 1981 mm, and thickness between 40 and 54 mm.

The aesthetics or appearance of a door may be varied significantly by its classification of type; panelled doors are quite different in appearance from flush doors.

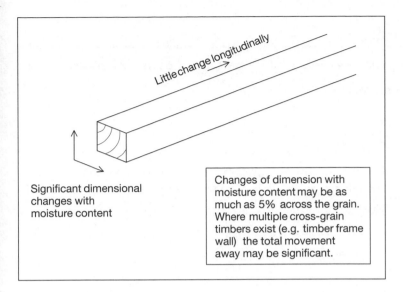

Little change longitudinally

Significant dimensional changes with moisture content

Changes of dimension with moisture content may be as much as 5% across the grain. Where multiple cross-grain timbers exist (e.g. timber frame wall) the total movement away may be significant.

Figure 10.9 ● Dimensional changes in timber with changing moisture content.

The material from which the door is made also reflects significantly on appearance: hardwood is quite different from PVC, for example.

Both heat insulation and sound insulation will be affected not only by the body construction of the door but by the quality of fit between the door and its frame. When timber doors are used an additional factor is the nature of the timber itself, as timber tends to be *hygroscopic* – it has the ability to absorb and lose moisture. As shown in Figure 10.9, the dimensional changes that occur as timber gains moisture and expands, and loses moisture and contracts, are not significant along the grain. However, across the grain dimension changes as large as 5% could be expected.

In this situation the gap between the door and the frame may change, allowing changes in resistance to heat flow and sound penetration.

Clearly, materials which are more dimensionally stable, such as PVC, have an advantage in this respect.

Durability mainly relates to resistance to the weather and to water in particular. Here again the hygroscopic nature of the material may have an effect on external doors if they are not maintained properly (paint, varnish, preservative stain etc.).

Certain timbers, such as hardwoods, are quite resistant naturally to moisture damage. If plywood was to be used in exterior doors a suitable grade could be chosen for its moisture-resisting qualities. Marine ply or WBP ply (water and boil proof) have high moisture resistance; see BS 1455.

When selecting doors for external and internal use their width needs to be considered for access for furniture such as settees, sideboards and wardrobes.

Review task

Name *three* performance characteristics that you would require from an external door.

What is hygroscopicity ?

Panelled doors

When we consider the types of door available it is best to commence with consideration of panelled doors, as the basic member composition tends to be used in other door types, as will be illustrated shortly.

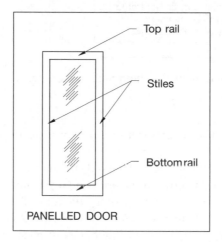

Figure 10.10 ● Ingredients of a panelled door.

The panelled door, as shown in Figure 10.10, has a basic perimeter which consists of two vertical stiles, a top rail and a bottom rail. The stiles and top rail are typically around 100 mm in width, while the bottom rail is traditionally wider, often 200 mm or more. If the door is to have a single panel, as in the figure, the perimeter frame is usually rebated to take the panel and the panel fixed in position using beads. The bead profile (Figure 10.11) may vary, as may the method fixing them in position.

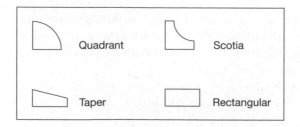

Figure 10.11 ● Beads for securing door panels.

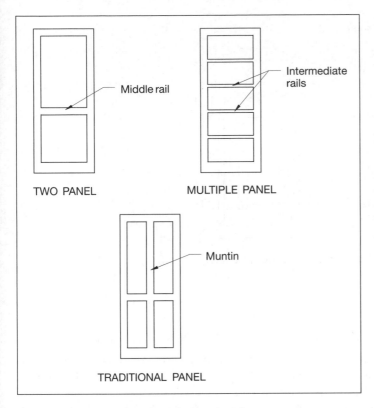

Figure 10.12 ● Varying the number of door panels.

If beads are nailed in position we tend to refer to them as *bradded*; alternatively, they may be screwed or fixed with cups and screws. The circular cups are used in conjunction with countersunk screws to allow for easy removal. This is necessary, as the head of the screw is not able to bite into the timber.

Figure 10.12 shows the creation of more than one panel using a middle rail, which traditionally is not in the middle of the door, intermediate rails (which are often little more than glazing bars in size), and a muntin used to divide the width of the door. For two- and multiple panel doors the bead is used extensively as the method of panel fixing, while with the four-panelled door the timber panels tend to be fixed into groves in the surrounding members as the door is assembled at the factory. The traditional four- (and six-) panel door will use panels which are shaped to enhance the appearance of the door and suggest strength.

'Raised and fielded' and 'bevel raised and fielded' are two of the traditional panel shapes used for four- and six-panelled doors (Figure 10.13).

As shown, the field of the panel is the flat section in the panel centre. This type of traditional panel profile can be enhanced even more by adding an ornamental bead around each panel perimeter. This bead is often termed a bolection moulding.

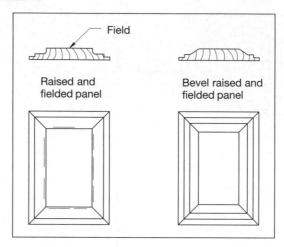

Figure 10.13 ● Traditional timber door panels.

Flush doors

Most flush doors (Figure 10.14) tend to use the internal perimeter timbers that feature on the panelled door, namely stiles and top and bottom rails. The name of this door emerges from the face finish, in that it is flat.

The figure shows that there are basically four forms that the flush door takes: hollow, skeleton, cellular and laminated. Forms of hollow door tend to be the cheapest available, while the laminated core is at the other end of the cost range.

Facings to flush doors are numerous, from hardboard (the cheapest door type), to plywood, veneered plywood and plastic laminate. With the hollow door there is little support to the face covering of the door, and this makes it vulnerable to damage if covered in one of the less strong facings such as hardboard.

If this door type is to be used externally it would require a facing capable of weather resistance, and an appropriate grade of plywood would be ideal. When used as an internal door, the appearance can be enhanced considerably by the use of hardwood veneered plywood facings.

The skeleton core uses internal horizontal members to provide some support to the face covering, and the cellular core can provide a more extensive face support as an alternative core. Different shapes of cellular core tend to be used by the different door manufacturers: diamond, honeycombed and square.

Where strength is needed from this door type the laminated door may be used. The laminate strips of timber which are glued together to complete the core have the grain of each laminate rotated to provide strength.

To prevent wear damage to the face covering of the door, a hardwood lipping is attached to the edges (usually only the two long edges) which extends through the full thickness of the door (Figure 10.15). If the two long edges of the door are protected in this way they will resist damage as the door opens and closes to its frame.

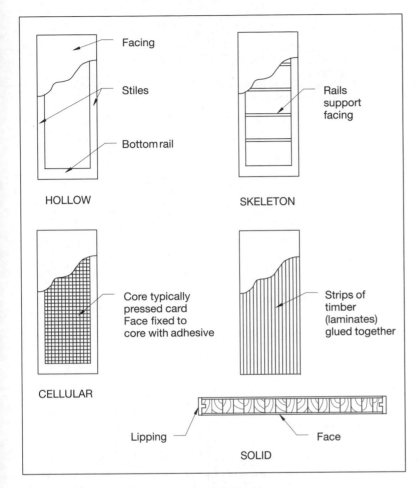

Figure 10.14 ● Different forms of flush door.

When we provide a door with handles (lever furniture) these are attached to a metal lock assembly which is recessed into the body of the door. These tend to be called mortice locks and mortice latches. As the joiner places this into the door body he will form a sinking or mortice in the door edge. With panelled doors the stile is generally not wide enough to accommodate the mortice lock or latch, and we therefore have to place an extra piece of timber inside the door during manu-facture to take the depth of the mortice assembly. This lock block required is also shown in Figure 10.15.

Matchboarded doors

Matchboarded doors (Figure 10.16) were formed originally out of floor boarding and used for exterior access doors to outbuildings and the like. The simplest form

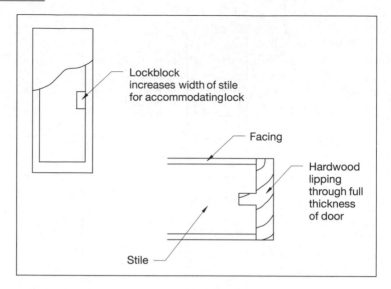

Figure 10.15 ● Lipping edges of flush doors.

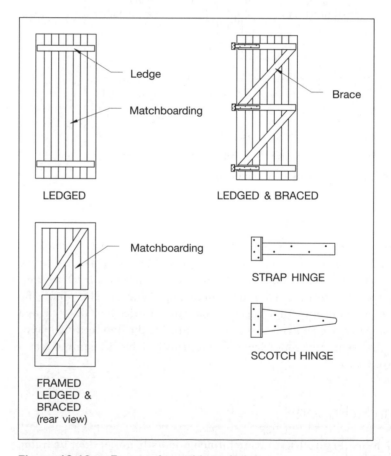

Figure 10.16 ● Forms of matchboarded door.

of matchboarded door possible is the ledged door, where just two cross ledges are used as the means of holding the boarding together.

For greater stability and strength braces were added as shown in the figure. Note the position of the hinges, with the braces sloping up from left to right. The ledge is the typical fixture point for the hinge. The best overall appearance and strength is achieved with the framed ledged and braced door, where effectively a perimeter frame is fitted around the matchboarding. From the front the door has a fairly flush face, with the matchboarding finishing in line with the perimeter enclosing framing. It is often the case that the matchboarding is tongued and grooved (just like floor boarding) and V jointed to enhance the appearance of the joint between boards.

Review task

Name *two* cores that could be used to flush doors.

What is *lever furniture* as applied to doors?

Frames and linings

Doors are traditionally hung from a timber frame which is machine rebated to take the closing edge of the door (Figure 10.17).

True frames tend to be found to external doors, where the overall dimensions tend to be approximately 100 × 75 mm. The gap between door edge and frame is needed to accommodate changes in frame dimension that are caused by changes in the frame and door moisture content. This will ensure that the door can still be

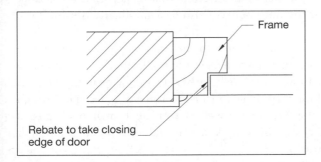

Figure 10.17 ● Door frame.

opened and that it does not have a tendency to stick (see BS 1186 for further information regarding moisture contents in timber at the time of manufacture of joinery components). Clearly the gap is also important in relation to preserving internal heat and in relation to sound entry, and it is often therefore the case that

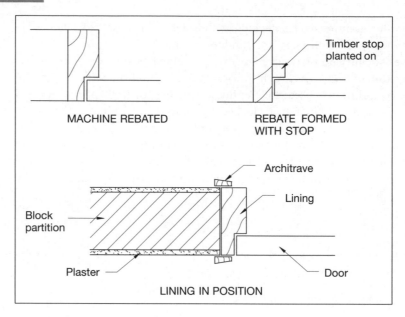

Figure 10.18 ● Door linings.

a compressible material is applied between the frame and the door edge to assist this as *draughtproofing*. As an alternative to providing doors and frames as separate items we can order a door already hung from a frame, and this is called a *door set*.

While frames are used to external doors a lining is more typical to internal doors. When an opening is formed in an internal wall or partition the timber lining will not only support the door but will also line and neatly finish off the opening.

Figure 10.18 shows the use of a lining to an internal door located in a blockwork partition. Here the extreme dimension of the lining is determined by the overall width of the partition. If the blockwork is 100 mm wide with 13 mm of plaster on either side, the lining would be finished to 126 mm to extend through the full width of the opening. Where the wall plaster meets a timber material such as a lining, there will always be a crack, and to hide this junction a timber architrave is used, as illustrated.

Like a door frame, the timber lining may have a rebate to receive the closing edges of the door, which is formed by machine. Alternatively, a rebate may be created by simply fixing on (planting on) another small section of timber as a *stop*.

Case study

Doors

Here we see two different examples of internal doors. The glazed door provides quite a different appearance and allows natural light to pass through, creating a feeling of openness. The flush door, by comparison, provides greater privacy and provides a decorative finish.

The choice of external door affects the aesthetics of the dwelling. In terms of functional performance, the use of glazed doors assists in providing a light interior; however, they are less secure than solid units.

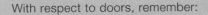

Reflective summary

With respect to doors, remember:

— The functional performance may be divided into items needed by external doors, or items needed by both external and internal doors.
  - *external* – e.g. security, heat insulation, weather protection
  - *external* and *internal* – e.g. appearance, width to allow furniture passage

— The range of door types includes panelled, flush and matchboarded doors.

— Flush doors may have a variety of face finishes and a variety of cores (hollow, skeleton, cellular and solid).

— Frames tend to be used with external doors, while internal doors are generally provided with linings which cover the body thickness of the wall or partition in which they are located.

Review task

Where would you expect to find a door frame used and where would you expect to find a door lining used?

For what reason would you use a *planted stop*?

Comparative study: doors and windows

Internal doors

Option	Advantages	Disadvantages	When to use
Hollow core flush doors	Cheap Readily available in a variety of finishes Often require no decoration	Less durable than solid doors Poor sound insulation Fixings and handles must locate pre-positioned blocks	These are the most common form of internal doors in dwellings Used where sound and fire resistance are not issues for consideration Almost ubiquitous in modern speculative building
Solid timber doors	Durable Good sound resistance High-quality appearance Possible 'Fire Resistance' rating if specifically designed as fire-resisting doors Flexibility in position of fixings and ironmongery	Expensive Often require applied decorative/protective finish	Selection is an issue of personal preference, although the use of solid doors tends to be more common in higher quality dwellings Where there is a requirement for fire resistance or sound insulation solid doors are generally utilised
Glazed doors	Allow the passage of light to areas that have limited access to natural light	Potential for danger due to glass at low level. This is generally avoided by use of safety glass, as required by the Building Regulations	Where natural light is to be maximised or when aesthetics demand

External doors

Option	Advantages	Disadvantages	When to use
PVCu	Durable No decorative maintenance requirement Security features	Appearance very modern Costly Difficult to cater for size adjustment	Increasingly common in dwellings due to availability and security advantages
Solid timber	Traditional appearance Durable, particularly if of hardwood form Security features Ability to adjust size on site by trimming	Costly if made in hardwood Requires protective finish for durability	Popular in a wide range of applications Subject to personal choice

chapter eleven

Internal finishes

Aims

After studying this chapter you should be able to:

- Appreciate the range of internal finishes typically applied to residential property
- Understand some of the criteria considered before selecting finishes
- Appreciate the types of wall plaster that could be used, the range and application of plasterboard for wall and ceiling finishes, and the use of a limited range of floor finishes

This chapter contains the following sections:

11.1 Functions of finishes and selection criteria

11.2 Wall finishes

11.3 Ceilings and ceiling finishes

11.4 Floor finishes

Hot links

- BS 1187: Specification for wood blocks for floors
- BS 1191: Specification for gypsum building plasters
- BS 1230: Gypsum plasterboard. Specification for plasterboard excluding materials submitted to secondary operations
- BS 4050: Specification for mosaic parquet panels
- BS 5385: Wall and floor tiling. Code of practice for the design and installation of ceramic floor tiles and mosaics
- BS 6431: Ceramic wall and floor tiles

- BS 8000: Part 11: Workmanship on building sites. Code of practice for wall and floor tiling. Ceramic tiles, terrazzo tiles and mosaics
- BS 8201: Code of practice for flooring of timber, timber products and wood based panel products
- BS 8212: Code of practice for dry lining and partitioning using gypsum plasterboard

11.1 Functions of finishes and selection criteria

Introduction

After studying this section you should appreciate the range of issues that may be examined before selecting internal finishes.

Overview

The basic function of internal finishes tends to be twofold: to create internal surfaces which may be kept clean with reasonable ease, and to create internal surfaces that are visually acceptable. In dwellings, the range of finishes to certain elements such as ceilings and walls is fairly limited, but slightly more scope exists where selecting finishes for floors.

Criteria

The criteria considered to satisfy ease of cleaning will tend to include:

- smoothness/texture
- absorption characteristics
- suitability for decoration
- durability

Examination of wall finishes, for example, would involve consideration of plaster as an accepted traditional material. Plaster is smooth and tends therefore not to harbour dust. Although it is porous to moisture it can be painted to reduce its porosity if necessary. It is ideal as a smooth finish for the application of accepted decoration such as wallpaper, and despite its natural porosity it is a fairly durable material in that its surface in particular is fairly hard.

Desired criteria to satisfy the visual acceptability of the finishes would typically include:

- smoothness/texture again
- the traditional nature of the finish

By their nature, finishes provided within property tend to be smooth in nature, while the decoration or subsequently applied material (e.g. carpet) may be the ultimate and variable finish provided. To an extent, the internal finish is the base for other materials subsequently applied, materials like those specifically considered in this section.

Most internal finishes used in houses today have evolved over time as the accepted norm, and it should be recognised that the floor element often has no internal finish, simply the finish resulting from the selection of a floor solution (floorboarding, or perhaps power floated concrete).

From the builder's perspective cost may also be an issue. Whether to have wet finished plastered walls (*in situ* plaster) of whether to dry line the walls with plasterboard may have a significant effect on speed and hence cost. Consideration of which finishes to apply, although limited in our choice range, may be viewed from different eyes: for example, the homeowner or the builder.

When we examine buildings other than houses, a number of other criteria emerge. We may want to know for example the lifespan of the finish, its maintenance requirements, its acoustic properties and its non-slip qualities. We may view the total cost for finishes (particularly the heavily burdened floor finishes) by examining the initial purchase and laying cost, together with the cleaning cost, maintenance cost, replacement cost, disruption and so on. In this way, performance is considered over the life of the building.

11.2   Wall finishes

Introduction

After studying this section you should be able to identify the nature of *in situ* wall plasters used in residential property. You should also understand the use of plasterboard dry lining finishes as an alternative to wet wall finishes.

Wall finish options

Wet plaster is the traditional way of finishing walls for houses. Over the years, plaster has been formed from a variety of materials: sand/lime, fibrous hair reinforced and so on. The modern and most widely used plaster today is gypsum based. BS 1191 outlines the specification for these plaster types, which are also often referred to as calcium sulphate plasters.

In their unretarded state, this form of plaster tends to be of little use apart from in situations requiring the material to set in minutes. Until recently these types were used in hospitals for the setting of broken bones. Once a retarder is added to the mix to slow the setting time the plaster is suitable for applying to walls and ceilings.

Gypsum plaster is also known as calcium sulphate plaster.

One of the processes undertaken to create the range of gypsum plasters covered by BS 1191: Part 2 is the application of heat. The chemical ingredients of gypsum or calcium sulphate contains two molecules of water: hence $2H_2O$. If this is heated until three-quarters of the water evaporates, half a molecule of water is left, and this form of the plaster which is extensively used is now termed hemi-hydrate gypsum plaster. Of course, we have already mentioned the retarder, so retarded hemi-hydrate tends to be the form that the plaster takes.

The British Standard also sets out the number, type, and thickness of coats of plaster recommended for different surfaces. As a result, a single coat or *skim coat* tends to be recommended for application to plasterboard, a two-coat application to blockwork, and perhaps a three-coat application to concrete (depending on its density).

The normal thickness of two-coat work to blockwork is 13 mm overall, and this is the most widely used specification in housing due to the popularity of blockwork.

It should be remembered also that the two coats tend to be in different plasters – undercoat plaster typically 10 mm thick, and a harder finish plaster 3 mm thick.

Plaster accessories

Metal accessories are available to reinforce certain locations on plaster that may be vulnerable to damage or where shrinkage cracks are anticipated. These include the external angle bead and the stop bead.

Both the external angle bead and the stop bead are formed of light gauge pressed metal. The solid metal portion of the bead provides the edge required, whilst the remainder is slotted and stretched to form expanded metal lathing (EML). Figure 11.1 is typical.

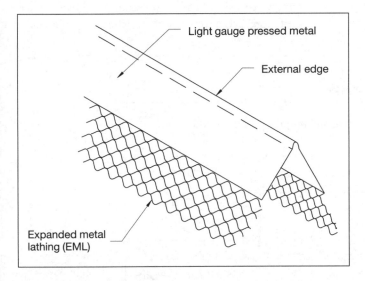

Figure 11.1 ● The external angle bead.

The expanded metal portion of the bead provides the means of fixing this bead to the wall using plaster dabs. Having located the bead on the corner of the wall or partition the plaster undercoats and finish coat are worked up to the edge, as shown in Figure 11.2.

When a timber lining is used as the frame, the usual way to finish the wall plaster and frame junction is to cover the meeting with a timber architrave. The reason for this is that the plaster will always shrink back from the timber lining and leave an unsightly crack, which needs to be covered (Figure 11.3).

Occasionally, it may be preferred to extend the door lining through the wall beyond the plaster surface, and this tends to make a feature of the lining. When this detail is used the possibility of using an architrave is discounted, but the crack which is expected between the lining and the plaster can be controlled by the use of a stop bead (Figure 11.4).

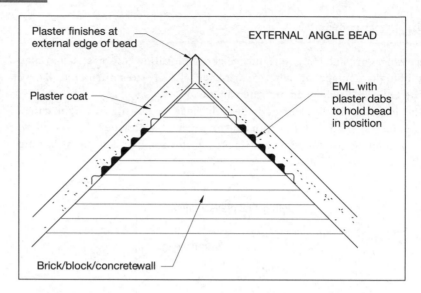

Figure 11.2 ● The external angle bead in position.

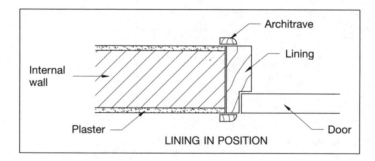

Figure 11.3 ● Covering the plaster/lining junction with an architrave.

 ## Review task

What is the basic chemical ingredient of gypsum plaster?

How many layers and what thickness would be appropriate when applying plaster to a blockwork surface?

Dry lining walls with plasterboard

Instead of using *in situ* (wet) plaster to finish internal walls to a property we can dry line the walls with plasterboard sheets. The plasterboard may be fixed to the wall in a variety of ways, but which ever method is chosen this technique may be considered to have a number of advantages over wet plaster:

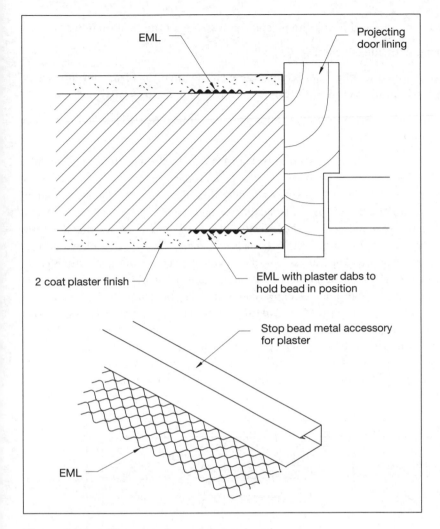

EML

Projecting
door lining

2 coat plaster finish

EML with plaster dabs to
hold bead in position

Stop bead metal accessory
for plaster

EML

Figure 11.4 ● The use of a metal stop bead.

- It creates a small void between the back of the plasterboard and the backing wall, which can be useful for threading cables for the electrical installation.

- The air void is a good insulator and this may assist the thermal insulating qualities of the wall.

- The thermal insulation qualities of the wall may be considerably assisted also by the use of thermal plasterboard, which can be supplied with insulation (e.g. polystyrene) bonded to the back (e.g. Gyproc Thermal Board, British Gypsum).

- Dry plasterboard means quicker completion of the wall finish with no real delay for the drying time which would be associated to wet plaster.

The three methods of fixing the plasterboard sheets to the wall include:

- fixing with adhesive dabs

- fixing onto a sawn timber batten frame (wedged vertical from the surface of the wall and sometimes preferred with uneven existing walls)

- fixing on to a proprietary metal channel (metal furring system, British Gypsum)

Fixing by plaster dabs is illustrated in Figure 11.5. As shown, the adhesive dabs tend to be located at the perimeter of the plasterboard sheets.

Figures 11.6, 11.7 and 11.8 show the detailing where dry lining meets a door lining, a window opening and a typical external corner.

An alternative to fixing plasterboard with adhesive dabs is to use the metal furring system. This uses light gauge metal channels which are fixed to the wall in a proprietary adhesive and set vertical using a spirit level. The centres of the channels coincide with the width of the plasterboard sheets, and fixing plasterboard is by self-tapping screws through the plasterboard and through the channel (Figure 11.9).

With dry lining techniques the tendency is not to cover them with a single skim coat of plaster, but instead to use better quality plasterboard sheets which have an ivory card face to the outside for direct decoration. With these plasterboards the fixture screw heads are filled and the face of the board rubbed with a proprietary slurry (sponge applied) to present an even surface on which paint can be directly applied.

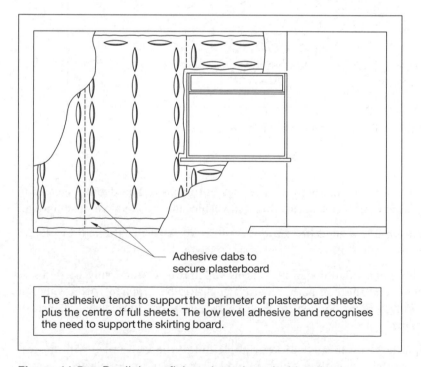

Adhesive dabs to secure plasterboard

The adhesive tends to support the perimeter of plasterboard sheets plus the centre of full sheets. The low level adhesive band recognises the need to support the skirting board.

Figure 11.5 ● Dry lining – fixing plasterboard with adhesive.

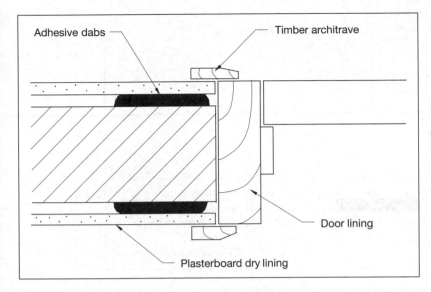

Figure 11.6 ● Dry lining junction with an internal door lining.

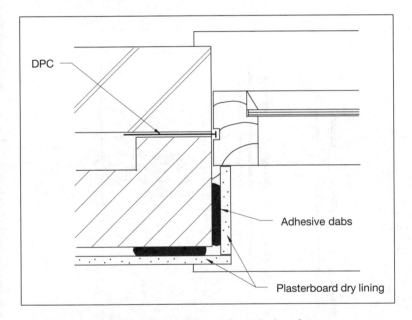

Figure 11.7 ● Dry lining meeting with a window frame.

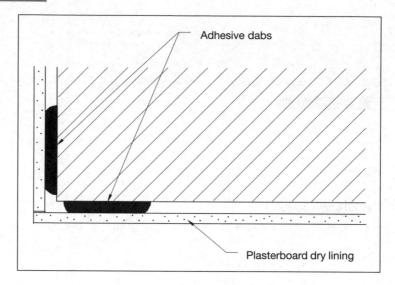

Figure 11.8 ● Dry lining to an external corner.

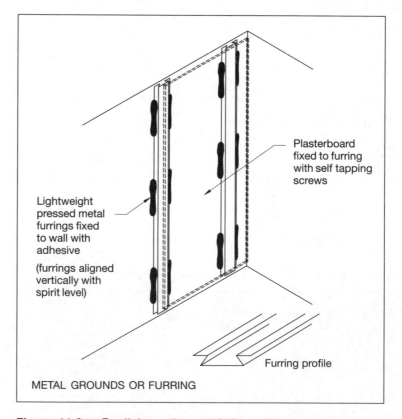

Figure 11.9 ● Dry lining – the metal channel system.

Wall tiling

Ceramic wall tiles are still popular for certain rooms of the house, such as the bathroom, kitchen or WC, where tiling may be full floor to ceiling height or to only part of the wall in the form of a dado (Figure 11.10).

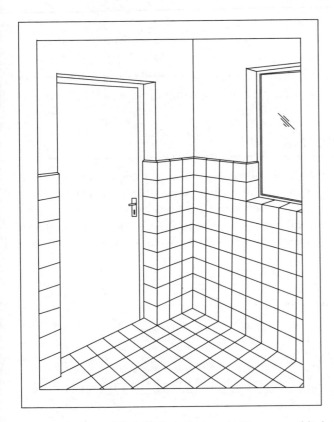

Figure 11.10 ● Wall tiled dado to a bathroom or kitchen.

As an alternative to large areas of tiles as illustrated, tile splashbacks are also often provided behind sinks and hand basins.

BS 8000 Part 11 covers the fixing of these tiles to walls and floors, while BS 6431 refers to tile quality.

Today, tile adhesive is often also capable of use as grout between the tiles. While the tiles themselves are impervious it is important to recognise the need to make the joints between them watertight with grout.

11.3 Ceilings and ceiling finishes

Introduction

After studying this section you should appreciate the forms of finish to ceilings.

Ceiling finish materials

Before the availability of plasterboard, ceilings to houses tended to be formed using the lath and plaster technique. Thin strips of sawn timber (not planed) were nailed to the underside of the joists with gaps left between each timber strip. The plasterer could then apply the plaster to the ceiling and force some of the material between the laths where it would achieve a key by swelling, as shown in Figure 11.11.

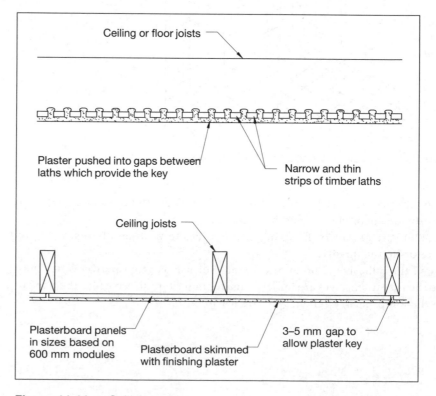

Figure 11.11 ● Ceiling options.

Modern ceilings by comparison tend to be formed in plasterboard sheets which are clout nailed (galvanised mild steel nails with large heads) to the joists. Joists are usually set at 400 mm centres for floors and for ceiling joists of roof solutions, as this suits the plasterboard sheets, which are produced in multiples of 400 mm. The largest sheets are 2400 mm × 1200 mm.

Setting the joists at 400 mm will ensure that there will always be timber against which the edge of the plasterboard can be nailed. Alternatively, 600 mm joist centres would suffice provided this satisfies the structural needs of the span in question.

A skim coat of plaster (less than 5 mm thick) is the normal way of finishing the plasterboard ceiling. Before the application of the plaster the joints between the plasterboard sheets are covered with a *scrim* reinforcement to resist cracking of the ceiling plaster along the lines of the plasterboard sheet edges. This scrim used to be in jute cloth, but the modern equivalent is plastic-based self-adhesive netting material applied across the joints from narrow rolls. Any deflection to the floor above the ceiling would otherwise tend to cause fracture of the plaster at the position of weakness: at the plasterboard sheet edge.

Plasterboard is covered by BS 1230. It is simply gypsum plaster sandwiched between two layers of card. The normal card is slightly rough to the touch and this helps the key to the wet plaster skim coat. Alternatively, the plasterboard can be obtained with a better quality ivory card face to one side to allow the board to be directly decorated rather than plastered.

The thickness of plasterboard sheets depends on the type of plasterboard in question but may be 9.5 mm, 12.5 mm or 19 mm thick. British Gypsum is our main plasterboard supplier and this company uses the name Gyproc as its trade name for plasterboard. Gyproc Wallboard is just one variety. The thickest sheet without attached insulation is Gyproc Plank, at 19 mm.

Plasterboard is formed by sandwiching gypsum plaster between two sheets of cardboard. Sheets have dimensions in multiples of 400 mm.

Review task

What thicknesses are available in plasterboard sheeting?

What sort of metal bead would you use to reinforce external plaster corners on a wall?

What is the purpose of scrim reinforcement?

11.4   Floor finishes

Introduction

After studying this section you should appreciate some of the timber finishes that may be applied to floors.

Overview

As stated in the introduction to this section, the scope for floor finishes in the home is a little limited. Many properties are constructed and sold without any floor finishes at all, only the floor surfaces as constructed: either timber boards, chipboard sheets, power floated concrete or screeded concrete. These of course will tend to be subsequently carpeted or similar to the requirements of the owner.

This brief section intends to focus on finishes that may be applied prior to the sale of the unit.

Timber finishes

There are really two timber solutions that might be regarded as traditional finishes to floors in dwellings: wood block flooring and hardwood strip flooring.

Whichever of these is used it should be remembered that timber is hygroscopic and as such will absorb moisture. This moisture may be from the air of the room in question or it may be from physical contact with moisture. In the latter case we need to ensure that suitable DPC material occurs between the finish and moisture source.

When timber absorbs moisture, its moisture content rises and expansion results. There is a need therefore to recognise the fact that timber floor finishes will move in use, and provision for movement must be incorporated into the laying procedure.

When hardwood strip flooring is used a degree of restrain may be gained by the nailing that often takes place in securing the strips to the joists of the floor structure (Figure 11.12).

The extent of the gap left around the perimeter of strip flooring will depend to a degree on the type of hardwood that is used. A significant difference between the dimensional changes due to moisture content changes exists between different hardwoods.

If the perimeter expansion gap is not to be covered by a skirting board, compressible fill may be used in the gap.

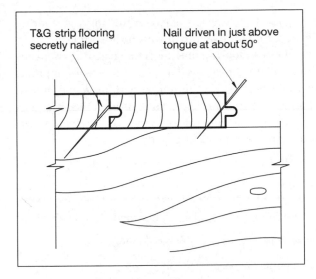

Figure 11.12 ● Secret nailing hardwood strip flooring.

When hardwood block flooring is used the extent of movement will be dictated by the laying pattern. Figure 11.13 shows the two most popular laying patterns: basket weave and herringbone.

Irrespective of the chosen pattern, this floor finish is provided with a two-block-wide plain margin around the perimeter of the floor. Beyond this, and between the margin and the enclosing walls, an expansion gap must be left to allow for movement in the blocks caused by changes in moisture content. It is easy to leave such a gap at the perimeter as we may simply cover this with the timber skirting board.

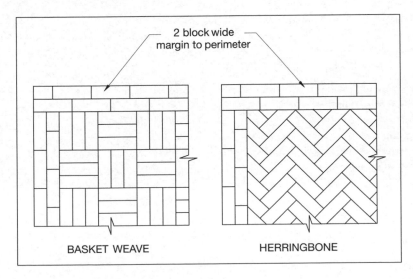

Figure 11.13 ● Wood block flooring.

Hygroscopicity means that the timber can absorb and lose moisture. Remember that the dimensional movement experienced by the timber is most noticeable across the grain.

A small tongued and grooved joint often exists between this form of flooring block, but the main means of securing is by laying in waterproof adhesive.

A similar appearance to wood block flooring may be achieved using the technique of parquet flooring. Here, instead of using hardwood blocks of approximately 25 mm thickness, the timber used is far thinner, at perhaps 6 mm or less. The veneers of timber associated with the parquet floor solution are sometimes board mounted to allow larger areas to be laid quickly. Once laid they are virtually indistinguishable from the hardwood block alternative.

Review task

Describe the secret nailing fixture method as applied to boarded floor finishes.

What are the *two* popular patterns for laying wood block flooring?

What distinguishes parquet flooring from wood block flooring?

Reflective summary

With reference to internal finishes, remember:

— Selection may typically be on the basis of smoothness of texture, absorption characteristics, suitability for decoration, durability or cost.

— Modern plasters tend to be gypsum based – these plasters are also known as calcium sulphate plasters.

— Metal bead accessories may be useful to reinforce the plaster finish or create the edge required.

— A dry lining finish to walls involves securing plasterboard to the walls.

— The old method of forming a plastered ceiling involved the use of narrow strips of timber called laths; hence the old *lath and plaster* ceiling.

— Floor joists and ceiling joists tend to be set at 400 mm centres to suit the dimensions of plasterboard sheets, which are produced in multiples of 400 mm.

— Timber floor finishes may move as they gain and lose moisture; this is because of timber's hygroscopic qualities.

Index